First Course on

POWER SYSTEMS

Ned Mohan

Oscar A. Schott Professor of Power Electronics and Systems
Department of Electrical and Computer Engineering
University of Minnesota
Minneapolis, MN 55455
USA

MNPERE
Minneapolis

To my Family: Mary, Michael and Tara
And,
To my Teachers: Eugene F. Hill and Harold A. Peterson

MATLAB is a registered trademark of The Mathworks, Inc.
SIMULINK is a registered trademark of The Mathworks, Inc.
PowerWorld is a registered trademark of the *PowerWorld* Corporation.
PSCAD/EMTDC is a registered trademark of the Manitoba HVDC Research Centre.

Published by:
    MNPERE
    P. O. Box 14503
    Minneapolis, MN 55414
    USA
    E-mail: MNPERE@AOL.COM
    http://www.MNPERE.com

ISBN 0-9715292-7-2

Printed in the United States of America.

PREFACE

In writing this new textbook, my sincere **hope** is to get the following type of reaction from undergraduates in courses where it is adopted – "Wow, in just one semester, I gained a thorough overview of the entire power systems from generation-to-load and learned the underlying fundamental principles that will be crucial to me as a practicing engineer and a lifelong learner, or if I choose to go into a graduate-level research-oriented career."

So why write another Power Systems textbook? Power Systems in many respects is a mature subject and many good textbooks abound. However, all textbooks this author is familiar with are written for use in two semesters and/or fail to cover the recent and potential changes in power systems. It is based on the author asking himself the following question: if students were to take **just one course** on Power Systems in their undergraduate curriculum, what knowledge should they graduate with that will be most helpful to them? This textbook is in response to this question and takes a balanced approach to cover many more topics in a way that also provides a deeper understanding of the subject matter in just a **one-semester** course.

A selected list of covered topics, some of them new, which are becoming increasingly important in present and future power systems, is as follows:

1. Changing Power Systems Landscape. Distributed generation (DG) (Chapter 1)
2. Energy sources including Renewable; Environmental Consequences (Chapter 3)
3. Loadability of transmission lines (Chapter 4)
4. High Voltage DC (HVDC) Transmission lines (Chapter 7)
5. Power Electronics based FACTS devices and their applications (Chapter 7)
6. Utility Loads: Voltage dependence and Power Factor; Power Quality (Chapter 8)
7. Synchronous generators and how they supply reactive power (Chapter 9)
8. Voltage Regulation and Stability; means to prevent voltage collapse (Chapter 10)
9. Qualitative discussion of Dynamic Stability (Chapter 11)
10. Automatic Generation Control (AGC); simulation using *Simulink* (Chapter 12)
11. Switching Transients and their calculations using *EMTDC* (Chapter 14)

A Simple Example Power System: The author was recently asked by a student the following question: "I am about to graduate and return to my native country where my family expects me to help design a much needed power infrastructure. I have taken courses in the energy related area here. Would I able to design such a system?" My answer was that it takes a great deal of combined experience of many experts to design a power system; taking a few courses by itself is not sufficient. However, it made me think that this question, although unique to this student, is pertinent to students all over the world, be it from developing countries or from countries where there is a huge basic infrastructure that is evolving, such as in the United States. Therefore, what if we teach students to design a simple 3-Bus power system as shown below which can be designed with paper-and-pencil and some simple computer programs specifically written for this objective, but that can be generalized to a very large interconnected system with buses that number in thousands?

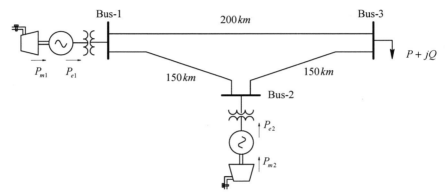

A 345-kV Example System.

Most of the topics in this textbook are covered with this example system in mind and they have been generalized to an n-Bus system.

What to cover? The intent of the course for which this textbook is designed is to teach students the basic fundamental concepts in Power Systems. But there are dilemmas. Take the case of Power Flow using Newton-Raphson method. Should we cover this method at all, rationalizing our decision on the basis that several professional tools are already available and most students are going to use such software rather than designing it? Although the answer to the preceding question is clear, this author would argue that we are not teaching in a trade school (needless to say there is nothing wrong with that, if that's the mission) and we shouldn't leave this subject completely as a "black box". However, we should teach it in a balanced manner perhaps coving it in 3 lectures rather than in 3 weeks. The same argument applies in covering many other topics.

Role of Software: Extending the earlier discussion further, if we agree to teach Newton-Raphson method for calculating power flow, it will be a total waste to do so without a simple numerical example. This is where *MATLAB* and *Simulink* (or similar software) can play an important role. *MATLAB* and *Simulink* are widely used in universities and students are often familiar with them prior to taking this course.

State-of-the-Art Software:
A win-win situation is if a simulation example of power flow in *MATLAB*, for example, is verified by a commercial software *PowerWorld*, whose evaluation version is free for educational purposes. Having done so, what-if type of studies can be done using this highly graphical software. This is the approach followed in this textbook, where the use of *PowerWorld* is made for power flow and fault-current calculations. *Simulink* is used for inter-area dynamic oscillations. Unfortunately, no easily accessible and free software for educational purposes is available for transient stability studies. Therefore, *MATLAB* is utilized on the 3-Bus example test power system. For switching transient calculations, writing a software code is impractical in a first course on Power Systems, and thus a software called *PSCAD/EMTDC* that is widely accepted in industry is used, whose evaluation version is free for educational purposes.

SOFTWARE LABORATORY
The course for which this book is written is intended to be accompanied by a laboratory component. In the past, such laboratories consisted of hardware experiments. However, unlike for the courses in Power Electronics and Electric Drives, it is difficult to design a hardware laboratory for Power Systems that is a tight accompaniment to the lecture course. Rather, a software laboratory is much better suited to illustrate and validate the concepts leaned in lectures. Based on this rationale, a software laboratory is developed, and the Manual that contains the Lab Exercises based on the Software Examples are supplied on the accompanying CD to this book. The connection between the book chapters and the laboratory exercises is shown in the Table below over a typical 13-week period.

Week	Book Chapters	Laboratory
1	Chapter 1: Overview Chapter 2: Fundamentals	Lab 1: Visit to a local substation; otherwise a virtual substation
2	Chapter 3: Energy Sources	Lab 2: Introduction to *PSCAD/EMTDC*; 3-phase circuits, vars, power-factor correction
3	Chapter 4: Transmission Lines	Lab 3: Transmission Lines using *PSCAD-EMTDC*
4	Chapter 5: Power Flow	Lab 4: Power Flow using *MATLAB* and *PowerWorld*
5	Chapter 6: Transformers	Lab 5: Including Transformers in Power Flow using *PowerWorld* and *MATLAB*

6	Chapter 7: HVDC, FACTS	Lab 6: Power Converters and HVDC using *PSCAD-EMTDC*, HVDC in *PowerWorld*
7	Chapter 8: Distribution Systems	Lab 7: Power Quality using *PSCAD-EMTDC*
8	Chapter 9: Synchronous Generators	Lab 8: Synchronous Generators and AVR using *PSCAD-EMTDC*.
9	Chapter 10: Voltage Stability	Lab 9: Voltage Regulation using *PowerWorld*
10	Chapter 11: Transient Stability	Lab 10: Transient Stability using *MATLAB*
11	Chapter 12: Interconnected Systems, Economic Dispatch	Lab 11: AGC using *Simulink*, and Economic Dispatch using *PowerWorld*
12	Chapter 13: Short-Circuit Faults, Relays, Circuit Breakers	Lab 12: Transmission Line Faults using *PowerWorld* and *MATLAB*
13	Chapter 14: Transient Over-Voltages, Surge Arrestors, Insulation Coordination	Lab 13: Over-voltages and Surge Arrestors using *PSCAD-EMTDC*

CD-ROM

The accompanying CD-ROM includes the following:

- Extremely useful for <u>Instructors</u>: PowerPoint-based slides in PDF format are included for every chapter to quickly prepare lectures and to review the material in class. All the slides on this accompanying CD can be printed.
- Student (Evaluation) versions of *PowerWorld* and *PSCAD/EMTDC* that are sufficient for educational purposes and are ready-to-use; nothing to download or purchase.
- Ready-to-execute examples using *PowerWorld* and *PSCAD/EMTDC*.
- Simulations and design examples using *MATLAB* and *Simulink*.
- Laboratory Manual containing all the Laboratory Exercises.

ACKNOWLEDGEMENTS

During the course of writing this textbook over several years, the author has benefited from the knowledge and advice of several individuals – many of them I consider my mentors. In the recent months leading to the publication of this book, I sincerely appreciate the help of two individuals from industry and academia: Jack Christofersen (retired after over 40 years of experience in the utility industry and now an independent consultant) who believed in this project from its inception and took a deep interest in its success, and Professor Ani Golé of the University of Manitoba for once again introducing me to *PSCAD/EMTDC*. I would also like to take this opportunity to thank my graduate students and post-docs with whom I often interacted and who have provided me their unique perspectives which I believe have been very influential in molding this book.

SUGGESTED REFERENCE BOOKS:

Over the years, this author has immensely benefited from the following books (in no particular order) and their authors are my teachers. These are excellent books that are highly recommended as references in this course:

1. Electric Utility Systems and Practices, 4th Edition by Homer M. Rustebakke (Editor), John Wiley & Sons, August 1983.

2. Powerplant Technology by M. M. El-Wakil, McGraw-Hill Companies, 1984.

3. Electric Power Research Institute (EPRI), *Transmission Line Reference Book: 345 kV and above*, 2nd edition, 1982.

4. Hermann W. Dommel, *EMTP Theory Book*, BPA, August 1986.

5. Prabha Kundur, *Power System Stability and Control*, McGraw Hill, 1994.

6. Paul Anderson, Analysis of Faulted Power Systems, IEEE Press, 1995.

7. G.T. Heydt, *Computer Analysis Methods for Power Systems*, Stars in a Circle Publications, 1996.

8. A. Burgen, V. Vittal, *Power Systems Analysis*, 2nd edition, Prentice Hall, 1999.

9. W. D. Stevenson, *Elements of Power System Analysis*, 4th edition, McGraw-Hill, 1982.

10. Electrical Transmission and Distribution Reference Book, Westinghouse Electric Corporation, 1950.

11. E. W. Kimbark, Direct Current Transmission, vol. 1, Wiley –Interscience, New York, 1971.

12. J. Casazza and F. Delea, Understanding Electric Power Systems: An Overview of the Technology and the Marketplace, IEEE Press and Wiley-Interscience, 2003.

13. C.W. Taylor, Power System Voltage Stability, McGraw-Hill, 1994 (for reprints, Email: cwtaylor@ieee.org).

14. N. Hingorani, L. Gyugyi, *Understanding FACTS : Concepts and Technology of Flexible AC Transmission Systems*, Wiley-IEEE Press, 1999.

15. Graham Rogers, Power System Oscillations, Kluwer, 2000.

16. Leon K. Kirchmayer, *Economic Operation of Power Systems*, John Wiley & Sons, 1958.

17. Nathan Cohn, *Control of Generation and Power Flow on Interconnected Systems*, John Wiley & Sons, 1967.

18. Leon K. Kirchmayer, *Economic Control of Interconnected Systems*, John Wiley & Sons, 1959.

19. A. Wood, B. Wollenberg, *Power Generation, Operation, and Control*, 2nd edition, Wiley-Interscience, 1996.

20. A. Phadke, J. Thorp, *Computer Relaying for Power Systems*, Institute of Physics Publishers, 2005.

CONTENTS

Chapter 1

POWER SYSTEMS: A CHANGING LANDSCAPE

Electric power systems are a technical wonder and, according to the National Academy of Engineering [1], electricity and its accessibility are the greatest engineering achievements of the twentieth century, ahead of computers and airplanes.

Electricity is a highly refined "commodity" without which it is difficult to imagine how a modern society could function. It has saved countless millions from the daily drudgery of backbreaking menial tasks. Electricity as a commodity is also unique that it must be consumed at the instant it is produced, since storing it for future use is still economically prohibitive in most cases.

1-1   NATURE OF POWER SYSTEMS

Power Systems encompass the generation of electricity to its ultimate consumption in operating computers to hairdryers! For example, the North American grid in the United States and Canada consists of thousands of generators, all operating in synchronism. These generators are interconnected by over two hundred thousand miles of transmission lines at 230 kV and above [2], as shown in Fig. 1-1. Such an interconnected system results in the continuity and the reliability of service if there is an outage in one part of the system, and provides electricity at the lowest cost by utilizing the lowest cost generation at a given time.

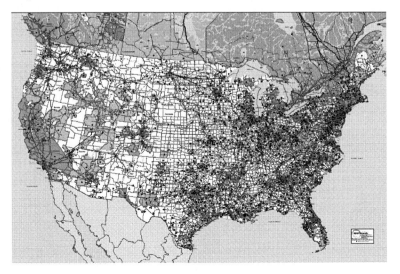

Fig. 1-1 Interconnected North American Power Grid [2].

The electric system in North America is made up of three regions, as shown in Fig. 1-2 [3], referred as Interconnections by the National Electric Reliability Council (NERC), which is a voluntary organization that has operated successfully since its formation in 1968. NERC's mission is to ensure that the bulk electric system in North America is reliable, adequate and secure, relying on reciprocity, peer pressure and the mutual self-interest of all those involved. These Interconnections are divided into 152 control areas (each control area includes the combination of the Balancing Authority and the Transmission Operator), where each control area controls its generation such as to maintain its interchange schedule with other control areas, and it also contributes to the frequency regulation of the Interconnection.

Fig. 1-2 NERC Interconnections [3]. Source: NERC.

Although power systems are almost always three phase, they are represented by the one-line diagram, as illustrated by Fig. 1-3.

Fig. 1-3 One-line diagram as an example.

The output of generators, often in locations remote to the load centers, is stepped up in voltage from a 20-kV level by transformers to a much higher voltage for transmission over long distances, and subsequently stepped down in voltage level and distributed to the consumers. A visit to the local utility substation will show many of the apparatus in Fig. 1-3 in operation day and night. A similar visit to a generation plant and the control center of the local utility will illustrate how these interconnected systems are kept operating in the most economical and reliable manner.

1-2   CHANGING LANDSCAPE OF POWER SYSTEMS AND UTILITY DEREGULATION

Power Systems of today are undergoing major changes in how they are evolving in their structure and how they are competing to meet the load demand. In the past and true to some extent today, as Fig. 1-4a shows, electric utilities were highly centralized, owning large central power plants to the transmission and distribution systems, all the way down to the consumer loads [4]. These utilities were monopolies where consumers had no choice but to buy power from their local utilities. For oversight purposes, utilities were highly regulated by Public Service Commissions that acted as consumer watchdogs, preventing utilities from price gouging, and as custodial of the environment by not allowing avoidable polluting practices.

Fig. 1-4 Changing landscape [4]. Source: ABB.

The structure and the operation of the power systems are beginning to change as Fig. 1-4b attempts to illustrate. Utilities have been forced to break up in separate generation, and transmission/distribution companies. There is Distributed Generation (DG) by independent power producers (IPP), who can generate electricity by whatever means, by wind for example, and must be allowed access to the transmission grid to sell power to consumers. The impetus for the breakup in the utility structure was provided by the enormous benefits of deregulation in the telecommunication and the airline industries that fostered a large degree of competition, resulting in much lower rates and much better service to the consumers. In spite of the inherent differences between these two industries and the utility industry, it was perceived that the utility deregulation would similarly profit the consumers with lower electricity rates. This deregulation is in transition with some states and countries pursuing it more aggressively and others more cautiously. To promote open competition, utilities are forced to restructure by unbundling their generation unit from their transmission and distribution units. The objective is that the independent Transmission System Operators (TSO) wheel power for a charge from anywhere and anyone to the customer site. This would foster competition allowing open transmission access to everyone, for example Independent Power Producers (IPP). Many such small IPPs have gone into business, producing power using gas turbines and windmills.

Operation in a reliable manner is ensured by the Independent System Operators (ISOs) and the financial transactions are governed by real-time bidding to buy and sell power. Energy traders have gotten into the act for profit: buying energy at lower prices and selling it at higher prices in the spot market. Utilities are signing long-term contracts for energy such as gas. This is all based on the rules of the financial world: forecasting, risks, options, reliability, etc.

As mentioned earlier, the outcome of this deregulation, still in transition, is far from certain. So far, consumers have seen little or no savings and in some cases it has been a disaster as during the California Energy Crisis. However, there is every reason to believe that the deregulation, now in progress, would continue with very little possibility that the clock would be turned back. In doing so, there are some fixes that are needed. The transmission grid has become a bottleneck with very little financial incentive for the Transmission System Operators to increase the capacity. If the transmission system is congested, TSO can charge higher prices. The number of transactions and the complexity of these transactions have increased drastically. These factors point to anticipated legislative action needed to maintain electric system reliability.

1-3   TOPICS IN POWER SYSTEMS

The purpose of this textbook is to provide a complete overview of power systems meeting present and future energy challenges. In doing so, fundamentals are to be clearly understood so that the details in any of the topics can be easily comprehended as a graduate student or as a lifelong learner while practicing this profession.

The chapters in this book are arranged to associate the lecture material to the laboratory exercises in a chronological manner.

As the present chapter describes, the power systems industry is undergoing major changes. In order to fully comprehend these changes and the underlying challenges, we need to understand the basics of power systems. The most basic aspect of power systems is generation. One has a choice of choosing certain resources for generating electricity, but there are always consequences to any selection. These are briefly discussed in

Chapter 3 which also describes the increasing role of renewable energy sources such as wind. However, prior to this, basic concepts that are fundamental to the analysis of power system circuits are briefly reviewed in Chapter 2.

AC transmission lines and cables are described in Chapter 4. Increasingly high voltage dc transmission (HVDC) is being used to enhance system stability. For purposes of planning and operating securely under contingencies caused by outages, it is important to know how power flows on various paths. The principles of power flow are examined in Chapter 5. Voltages produced by generators are stepped up by transformers for long distance hauling of power over transmission lines. Transformers are described in Chapter 6. Moreover, there is a growing role of power electronics in power systems in the form of flexible ac transmission systems (FACTS). The principles behind HVDC and FACTS are described in Chapter 7. Through several changes in voltage levels, made possible by transformers, transmission, sub-transmission and distribution networks provide electricity to consumer loads. Chapter 8 describes these loads and the role of power electronics that is changing their nature. This chapter also describes how these loads react to voltage fluctuations and the power quality.

For generating electricity, steam and natural gas are utilized to run turbines that provide mechanical input to synchronous generators to produce three-phase electrical voltages. Synchronous generators are described in Chapter 9. Transmission lines are being loaded more than ever, making the voltage stability a concern, as discussed in Chapter 10. Maintaining stability so that various generators operate in synchronism is described in Chapter 11, which discusses how the stability in an interconnected system, with thousands of generators operating in synchronism, can be maintained in response to transient conditions, such as transmission-line faults, where there is a mismatch between the mechanical power input to the turbines and the electrical power that can be transmitted. Chapter 12 discusses economic dispatch where generators are loaded such as to provide the overall economy of operation. The operation of interconnected systems, so that the power system frequency and voltages are maintained at their nominal values and the purchasing-and-selling agreements between various utilities are honored, are also described in Chapter 12.

Power systems are spread over large areas. Being exposed to the elements of nature, they are subjected to occasional faults against which they must be designed and protected so that such events result only in momentary loss of power, and no permanent equipment damage accrues. Short-circuits on transmission systems is discussed in Chapter 13, which describes how relays detect faults and cause circuit breakers to open the circuit, interrupting the fault current, and then re-close to bring the operation back to normal as soon as possible. Lightening strikes and switching of extra-high voltage transmission lines during reenergizing, particularly with trapped charge, can result in very high voltage surges which can cause insulation to flashover. To avoid this, surge arresters are used and are properly coordinated with the insulation level of the power systems apparatus to prevent damage. These topics are discussed in Chapter 14.

REFERENCES
1. National Academy of Engineering (www.nae.edu).
2. PennWell MAPSearch (www.mapsearch.com/paper_products.cfm).
3. National Electric Reliability Council (www.nerc.com).
4. ABB Corporation (www.abb.com).

PROBLEMS

1-1   What are the advantages of a highly interconnected system?

1-2   What are the changes taking place in the utility industry?

1-3   What are the different topics in power systems for understanding its basic nature?

CHAPTER 2

REVIEW OF BASIC ELECTRIC CIRCUITS AND ELECTROMAGNETIC CONCEPTS

2-1   INTRODUCTION

The purpose of this chapter is to review elements of the basic electric circuit theory that are essential to the study of electric power circuits: use of phasors to analyze circuits in sinusoidal steady state, the real and reactive powers, the power factor, analysis of three-phase circuits, power flow in ac circuits and per-unit quantities.

In this book, we will use MKS units and the IEEE-standard letters and graphic symbols whenever possible. The lowercase letters v and i are used to represent instantaneous values of voltages and currents that vary as functions of time. A current's positive direction is indicated by an arrow, as shown in Fig. 2-1. Similarly, the voltage polarities must be indicated. The voltage v_{ab} refers to the voltage of node "a" with respect to node "b," thus $v_{ab} = v_a - v_b$.

Fig. 2-1 Convention for voltages and currents.

2-2   PHASOR REPRESENTATION IN SINUSOIDAL STEADY STATE

In linear circuits with sinusoidal voltages and currents of frequency f applied for a long time so that steady state has been reached, all circuit voltages and currents are at a frequency $f (= \omega / 2\pi)$. To analyze such circuits, calculations are simplified by means of phasor-domain analysis. The use of phasors also provides a deeper insight with relative ease into the circuit behavior.

In the phasor domain, the time-domain variables $v(t)$ and $i(t)$ are transformed into phasors which are represented by the complex variables $\overline{V}$ and $\overline{I}$. Note that these phasors are expressed by uppercase letters with a bar "-" on top. In a complex (real and imaginary) plane, these phasors can be drawn with a magnitude and an angle. A cosinusoidal time function is taken as a reference phasor; for example, the voltage expression in Eq. 2-1 below is represented by a phasor, which is entirely real with an angle of zero degrees:

$$v(t) = \sqrt{2}\,V\cos\omega t \qquad\qquad \Leftrightarrow \qquad \overline{V} = V\angle 0 \qquad\qquad (2\text{-}1)$$

Similarly,

$$i(t) = \sqrt{2}\,I\cos(\omega t - \phi) \qquad \Leftrightarrow \qquad \overline{I} = I\angle -\phi \qquad\qquad (2\text{-}2)$$

where V and I are the rms values of the voltage and current. These voltage and current phasors are drawn in Fig. 2-2. In Eqs. 2-1 and 2-2, the frequency ω is implicitly associated with each phasor. Knowing this frequency, a phasor expression can be re-transformed back into a time-domain expression.

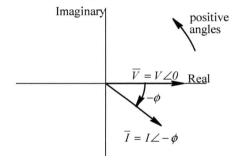

Fig. 2-2 Phasor diagram.

Using phasors, we can convert differential equations into easily solvable algebraic equations containing complex variables. Consider the circuit of Fig. 2-3a in a sinusoidal steady state with an applied voltage at a frequency $f(=\omega/2\pi)$.

In order to calculate the current in this circuit, remaining in time domain would require to solve the following differential equation:

$$Ri(t) + L\frac{di(t)}{dt} + \frac{1}{C}\int i(t)\bullet dt = \sqrt{2}\,V\cos(\omega t) \qquad\qquad (2\text{-}3)$$

Using phasors, we can redraw the circuit of Fig. 2-3a in Fig. 2-3b, where the inductance L is represented by $j\omega L$ and the capacitance C by $-j/(\omega C)$.

Fig. 2-3 A circuit (a) in time-domain and (b) in phasor-domain; (c) impedance triangle.

In the phasor-domain circuit, the impedance Z of the series-connected elements is obtained by the impedance triangle of Fig. 2-3c as

$$Z = R + jX_L - jX_c \qquad (2\text{-}4)$$

where

$$X_L = \omega L , \text{ and } \quad X_c = \frac{1}{\omega C} \qquad (2\text{-}5)$$

This impedance can be expressed as

$$Z = |Z| \angle \phi \qquad (2\text{-}6a)$$

where

$$|Z| = \sqrt{R^2 + \left(\omega L - \frac{1}{\omega C}\right)^2} \qquad \text{and} \qquad \phi = \tan^{-1}\left[\frac{\left(\omega L - \frac{1}{\omega C}\right)}{R}\right] \qquad (2\text{-}6b)$$

It is important to recognize that while Z is a complex quantity, it is <u>not</u> a phasor and does <u>not</u> have a corresponding time-domain expression.

▲ **Example 2-1** Calculate the impedance seen from the terminals of the circuit in Fig. 2-4 under a sinusoidal steady state at a frequency $f = 60 Hz$.

Fig. 2-4 Impedance network of Example 2-1.

Solution $Z = j0.1 + \dfrac{2 \times (\text{-j}5)}{(2\text{-j}5)} = 1.72 - j0.59 = 1.82 \angle -18.9° \ \Omega$.   ▲

Using the impedance in Eq. 2-6, the current in Fig. 2-3b can be obtained as

$$\overline{I} = \frac{\overline{V}}{Z} = \left(\frac{V}{|Z|}\right)\angle -\phi \qquad (2\text{-}7)$$

where $I = \dfrac{V}{|Z|}$ and ϕ is as calculated from Eq. 2-6b. Using Eq. 2-2, the current can be expressed in the time domain as

$$i(t) = \frac{\sqrt{2}\,V}{|Z|}\cos(\omega t - \phi) \qquad (2\text{-}8)$$

In the impedance triangle of Fig. 2-3c, a positive value of the phase angle ϕ implies that the current lags behind the voltage in the circuit of Fig. 2-3a. Sometimes, it is convenient to express the inverse of the impedance, which is called admittance:

$$Y = \frac{1}{Z} \qquad (2\text{-}9)$$

The phasor-domain procedure for solving $i(t)$ is much easier than solving the differential-integral equation given by Eq. 2-3.

▲ **Example 2-2**   Calculate the current $\overline{I}_1$ and $i_1(t)$ in the circuit of Fig. 2-5 if the applied voltage has an rms value of $120V$ and a frequency of $60\,Hz$. Assume $\overline{V}_1$ to be the reference phasor.

Fig. 2-5 Circuit of Example 2-2.

Solution   With $\overline{V}_1$ as the reference phasor, it can be written as $\overline{V}_1 = 120\angle 0^\circ V$. The input impedance of the circuit seen from the applied voltage terminals is

$$Z_{in} = (0.3 + j0.5) + \frac{(j15)(7 + j0.2)}{(j15) + (7 + j0.2)} = 6.775\angle 29.03^\circ\ \Omega .$$

Therefore, the current $\overline{I}_1$ can be obtained as

$$\overline{I_1} = \frac{\overline{V_1}}{Z_{in}} = \frac{120\angle 0°}{6.775\angle 29.03°} = 17.712\angle -29.03° A$$

hence $i_1(t) = 25.048\cos(\omega t - 29.03°)A$.   ▲

2-3   POWER, REACTIVE POWER, AND POWER FACTOR

Consider the generic circuit of Fig. 2-6 in a sinusoidal steady state. Each sub-circuit may consist of passive (R-L-C) elements and active voltage and current sources. Based on the arbitrarily chosen voltage polarity and the current direction shown in Fig. 2-6, the instantaneous power $p(t) = v(t)i(t)$ is delivered by sub-circuit 1 and absorbed by sub-circuit 2. This is because in sub-circuit 1, the positively-defined current is coming out of the positive-polarity terminal (the same as in a generator). On the other hand, the positively-defined current is entering the positive-polarity terminal in sub-circuit 2 (the same as in a load). A negative value of $p(t)$ reverses the roles of sub-circuit 1 and sub-circuit 2.

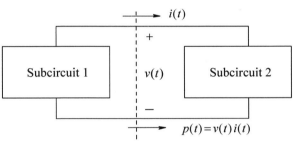

Figure 2-6 A generic circuit divided into two sub-circuits.

Under a sinusoidal steady state condition at a frequency f, the complex power S, the reactive power Q, and the power factor express how "effectively" the real (average) power P is transferred from one sub-circuit to the other. If $v(t)$ and $i(t)$ are in phase, the instantaneous power $p(t) = v(t)i(t)$, as shown in Fig. 2-7a, pulsates at twice the steady state frequency as shown below (V and I are the rms values):

$$p(t) = \sqrt{2}V\cos\omega t \cdot \sqrt{2}I\cos\omega t = 2VI\cos^2\omega t = VI + VI\cos 2\omega t \quad (i \text{ in phase with } v) \quad (2\text{-}10)$$

But, at all times, $p(t) \geq 0$, and therefore the power always flows in one direction: from sub-circuit 1 to sub-circuit 2. The average over one cycle of the second term on the right-side of Eq. 2-10 is zero, and therefore the average power is $P = VI$. Now consider the waveforms of Fig. 2-7b, where the $i(t)$ waveform lags behind the $v(t)$ waveform by a phase angle $\phi(t)$. Here, $p(t)$ becomes negative during a time interval of (ϕ/ω) during each half-cycle as calculated below:

$$p(t) = \sqrt{2}V \cos \omega t \cdot \sqrt{2}I \cos(\omega t - \phi) = VI \cos \phi + VI \cos(2\omega t - \phi) \qquad (2\text{-}11)$$

A negative instantaneous power implies power flow in the opposite direction. This back-and-forth flow of power indicates that the real (average) power is not optimally transferred from one sub-circuit to the other, as is the case in Fig. 2-7a. Therefore, the average power $P(=VI\cos\phi)$ in Fig. 2-7b is less than that in Fig. 2-7a.

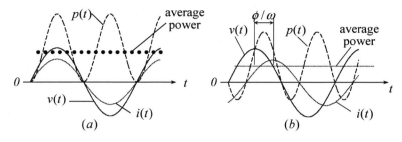

Figure 2-7 Instantaneous power with sinusoidal currents and voltages.

The circuit of Fig. 2-6 is redrawn in Fig. 2-8a in the phasor domain. The voltage and the current phasors are defined by their magnitudes and phase angles as

$$\overline{V} = V\angle\phi_v \qquad \text{and} \qquad \overline{I} = I\angle\phi_i \qquad (2\text{-}12)$$

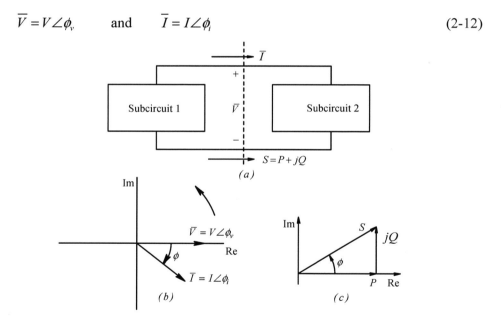

Fig. 2-8 (a) Circuit in phasor-domain; (b) phasor diagram with $\phi_v = 0$; (c) power triangle.

In Fig. 2-8b, the voltage $\overline{V}$ is taken as a reference phasor along the real-axis (Re) so that $\phi_v = 0$, and ϕ_i is assumed to have a negative value. The complex power S is defined as

$$S = \overline{V}\,\overline{I}^* \qquad (\text{* indicates complex conjugate}) \qquad (2\text{-}13)$$

Therefore, substituting the expressions for voltage and current into Eq. 2-13, and noting that $\overline{I}^* = I\angle-\phi_i$,

$$S = V\angle\phi_v \, I\angle-\phi_i = V\,I\angle(\phi_v - \phi_i) \tag{2-14}$$

The difference between the two phase angles is defined as

$$\phi = \phi_v - \phi_i \tag{2-15}$$

Therefore,

$$S = V\,I\angle\phi = P + jQ \tag{2-16}$$

where

$$P = V\,I\cos\phi \tag{2-17}$$

$$Q = V\,I\sin\phi \tag{2-18}$$

In Eq. 2-17, $I\cos\phi$ is the current component that is in phase with the voltage phasor in Fig. 2-8b, and results in real power transfer P. Whereas, from Eq. 2-18, $I\sin\phi$ is the current component that is at 90^0 angle to the voltage phasor in Fig. 2-8b, and results in the reactive power Q but no average real power.

The power triangle corresponding to the phasors in Fig. 2-8b is shown in Fig. 2-8c. From Eq. 2-16, the magnitude of S, also called the "apparent power," is

$$|S| = \sqrt{P^2 + Q^2} \tag{2-19}$$

and

$$\phi = \tan^{-1}\left(\frac{Q}{P}\right) \tag{2-20}$$

The above quantities have the following units: P: W (Watts); Q: Var (Volt-Amperes Reactive); $|S|$: VA (Volt-amperes); and ϕ_v, ϕ_i, ϕ: radians, measured positively in a counter-clockwise direction with respect to the real-axis that is drawn horizontally from left to right.

The physical significance of the apparent power $|S|$, P, and Q should be understood. The cost of most electrical equipment such as generators, transformers, and transmission lines is proportional to $|S|(=V\,I)$, since their electrical insulation level and the magnetic core size for a given line-frequency depend on the voltage V and the conductor size depends on the rms current I. The real power P has a physical significance since it represents the useful work being performed plus the losses. Under most operating conditions, it is desirable to have the reactive power Q be zero, otherwise it results in increased $|S|$.

To support the above discussion, another quantity called the power factor is defined. The power factor is a measure of how effectively a load draws real power:

$$\text{power factor} = \frac{P}{|S|} = \frac{P}{VI} = \cos\phi \tag{2-21}$$

which is a dimension-less quantity. Ideally, the power factor should be 1.0 (that is, Q should be zero) in order to draw real power with a minimum current magnitude and hence minimize losses in electrical equipment, and transmission and distribution lines. An inductive load draws power at a lagging power factor where the load current lags behind the voltage. Conversely, a capacitive load draws power at a leading power factor where the load current leads the load voltage.

▲ **Example 2-3** Calculate P, Q, S, and the power factor of operation at the terminals in the circuit of Fig. 2-5 in Example 2-2.

Solution

$$P = V_1 I_1 \cos\phi = 120 \times 17.712 \cos 29.03^0 = 1858.4 \ W$$

$$Q = V_1 I_1 \sin\phi = 120 \times 17.712 \times \sin 29.03^0 = 1031.3 \ VAR$$

$$|S| = V_1 I_1 = 120 \times 17.7 = 2125.4 \ VA$$

From Eq. 2-20, $\phi = \tan^{-1}\dfrac{Q}{P} = 29.03^0$ in the power triangle of Fig. 2-8c. Note that the angle of S in the power triangle is the same as the impedance angle ϕ in Example 2-2. The power factor of operation is

$$\text{power factor} = \cos\phi = 0.874 \qquad\qquad ▲$$

Note the following for the inductive impedance in the above example: 1) The impedance is $Z = |Z| \angle\phi$, where ϕ is positive. 2) The current lags the voltage by the impedance angle ϕ. This corresponds to a lagging power factor of operation. 3) In the power triangle, the impedance angle ϕ relates P, Q, and S. 4) An inductive impedance, when applied a voltage, draws a positive reactive power (vars). If the impedance were to be capacitive, the phase angle ϕ would be negative and the impedance would draw a negative reactive power (that is, the impedance would supply a positive reactive power).

2-3-1 Sum of Real and Reactive Powers in a Circuit

In a circuit, all the real powers supplied to the various components sum to the total real power supplied:

$$\text{Total Real Power Supplied} = \sum_k P_k = \sum_k I_k^2 R \qquad (2\text{-}22)$$

Similarly, all the reactive powers supplied to the various components sum to the total reactive power supplied:

$$\text{Total Reactive Power Supplied} = \sum_k Q_k = \sum_k I_k^2 X \qquad (2\text{-}23)$$

where Q_k is negative if a component is supplying reactive power; such is the case with a capacitor.

▲ **Example 2-4** In the circuit of Fig. 2-5 in Example 2-2, calculate P and Q associated with each element and calculate the total real and reactive powers supplied at the terminals. Confirm these calculations by comparing with P and Q calculated in Example 2-3.

Solution   From Example 2-2, $\overline{I}_1 = 17.712 \angle - 29.03^0 \, A$.

$$\overline{I}_m = \overline{I}_1 \frac{R_2 + jX_2}{(R_2 + jX_2) + jX_m} = 7.412 \angle - 92.66^0 \, A, \text{ and } \overline{I}_2 = \overline{I}_1 - \overline{I}_m = 15.876 \angle - 4.3^0 \, A.$$

Therefore, $P_{R_1} = R_1 I_1^2 = 0.3 \times 17.172^2 = 94.11 W$, $P_{R_2} = R_2 I_2^2 = 7 \times 15.876^2 = 1764.3 W$, and

$$\sum P = P_{R_1} + P_{R_2} = 1858.4 W$$

For the reactive vars, $Q_{X_1} = X_1 I_1^2 = 0.5 \times 17.172^2 = 156.851 \, VAR$,

$$Q_{X_2} = X_2 I_2^2 = 0.2 \times 15.876^2 = 50.409 \, VAR \text{ , and}$$

$$Q_{X_3} = X_m I_m^2 = 15 \times 7.412^2 = 821.021 \, VAR.$$

Therefore,

$$\sum Q = Q_{X_1} + Q_{X_2} + Q_{X_m} = 1031.3 VAR$$

Note that $\sum P$ and $\sum Q$ are equal to P and Q at the terminals, as calculated in Example 2-3.   ▲

2-3-2 Power Factor Correction

As explained earlier, utilities prefer that loads draw power at the unity power factor, so that the current for a given power drawn is minimum, thus resulting in the least amount of I^2R losses in the resistances associated with transmission and distribution lines and other apparatus. This power factor correction can be accomplished by compensating or nullifying the reactive power drawn by the load by connecting a reactance in parallel that draws the same reactive power in magnitude but of opposite sign. This is illustrated by the example below.

▲ **Example 2-5** In the circuit of Fig. 2-5 in Example 2-3, the complex power drawn by the load impedance was calculated as $P_L + jQ_L = (1858.4 + j1031.3)VA$. Calculate the reactance in parallel that will result in the overall power factor to be unity, as seen from the voltage source.

Solution The load is drawing reactive power $Q_L = 1031.3 VAR$. Therefore, as shown in Fig. 2-9, a capacitive reactance must be connected in parallel with the network to supply $Q_C = 1031.3 VAR$ such that only the real power is drawn from the voltage source.

Fig. 2-9 Power factor correction in Example 2-5.

Since the voltage across the capacitive reactance is given, the capacitive reactance can be calculated as

$$X_C = \frac{V^2}{Q_C} = \frac{120^2}{1031.3} = 13.963\Omega. \qquad ▲$$

2-4   THREE-PHASE CIRCUITS

Basic understanding of three-phase circuits is essential to the study of electric power systems. Nearly all electricity, with only a few exceptions, is generated by means of three-phase ac generators. Figure 2-10 shows a one-line diagram of a three-phase transmission and distribution system. Generated voltages (usually below 25 kV) are stepped-up by means of transformers to 230 kV to 500 kV levels for transferring power long distances over transmission lines from the generation site to load centers. At the receiving-end of the transmission lines near load centers, these three-phase voltages are stepped-down by transformers. Most motor loads above a few kW in power rating operate from three-phase voltages.

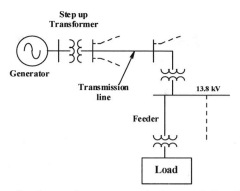

Fig. 2-10 One-line diagram of a three-phase transmission and distribution system.

Three-phase ac circuits are either wye or delta connected. We will investigate these under sinusoidal steady state, balanced condition, which implies that all three voltages are equal in magnitude and displaced by 120^0 ($2\pi/3$ radians) with respect to each other. The phase sequence of voltages is commonly assumed to be $a-b-c$, where the phase "a" voltage leads the phase "b" voltage by 120^0, and phase "b" leads phase "c" by 120^0 ($2\pi/3$ radians), as shown in Fig. 2-11. This applies to both the time-domain representation in Fig. 2-11a and the phasor-domain representation in Fig. 2-11b. Notice that in the $a-b-c$ sequence voltages plotted in Fig. 2-11a, first v_{an} reaches its positive peak, and then v_{bn} reaches its positive peak $2\pi/3$ radians later, and so on. We can represent these voltages in the phasor form in Fig. 2-11b as

$$\overline{V}_{an} = V_{ph}\angle 0^0, \quad \overline{V}_{bn} = V_{ph}\angle -120^0, \quad \text{and} \quad \overline{V}_{cn} = V_{ph}\angle -240^0 \qquad (2\text{-}24)$$

where V_{ph} is the rms phase-voltage magnitude and the phase "a" voltage is assumed to be the reference (with an angle of zero degrees).

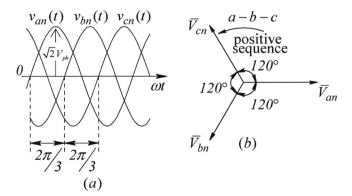

Fig. 2-11 Three-phase voltages in time and phasor domain.

For a balanced set of voltages given by Eq. 2-24, at any instant, the sum of these phase voltages equals zero:

$$\overline{V}_{an} + \overline{V}_{bn} + \overline{V}_{cn} = 0 \qquad \text{and} \qquad v_{an}(t) + v_{bn}(t) + v_{cn}(t) = 0 \qquad (2\text{-}25)$$

2-4-1 Per-Phase Analysis in Balanced Three-Phase Circuits

A three-phase circuit can be analyzed on a per-phase basis, provided that it has a balanced set of source voltages and equal impedances in each of the phases. Such a wye-connected circuit is shown in Fig. 2-12a.

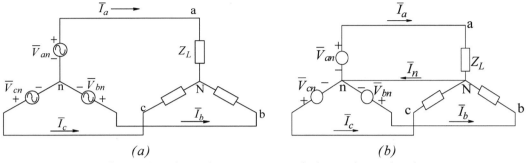

(a)   (b)

Fig. 2-12 Balanced wye-connected, three-phase circuit.

In such a circuit, the source neutral "n" and the load neutral "N" are at the same potential. Therefore, "hypothetically" connecting these with a zero impedance wire, as shown in Fig. 2-12b, does not change the original three-phase circuit, which can now be analyzed on a per-phase basis. Selecting phase "a" for this analysis, the per-phase circuit is shown in Fig. 2-13a.

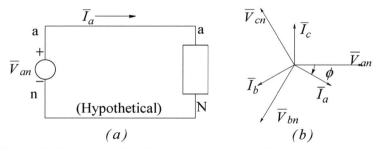

(a)   (b)

Fig. 2-13 Per-phase circuit and the corresponding phasor diagram.

If $Z_L = |Z_L| \angle \phi$, using the fact that in a balanced three-phase circuit, phase quantities are displaced by 120^0 with respect to each other, we find that

$$\overline{I}_a = \frac{\overline{V}_{an}}{Z_L} = \frac{V_{ph}}{|Z_L|} \angle -\phi \quad \overline{I}_b = \frac{\overline{V}_{bn}}{Z_L} = \frac{V_{ph}}{|Z_L|} \angle (-\phi - \frac{2\pi}{3}) \quad \overline{I}_c = \frac{\overline{V}_{cn}}{Z_L} = \frac{V_{ph}}{|Z_L|} \angle (-\phi - \frac{4\pi}{3}) \quad (2\text{-}26)$$

The three-phase voltage and current phasors are shown in Fig. 2-13b. The total real and reactive powers in a balanced three-phase circuit can be obtained by multiplying the per-phase values by a factor of 3. The total power factor is the same as its per-phase value.

2-4-2 Per-Phase Analysis of Balanced Circuits including Mutual Couplings

Most three-phase apparatus such as generators, transmission lines and motors consist of mutually coupled phases. For example, in a three-phase synchronous generator, the current in a phase winding produces flux lines that link not only that phase winding but the other phase windings as well. In general, in a balanced three-phase circuit, this can be represented as shown in Fig. 2-14a where Z_{self} is the impedance of a phase by itself, and Z_{mutual} represents mutual coupling. Therefore,

$$\overline{V}_{aA} = Z_{self}\overline{I}_a + Z_{mutual}\overline{I}_b + Z_{mutual}\overline{I}_c \tag{2-27}$$

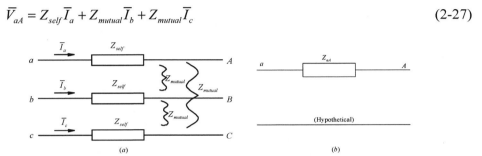

Fig. 2-14 Balanced three-phase network with mutual couplings.

In a balanced three-phase circuit under balanced excitation, three currents sum to zero: $\overline{I}_a + \overline{I}_b + \overline{I}_c = 0$. Therefore, making use of this condition in Eq. 2-25,

$$\overline{V}_{aA} = (Z_{self} - Z_{mutual})\overline{I}_a = Z_{aA}\overline{I}_a \tag{2-28}$$

where,

$$Z_{aA} = Z_{self} - Z_{mutual} \tag{2-29}$$

and the per-phase representation is as shown in Fig. 2-14b.

2-4-3 Line-to-Line Voltages

In the balanced wye-connected circuit of Fig. 2-12a, it is often necessary to consider the line-to-line voltages, such as those between phases "a" and "b," and so on. Based on the previous analysis, we can refer to both neutral points "n" and "N" by a common term "n," since the potential difference between n and N is zero. Therefore, in Fig. 2-12a, as shown in the phasor diagram of Fig. 2-15,

$$\overline{V}_{ab} = \overline{V}_{an} - \overline{V}_{bn}, \quad \overline{V}_{bc} = \overline{V}_{bn} - \overline{V}_{cn}, \quad \text{and} \quad \overline{V}_{ca} = \overline{V}_{cn} - \overline{V}_{an} \tag{2-30}$$

Either using Eqs. 2-24 and 2-30, or graphically from Fig. 2-15, we can show the following where V_{ph} is the rms magnitude of each of the phase voltages:

$$\overline{V}_{ab} = \sqrt{3}V_{ph}\angle\frac{\pi}{6}$$

$$\overline{V}_{bc} = \sqrt{3}V_{ph}\angle(\frac{\pi}{6} - \frac{2\pi}{3}) = \sqrt{3}V_{ph}\angle - \frac{\pi}{2}$$

$$\overline{V}_{ca} = \sqrt{3}V_{ph}\angle(\frac{\pi}{6} - \frac{4\pi}{3}) = \sqrt{3}V_{ph}\angle - \frac{7\pi}{6}$$

(2-31)

Fig. 2-15 Line-to-line voltages in a three-phase circuit.

Comparing Eqs. 2-24 and 2-31, we see that the line-to-line voltages have an rms value that is $\sqrt{3}$ times the phase voltage (rms):

$$V_{LL} = \sqrt{3}V_{ph}$$

(2-32)

and $\overline{V}_{ab}$ leads $\overline{V}_{an}$ by $\pi/6$ radians (30^0).

▲ **Example 2-6** In residential buildings where three-phase voltages are brought in, the rms value of the line-line voltage is $V_{LL} = 208V$. Calculate the rms value of the phase voltages.

Solution From Eq. 2-32,

$$V_{ph} = \frac{V_{LL}}{\sqrt{3}} = 120V$$

▲

2-4-4 Delta-Connected Loads

In ac-motor drives or transformers, for example, the three phase-windings may be connected in a delta configuration. Under a totally balanced condition, it is possible to replace the delta-connected load with an equivalent wye-connected load similar to that in Fig. 2-12a. We can then apply a per-phase analysis using Fig. 2-13. To discuss delta-wye transformation, consider the delta-connected load impedances of Fig. 2-16a. In terms of the currents drawn, these delta-connected impedances are equivalent to the wye-connected impedances in the circuit of Fig. 2-16b, which is easy to analyze on a per-phase basis, where

$$Z_y = \frac{Z_\Delta}{3} \tag{2-33}$$

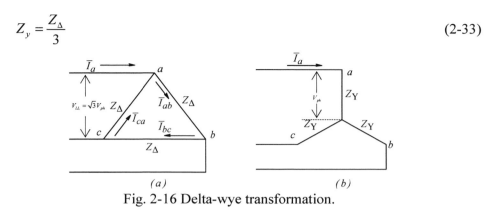

(a)   *(b)*

Fig. 2-16 Delta-wye transformation.

2-4-5   Power, Reactive Power and Power Factor In Three-Phase Circuits

We saw earlier that the per-phase analysis is valid for balanced three-phase circuits in sinusoidal steady state. This implies that the real and reactive powers drawn by each phase are the same as if were a single-phase load. Therefore, the total average real power and the reactive power in a three-phase circuit are ($V = V_{ph}$ and $I = I_{ph}$)

$$P_{3-phase} = 3 \times P_{per-phase} = 3VI\cos\phi \tag{2-34}$$

$$Q_{3-phase} = 3 \times Q_{per-phase} = 3VI\sin\phi \tag{2-35}$$

and the total apparent volt-ampers are

$$\left|S\right|_{3-phase} = 3 \times \left|S_{per-phase}\right| = 3VI \tag{2-36}$$

Therefore, the power factor in a three-phase circuit is the same as the per-phase power factor

$$\text{power factor} = \frac{P_{3-phase}}{\left|S\right|_{3-phase}} = \frac{3VI\cos\phi}{3VI} = \cos\phi \tag{2-37}$$

However, there is one very important difference between three-phase and single-phase circuits in terms of the instantaneous power. In both circuits, in each phase, the instantaneous power is pulsating as given by Eq. 2-11 and repeated below for phase-a, where the phase current lags by a phase angle $\phi(t)$ behind the phase voltage, which is considered to be the reference phasor:

$$p_a(t) = \sqrt{2}V\cos\omega t \cdot \sqrt{2}I\cos(\omega t - \phi) = VI\cos\phi + VI\cos(2\omega t - \phi) \tag{2-38}$$

2-15

Similar expressions can be written for phases b and c:

$$p_b(t) = \sqrt{2}V \cos(\omega t - 2\pi/3) \cdot \sqrt{2}I \cos(\omega t - \phi - 2\pi/3)$$
$$= VI \cos\phi + VI \cos(2\omega t - \phi - 4\pi/3) \tag{2-39}$$

$$p_c(t) = \sqrt{2}V \cos(\omega t - 4\pi/3) \cdot \sqrt{2}I \cos(\omega t - \phi - 4\pi/3)$$
$$= VI \cos\phi + VI \cos(2\omega t - \phi - 8\pi/3) \tag{2-40}$$

Addition of the three instantaneous powers in Eqs. 2-38 through 2-40 results in

$$p_{3-phase}(t) = 3VI \cos\phi = P_{3-phase} \quad \text{(from Eq. 2-34)} \tag{2-41}$$

which shows that the combined three-phase power in steady state is a constant, equal to its average value, even on an instantaneous basis. This is in contrast to the pulsating power, shown in Fig. 2-7, in single-phase circuits. The non-pulsating total instantaneous power in three-phase circuits results in non-pulsating torque in motors and generators, and is the reason for preferring three-phase motors and generators over their single-phase counterparts.

▲ **Example 2-7** In the three-phase circuit of Fig. 2-12a, $V_{LL} = 208V$, $|Z_L| = 10\Omega$, and the per-phase power factor is 0.8 (lagging). Calculate the capacitive reactance needed, in parallel with the load impedance in each phase, to make the power factor 0.95 (lagging).

Solution   The three-phase circuit of Fig. 2-12a can be represented by the per-phase circuit of Fig. 2-13a. Assuming the input voltage to the reference phasor,

$$\overline{V}_{an} = \frac{208}{\sqrt{3}} \angle 0 = \underbrace{120}_{(=V)} \angle 0V.$$ The current $\overline{I}_L$ drawn by the load lags the voltage by an angle

$\phi_L = \cos^{-1}(0.8) = 36.87^0$, and

$$\overline{I}_L = \frac{V(=120)}{|Z_L|} \angle - \phi_L = 12\angle -36.87^0\, A.$$

Therefore, the per-phase real power P_L, and the reactive var (volt-amperes reactive) Q_L drawn by the load are

$$P_L = \frac{V^2}{|Z_L|}(\text{power Factor}) = 1152W, \text{ and } Q_L = \frac{V^2}{|Z_L|}\sin\phi_L = 864VAR.$$

To make the net power factor is to be 0.95 (lagging), a power-factor-correction capacitor of an appropriate value is connected in parallel with the load in each phase. Now, the net current into the combination of the load impedance and the power-factor-correction capacitor is at an angle of $\phi_{net} = \cos^{-1}(0.95) = 18.195^0$ (lagging). The net real power P_{net}

2-16

drawn from the source still equals P_L, that is, $P_{net} = P_L$. Using the power-triangle of Fig. 2-8c, the net reactive var drawn from the source is

$$Q_{net} = P_{net} \tan(\phi_{net}) = 378.65 VAR. \text{ Since, } Q_{net} = Q_L - Q_{cap},$$

$$Q_{cap} = Q_L - Q_{net} = 864.0 - 378.65 = 485.35 VAR.$$

Therefore, the capacitive reactance needed in parallel is

$$X_{cap} = \frac{V^2}{Q_{cap}} = 29.67\Omega. \qquad \blacktriangle$$

2-5   REAL AND REACTIVE POWER TRANSFER BETWEEN AC SYSTEMS

In this course, it will be important to calculate power flow between ac systems connected by transmission lines. Simplified ac systems can be represented by two ac voltage sources of the same frequency connected through a reactance X in series as shown in Fig. 2-17a, where the series resistance has been neglected for simplification.

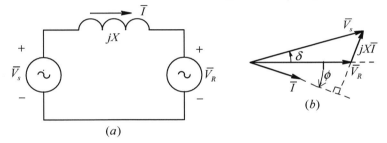

Fig. 2-17 Power transfer between two ac systems.

The phasor diagram for the system of Fig. 2-17a, where the voltage $\overline{V}_R$ is assumed to be the reference voltage with its phase angle to be zero, is shown in Fig. 2-17b. Based on the load, the current may be at some arbitrary phase angle ϕ. In the circuit of Fig. 2-17a,

$$\overline{I} = \frac{\overline{V}_S - \overline{V}_R}{jX} \qquad (2\text{-}42)$$

At the receiving-end, the complex power can be written as

$$S_R = P_R + jQ_R = V_R \overline{I}^* \qquad (2\text{-}43)$$

Using the complex conjugate from Eq. 2-42 into Eq. 2-43

$$P_R + jQ_R = V_R \left(\frac{V_S \angle(-\delta) - V_R}{-jX} \right) = \underbrace{\frac{V_S V_R \sin\delta}{X}}_{(=P_R)} + j\underbrace{\left(\frac{V_S V_R \cos\delta - V_R^2}{X} \right)}_{(=Q_R)} \qquad (2\text{-}44)$$

$$\therefore \qquad P_R = \underbrace{\frac{V_S V_R}{X}}_{(=P_{max})} \sin\delta \qquad \text{where} \qquad P_{max} = \frac{V_S V_R}{X} \tag{2-45}$$

which is the same as the sending end power P_S assuming no transmission-line losses. The discussion above shows that the real power P flows "downhill" on the phase angles of the voltages, and not on their magnitudes. It is plotted in Fig. 2-18 for positive values of δ.

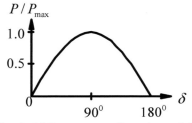

Fig. 2-18 Power as a function of δ.

Focusing on the reactive power, from Eq. 2-44,

$$Q_R = \frac{V_S V_R \cos\delta}{X} - \frac{V_R^2}{X} \tag{2-46}$$

If the power transfer between the two systems is zero, then, from Eq. 2-45, $\sin\delta$ and the angle δ are equal to zero. Under this condition, from Eq. 2-46,

$$Q_R = \frac{V_S V_R}{X} - \frac{V_R^2}{X} = \frac{V_R}{X}(V_S - V_R) \qquad \text{(if } P_R = 0 \text{)} \tag{2-47}$$

which shows that the reactive power at the receiving-end is related to the difference $(V_S - V_R)$ between the two voltage magnitudes.

The real and the reactive power transfers given by Eq. 2-45 through 2-47 are extremely important in the discussion of power and reactive power flows in later chapters.

2-6 APPARATUS RATINGS, BASE VALUES AND PER-UNIT QUANTITIES

2-6-1   Ratings

All power apparatus such as generators, transformers or the transmission lines have a voltage rating V_{rated}, which is the nominal voltage that an apparatus is designed to be operated at, based on its insulation or to avoid magnetic saturation at the operating frequency, whichever may be more limiting. Similarly, each apparatus has a current rating I_{rated}, which is the nominal current, usually specified in terms of rms, which the apparatus is designed to be operated at in steady state, and beyond which excessive I^2R heating may cause damage to the apparatus.

2-6-2 Base Values and Per-Unit Values

The parameters of an apparatus are specified in per-unit as a fraction of the appropriate base values. Often, the rated voltage and the rated current are chosen as base values and the other base quantities are calculated based on these two base values. There are several reasons for specifying apparatus parameters in per-unit:

1. Regardless of the size of the equipment, the per-unit values based on the apparatus voltage and current ratings lie in a narrow range and hence are easy to check or estimate, and

2. Power systems under study involve several transformers and hence such a system has several voltage and current ratings as we will study in the chapter on transformers. In such a system, a set of base values is chosen that is common to the entire system. Using parameters in per-unit of these common base values highly simplifies the analysis, where the voltage and current transformation due to the turns-ratio of the transformers are eliminated from calculations, as discussed in the chapter dealing with calculations of power flow.

With V_{base} and I_{base}, the other base quantities can be calculated as follows:

$$R_{base}, X_{base}, Z_{base} = \frac{V_{base}}{I_{base}} \qquad \text{(in } \Omega \text{)} \qquad (2\text{-}48)$$

$$G_{base}, B_{base}, Y_{base} = \frac{I_{base}}{V_{base}} \qquad \text{(in } \mho \text{)} \qquad (2\text{-}49)$$

$$P_{base}, Q_{base}, (VA)_{base} = V_{base} I_{base} \qquad \text{(in Watt, VAR, or VA)} \qquad (2\text{-}50)$$

In terms of these base quantities, the per-unit quantities can be specified as

$$\text{Per-Unit Value} = \frac{\text{actual value}}{\text{base value}} \qquad (2\text{-}51)$$

As mentioned earlier, the parameters of an apparatus are specified in per-unit of the base values that usually equal its rated voltage and current. Another benefit of using per-unit quantities is that their values remain the same on per-phase basis or a total three-phase basis. For example, if we are considering per-phase power, the power in Watts is one-third of the total power and so is its base value compared to that in the three-phase case.

▲ **Example 2-8** In Example 2-7, calculate the per-unit values of the per-phase voltage, the load impedance, the load current, and the load real and reactive powers, if the line-line voltage base is 208 V (rms) and the base value of the three-phase power is 5.4 kW.

Solution   Given that $V_{LL,base} = 208V$, $V_{ph,base} = 120V$. The base value of the per-phase

power is $P_{ph,base} = \dfrac{5400}{3} = 1800W$. Therefore,

$$I_{base} = \frac{P_{ph,base}}{V_{ph,base}} = 15\,A \text{, and } Z_{base} = \frac{V_{ph,base}}{I_{base}} = 8\Omega \,.$$

With these base values, $\overline{V}_{ph} = 1.0\angle 0\,pu$, $\overline{I} = 0.8\angle -36.87^0\,pu$, $Z_L = 1.25\angle -36.87^0\,pu$,

$P_L = 0.64\,pu$, and $Q_L = 0.48\,pu$. ▲

2-7 ENERGY EFFICIENCIES OF POWER SYSTEM APPARATUS

Power system apparatus must be energy efficient and reliable, have a high power density thus reducing their size and weight, and be low cost to make the overall system economically feasible. High energy efficiency is important for several reasons: it lowers operating costs by avoiding the cost of wasted energy, contributes less to global warming, and reduces the need for cooling therefore increasing power density.

The energy efficiency η of an apparatus in Fig. 2-19 is

$$\eta = \frac{P_o}{P_{in}} \tag{2-52}$$

which, in terms of the output power P_o and the power loss P_{loss} within the apparatus is

$$\eta = \frac{P_o}{P_o + P_{loss}} \tag{2-53}$$

Fig. 2-19 Energy Efficiency $\eta = P_o / P_{in}$.

In power systems, the apparatus such as transformers and generators have percentage energy efficiencies in upper 90's, and there is constant pursuit to increase them further.

2-8 ELECTROMAGNETIC CONCEPTS

Many of the apparatus used in power systems, like transformers, synchronous generators, transmission lines and motor loads require a basic understanding of electromagnetic concepts which will be reviewed in this section.

2-8-1   Ampere's Law

When a current i is passed through a conductor, a magnetic field is produced. The direction of the magnetic field depends on the direction of the current. As shown in Fig.

2-20

2-20a, the current through a conductor, perpendicular and *into* the paper plane, is represented by "×"; this current produces magnetic field in a clockwise direction. Conversely, the current *out of* the paper plane, represented by a dot, produces magnetic field in a counter-clockwise direction, as shown in Fig. 2-20b.

Fig. 2-20 Ampere's Law.

The magnetic-field intensity H produced by current-carrying conductors can be obtained by means of Ampere's Law, which in its simplest form states that, at anytime, the line (contour) integral of the magnetic field intensity along *any* closed path equals the total current enclosed by this path. Therefore, in Fig. 2-20c,

$$\oint H d\ell = \Sigma i \tag{2-54}$$

where $\oint$ represents a contour or a closed-line integration. Note that the scalar H in Eq. 2-54 is the component of the magnetic field intensity (a vector field) in the direction of the differential length $d\ell$ along the closed path. Alternatively, we can express the field intensity and the differential length to be vector quantities, which will require a dot product on the left side of Eq. 2-54.

▲ **Example 2-9** Consider the coil in Fig. 2-21, which has $N = 25$ turns and the toroid has an inside diameter $ID = 5\,cm$ and an outside diameter $OD = 5.5\,cm$.

Fig. 2-21 Example 2-9.

For a current $i = 3\,A$, calculate the field intensity H along the mean-path length within the toroid.

Solution   Due to symmetry, the magnetic field intensity H_m along a circular contour within the toroid is constant. In Fig. 2-21, the mean radius $r_m = \frac{1}{2}(\frac{OD+ID}{2})$. Therefore, the mean path of length $\ell_m (= 2\pi r_m = 0.165m)$ encloses the current i N-times, as shown in Fig. 2-21b. Therefore, from Ampere's Law in Eq. 2-54, the field intensity along this mean path is

$$H_m = \frac{Ni}{\ell_m} \qquad (2\text{-}55)$$

which for the given values can be calculated as

$$H_m = \frac{25\times3}{0.165} = 454.5\ A/m .$$

If the width of the toroid is much smaller than the mean radius r_m, it is reasonable to assume a uniform H_m throughout the cross-section of the toroid.   ▲

The field intensity in Eq. 2-55 has the units of [A/m], noting that "turns" is a unit-less quantity. The product Ni is commonly referred to as the ampere-turns or mmf F that produces the magnetic field. The current in Eq. 2-55 may be dc, or time varying. If the current is time varying, the relationship in Eq. 2-55 is valid on an instantaneous basis; that is, $H_m(t)$ is related to $i(t)$ by N/ℓ_m.

2-8-2   FLUX DENSITY B AND THE FLUX ϕ

At any instant of time t for a given H-field, the density of flux lines, called the flux density B (in units of $[T]$ for Tesla) depends on the permeability μ of the material on which this H-field is acting. In air,

$$B = \mu_o H \qquad \mu_o = 4\pi \times 10^{-7} \left[\frac{henries}{m} \right] \qquad (2\text{-}56)$$

where μ_o is the permeability of air or free space.

2-8-3   Ferromagnetic Materials

Ferromagnetic materials guide magnetic fields and, due to their high permeability, require small ampere-turns (a small current for a given number of turns) to produce the desired flux density. These materials exhibit the multi-valued nonlinear behavior shown by their B-H characteristics in Fig. 2-22a. Imagine that the toroid in Fig. 2-21 consists of a ferromagnetic material such as silicon steel. If the current through the coil is slowly varied in a sinusoidal manner with time, the corresponding H-field will cause one of the hysteresis loops shown in Fig. 2-22a to be traced. Completing the loop once results in a net dissipation of energy within the material. This energy loss per cycle is referred as the hysteresis loss.

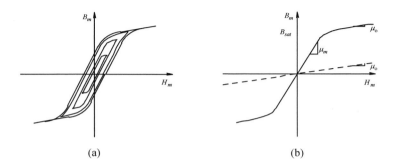

(a)   (b)

Fig. 2-22 B-H characteristic of ferromagnetic materials.

Increasing the peak value of the sinusoidally-varying H-field will result in a bigger hysteresis loop. Joining the peaks of the hysteresis loop, we can approximate the B-H characteristic by the single curve shown in Fig. 2-22b. At low values of magnetic field, the B-H characteristic is assumed to be linear with a constant slope, such that

$$B_m = \mu_m H_m \qquad\qquad\qquad\qquad (2\text{-}57a)$$

where μ_m is the permeability of the ferromagnetic material. Typically, the μ_m of a material is expressed in terms of a permeability μ_r relative to the permeability of air:

$$\mu_m = \mu_r \mu_o \qquad\qquad (\mu_r = \frac{\mu_m}{\mu_o}) \qquad\qquad (2\text{-}57b)$$

In ferromagnetic materials, μ_m can be several thousand times larger than μ_o .

In Fig. 2-22b, the linear relationship (with a constant μ_m) is approximately valid until the "knee" of the curve is reached, beyond which the material begins to saturate. Ferromagnetic materials are often operated up to a maximum flux density, slightly above the "knee" of 1.6 T to 1.8 T , beyond which many more ampere-turns are required to increase flux density only slightly. In the saturated region, the incremental permeability of the magnetic material approaches μ_o , as shown by the slope of the curve in Fig. 2-22b.

In this course, we will assume that the magnetic material is operating in its linear region and therefore its characteristic can be represented by $B_m = \mu_m H_m$, where μ_m remains constant.

2-8-4 Flux ϕ

Magnetic flux lines form closed paths, as shown in Fig. 2-23's toroidal magnetic core, which is surrounded by the current-carrying coil.

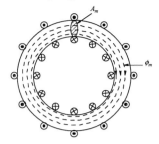

Fig. 2-23 Toroid with flux ϕ_m.

The flux in the toroid can be calculated by selecting a circular area A_m in a plane perpendicular to the direction of the flux lines. As discussed in Example 2-9, it is reasonable to assume a uniform H_m and hence a uniform flux-density B_m throughout the core cross-section. Substituting for H_m from Eq. 2-55 into Eq. 2-57a,

$$B_m = \mu_m \frac{Ni}{\ell_m} \tag{2-58}$$

where B_m is the density of flux lines in the core. Therefore, making the assumption of a uniform B_m, the flux ϕ_m can be calculated as

$$\phi_m = B_m A_m \tag{2-59}$$

where flux has the units of Weber [Wb]. Substituting for B_m from Eq. 2-58 into Eq. 2-57,

$$\phi_m = A_m \left(\mu_m \frac{Ni}{\ell_m} \right) = \frac{Ni}{\underbrace{\left(\dfrac{\ell_m}{\mu_m A_m} \right)}_{\mathfrak{R}_m}} \tag{2-60}$$

where Ni equals the ampere-turns (or mmf F) applied to the core, and the term within the brackets on the right side is called the reluctance $\mathfrak{R}_m$ of the magnetic core. From Eq. 2-60

$$\mathfrak{R}_m = \frac{\ell_m}{\mu_m A_m} \; [A/Wb] \tag{2-61}$$

Eq. 2-60 makes it clear that the reluctance has the units [*A/Wb*]. Eq. 2-61 shows that the reluctance of a magnetic structure, for example the toroid in Fig. 2-23, is linearly proportional to its magnetic path length and inversely proportional to both its cross-sectional area and the permeability of its material.

Eq. 2-60 shows that the amount of flux produced by the applied ampere-turns F ($= Ni$) is inversely proportional to the reluctance $\mathfrak{R}$; this relationship is analogous to Ohm's Law ($I = V/R$) in electric circuits in dc steady state.

2-8-5 Flux Linkage

If all turns of a coil, for example the one in Fig. 2-23, are linked by the same flux ϕ, then the coil has a flux linkage λ, where

$$\lambda = N\phi \tag{2-62}$$

In the absence of magnetic saturation, the flux-linkage λ is related to the coil current i by the coil inductance, as illustrated in the next section.

2-8-6 INDUCTANCES

At any instant of time in the coil of Fig. 2-24a, the flux linkage of the coil (due to flux lines entirely in the core) is related to the current i by a parameter defined as the inductance L_m:

$$\lambda_m = L_m i \tag{2-63}$$

where the inductance $L_m (= \lambda_m / i)$ is constant if the core material is in its linear operating region. The coil inductance in the linear magnetic region can be calculated by multiplying all the factors shown in Fig. 2-24b, which are based on earlier equations:

$$L_m = \left(\frac{N}{\ell_m}\right)\mu_m A_m N = \frac{N^2}{\left(\dfrac{\ell_m}{\mu_m A_m}\right)} = \frac{N^2}{\mathfrak{R}_m} \tag{2-64}$$

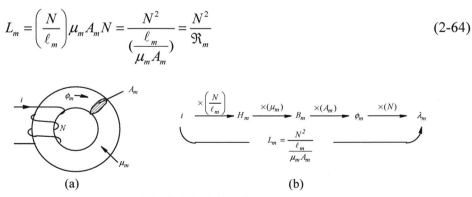

(a)   (b)

Fig. 2-24 Coil inductance.

Eq. 2-64 indicates that the inductance L_m is strictly a property of the magnetic circuit (i.e., the core material, the geometry, and the number of turns), provided that the operation is in the linear range of the magnetic material, where the slope of its *B-H* characteristic can be represented by a constant μ_m.

▲ **Example 2-10**   In the rectangular toroid of Fig. 2-25, $w = 5\,mm$, $h = 15\,mm$, the mean path length $\ell_m = 18\,cm$, $\mu_r = 5000$, and $N = 100$ turns.   Calculate the coil inductance L_m, assuming that the core is unsaturated.

Fig. 2-25 Rectangular toroid.

Solution   From Eq. 2-61,

$$\mathfrak{R}_m = \frac{\ell_m}{\mu_m A_m} = \frac{0.18}{5000 \times 4\pi \times 10^{-7} \times 5 \times 10^{-3} \times 15 \times 10^{-3}} = 38.2 \times 10^4 \, \frac{A}{Wb}.$$

Therefore, from Eq. 2-64,

$$L_m = \frac{N^2}{\mathfrak{R}_m} = 26.18\,mH.$$

▲

2-8-7   FARADAY'S LAW: INDUCED VOLTAGE IN A COIL DUE TO TIME-RATE OF CHANGE OF FLUX LINKAGE

In our discussion so far, we have established in magnetic circuits relationships between the electrical quantity i and the magnetic quantities H, B, ϕ, and λ.   These relationships are valid under dc (static) conditions, as well as at any instant when these quantities are varying with time.   We will now examine the voltage across the coil under time-*varying* conditions.   In the coil of Fig. 2-7, Faraday's Law dictates that the time-rate of change of flux-linkage equals the voltage across the coil at any instant:

$$e(t) = \frac{d}{dt}\lambda(t) = N\frac{d}{dt}\phi(t) \tag{2-65}$$

This assumes that all flux lines link all *N*-turns such that $\lambda = N\phi$.   The polarity of the emf $e(t)$ and the direction of $\phi(t)$ in the above equation are yet to be justified.

Fig. 2-26 Voltage polarity and direction of flux and current.

The above relationship is valid, no matter what is causing the flux to change. One possibility is that a second coil is placed on the same core. When the second coil is supplied by a time-varying current, mutual coupling causes the flux ϕ through the coil shown in Fig. 2-26 to change with time. The other possibility is that a voltage $e(t)$ is applied across the coil in Fig. 2-26, causing the change in flux, which can be calculated by integrating both sides of Eq. 2-65 with respect to time:

$$\phi(t) = \phi(0) + \frac{1}{N}\int_0^t e(\tau)\cdot d\tau \qquad (2\text{-}66)$$

where $\phi(0)$ is the initial flux at $t=0$ and τ is a variable of integration.

Recalling the Ohm's Law equation $v = Ri$, the current direction through a resistor is defined to be into the terminal chosen to be of the positive polarity. This is the passive sign convention. Similarly, in the coil of Fig. 2-26, we can establish the voltage polarity and the flux direction in order to apply Faraday's Law, given by Eqs. 2-65 and 2-66. If the flux direction is given, we can establish the voltage polarity as follows: first determine the direction of a hypothetical current that will produce flux in the same direction as given. Then, the positive polarity for the voltage is at the terminal which this hypothetical current is entering. Conversely, if the voltage polarity is given, imagine a hypothetical current entering the positive-polarity terminal. This current, based on how the coil is wound, for example in Fig. 2-26, determines the flux direction for use in Eqs. 2-65 and 2-66. Following these rules to determine the voltage polarity and the flux direction is easier than applying Lenz's Law (not discussed here).

▲ **Example 2-11** In the structure of Fig. 2-26, the flux $\phi_m (= \hat{\phi}_m \sin \omega t)$ linking the coil is varying sinusoidally with time, where $N = 300$ turns, $f = 60\,Hz$, and the cross-sectional area $A_m = 10\,cm^2$. The peak flux density $\hat{B}_m = 1.5\,T$. Calculate the expression for the induced voltage with the polarity shown in Fig. 2-26. Plot the flux and the induced voltage as functions of time.

Solution From Eq. 2-59, $\hat{\phi}_m = \hat{B}_m A_m = 1.5 \times 10 \times 10^{-4} = 1.5 \times 10^{-3}\,Wb$.

From Faraday's Law in Eq. 2-63, the induced voltage below is

$$e(t) = \omega N \hat{\phi}_m \cos \omega t = 2\pi \times 60 \times 300 \times 1.5 \times 10^{-3} \times \cos \omega t = 169.65 \cos \omega t \ V \ .$$

The induced voltage and the flux waveform are plotted in Fig. 2-27, from which we can concluded that the induced voltage phasor leads the flux phasor by 90^0.

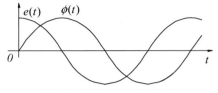

Fig. 2-27 Example 2-11.

▲

Example 2-11 illustrates that the voltage is induced due to $d\phi/dt$, regardless of whether any current flows in that coil.

2-8-8   LEAKAGE AND MAGNETIZING INDUCTANCES

Just as conductors guide currents in electric circuits, magnetic cores guide *flux* in *magnetic circuits*.   But there is an important difference.   In electric circuits, the conductivity of copper is approximately 10^{20} times higher than that of air, allowing leakage currents to be neglected at dc or at low frequencies such as 60 *Hz*.   In magnetic circuits, however, the permeabilities of magnetic materials are only around 10^4 times greater than that of air.   Because of this relatively low ratio, not all the flux is confined to the core in the structure of Fig. 2-28a, and the core window also has flux lines which are called "leakage".   Note that the coil shown in Fig. 2-28a is drawn schematically.   In practice, the coil consists of multiple layers and the core is designed to fit as snugly to the coil as possible, thus minimizing the unused "window" area.

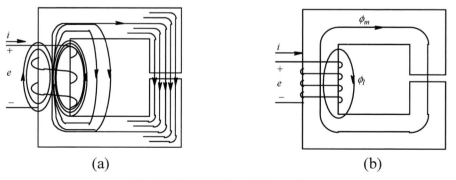

(a)   (b)

Fig. 2-28 Including leakage flux.

The leakage effect makes accurate analysis of magnetic circuits more difficult, so that it requires sophisticated numerical methods, such as finite element analysis.   However, we can account for the effect of leakage fluxes by making certain approximations. We can divide the total flux ϕ into two parts: the magnetic flux ϕ_m, which is completely confined to the core and links all N turns, and the leakage flux, which is partially or entirely in air and is represented by an "equivalent" leakage flux ϕ_ℓ, which also links all N turns of the coil but does not follow the entire magnetic path, as shown in Fig. 2-28b. Thus,

$$\phi = \phi_m + \phi_\ell \tag{2-67}$$

where ϕ is the equivalent flux which links all N turns. Therefore, the total flux linkage of the coil is

$$\lambda = N\phi = \underbrace{N\phi_m}_{\lambda_m} + \underbrace{N\phi_\ell}_{\lambda_\ell} = \lambda_m + \lambda_\ell \tag{2-68}$$

The total inductance (called the self-inductance) can be obtained by dividing both sides of Eq. 2-68 by the current i :

$$\underbrace{\frac{\lambda}{i}}_{L_{self}} = \underbrace{\frac{\lambda_m}{i}}_{L_m} + \underbrace{\frac{\lambda_\ell}{i}}_{L_\ell} \tag{2-69}$$

Therefore,

$$L_{self} = L_m + L_\ell \tag{2-70}$$

where L_m is often called the *magnetizing inductance* due to ϕ_m in the magnetic core, and L_ℓ is called the *leakage inductance* due to the leakage flux ϕ_ℓ. From Eq. 2-70, the total flux linkage of the coil can be written as

$$\lambda = (L_m + L_\ell)i \tag{2-71}$$

Hence, from Faraday's Law in Eq. 2-65,

$$e(t) = L_\ell \frac{di}{dt} + \underbrace{L_m \frac{di}{dt}}_{e_m(t)} \tag{2-72}$$

This results in the circuit of Fig. 2-29a. In Fig. 2-29b, the voltage drop due to the leakage inductance can be shown separately so that the voltage induced in the coil is solely due to the magnetizing flux. The coil resistance R can then be added in series to complete the representation of the coil.

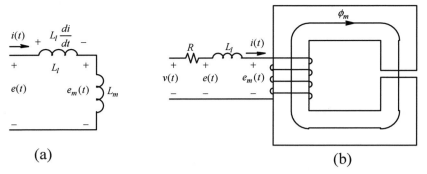

(a)   (b)

Fig. 2-29 Analysis including the leakage flux.

REFERENCES

Any textbooks in basic electric circuits and electromagnetic field theory.

PROBLEMS

2-1   Express the following voltages as phasors: (a) $v_1(t) = \sqrt{2} \times 100\cos(\omega t - 30^0)\ V$ and (b) $v_2(t) = \sqrt{2} \times 100\cos(\omega t + 30^0)\ V$.

2-2   The series R-L-C circuit of Fig. 2-3a is in a sinusoidal steady state at a frequency of 60 Hz. V=120 V, R = 1.5 Ω, L= 20 mH, and C=100 μF . Calculate $i(t)$ in this circuit by solving the differential equation Eq. 2-3.

2-3   Repeat Problem 2-2 using the phasor-domain analysis.

2-4   In a linear circuit in sinusoidal steady state with only one active source $\overline{V} = 90\angle 30^\circ\ V$, the current in a branch is $\overline{I} = 5\angle 15^o\ A$. Calculate the current in the same branch if the source voltage were to be $100\angle 0^0 V$.

2-5   To the circuit of Example 2-1, if a voltage $100\angle 0^0 V$ is applied, calculate P , Q , and the power factor. Show that $Q = \sum_k I_k^2 X_k$.

2-6   Show that a series-connected load with R_s and X_s , as shown below in Fig. P2-6a can be represented by a parallel combination, as shown in Fig. 2-6b, where $R_p = (R_s^2 + X_s^2)/ R_s$ and $X_p = (R_s^2 + X_s^2)/ X_s$.

(a)   (b)

Fig. P2-6

2-7 Using the results of the series-parallel conversion in Problem 2-6, calculate the equivalent R_p and X_p to represent the circuit of Example 2-2.

2-8 Confirm the calculations of the equivalent R_p and X_p in Problem 2-7 by using P and Q calculated in Example 2-3, recognizing that in the parallel representation, P is entirely associated with R_p, and Q entirely with X_p.

2-9 In Example 2-5, calculate the compensating capacitor in parallel, necessary to make the overall power factor to 0.9 (leading).

2-10 An inductive load connected to a 120-V (rms), 60-Hz ac source draws 5 kW at a power factor of 0.8. Calculate the capacitance required in parallel with the load in order to bring the combined power factor to 0.95 (lagging).

2-11 A positive sequence (a-b-c), balanced, wye-connected voltage source has the phase-a voltage given as $\overline{V}_a = \sqrt{2} \times 100 \angle 30^o V$. Obtain the time-domain voltages $v_a(t)$, $v_b(t)$, $v_c(t)$, $v_{ab}(t)$, and show all of these as phasors.

2-12 A balanced three-phase inductive load is supplied in steady state by a balanced, wye-connected, three-phase voltage source with a phase voltage of 120 V rms. The load draws a total of 10 kW at a power factor of 0.9. Calculate the rms value of the phase currents and the magnitude of the per-phase load impedance, assuming a wye-connected load. Draw a phasor diagram showing all three voltages and currents.

2-13 Repeat Problem 2-12, assuming a delta-connected load.

2-14 The balanced circuit of Fig. 2-14 shows the impedance of 3-phase cables connecting the source terminals (a, b, c) to the load terminals (A, B, C), where $Z_{self} = (0.3 + j1.5)\Omega$ and $Z_{mutual} = j0.5\Omega$. Calculate $\overline{V}_A$ if $\overline{V}_a = 1000 \angle 0^0 V$ and $\overline{I}_a = 10 \angle -30^0 A$, where $\overline{V}_a$ and $\overline{V}_A$ are voltages with respect to a common neutral.

2-15 Similar to the calculation in section 2-4-2, in the balanced circuit of Fig. P2-15, calculate the per-phase capacitive currents in terms of the voltages, capacitances and the frequency.

Fig. P2-15

2-16   In the circuit of Fig. 2-17a, the power transfer is 1 kW from side 1 to 2. $V_S = 100V$, $\overline{V}_R = 95\angle 0^0 V$, and $X = 1.5\Omega$. Calculate the current, the phase angle of $\overline{V}_S$, and Q_R supplied to the receiving-end.

2-17   In a radial system represented by the circuit of Fig. 2-17a, $X = 1.5\Omega$. Consider the source voltage to be constant at $\overline{V}_S = 100\angle 0^0$. Calculate and plot V_S / V_R if the load varies in a range from 0 to 1 kW at the following three power factors: unity, 0.9 (lagging), 0.9 (leading).

2-18   Repeat Example 2-8 if the base 3-phase power is changed to 3.6 kW but all else remains the same.

2-19   Repeat Example 2-8 if the base line-line voltage is changed to 240V but all else remains the same.

2-20   Repeat Example 2-8 if the base line-line voltage is changed to 240V *and* the base 3-phase power is changed to 3.6 kW.

2-21   In Example 2-9, calculate the field intensity within the core: a) very close to the inside diameter and b) very close to the outside diameter. c) Compare the results with the field intensity along the mean path.

2-22   In Example 2-9, calculate the reluctance in the path of flux lines if $\mu_r = 2000$.

2-23   Consider the core of dimensions given in Example 2-9. The coil requires an inductance of $25\,\mu H$. The maximum current is $3\,A$ and the maximum flux density is not to exceed $1.3\,T$. Calculate the number of turns N and the relative permeability μ_r of the magnetic material that should be used.

2-24   In Problem 2-23, assume the permeability of the magnetic material to be infinite. To satisfy the conditions of maximum flux density and the desired inductance, a small air gap is introduced. Calculate the length of this air gap (neglecting the effect of flux fringing) and the number of turns N.

CHAPTER 3

ELECTRIC ENERGY AND THE ENVIRONMENT

3-1 INTRODUCTION

Figure 3-1a shows the production and consumption of energy by various means in the United States in 2004, which indicates that the consumption is nearly 100 Quadrillion (10^{15}) BTUs where as the production is only 70 Quadrillion BTUs, and the rest is being imported. (Approximately, 10,000 BTUs equal 2.93 kWh.) As shown in Fig. 3-1b, out of this total energy consumption, 38.9 Quadrillion BTUs, also 38.9%, since the consumption is nearly 100 Quadrillion BTUs, are used for generating electric power which is used in various sectors, where the primary consumption figures indicate sources other than electricity. Therefore, adding all the sectors, the total consumption minus the primary consumption equals electric energy consumption.

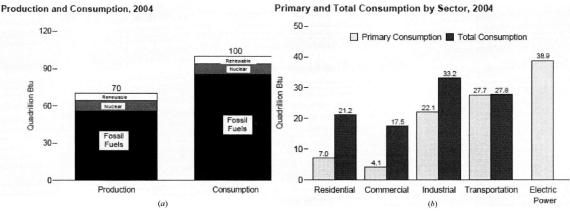

Fig. 3-1 Production and consumption of energy in the United States in 2004 [1].

Present installed generation capacity in the United States is approximately 10^6 MW, which is a substantial percentage of the world's total, and corresponds to roughly 3 kW per capita. Fig. 3-2 shows electric power generation by various fuel sources in 2004. In the coming years and decades, energy including electric energy is going to become increasingly a precious commodity. Therefore, how we use it will be critical from the geopolitical, social and the environmental points of view. In this chapter, we will briefly examine the present and the potential choices and their environment consequences.

Fig. 3-2 Electric power generation by various fuel types in the U.S. in 2005 [1].

3-2 CHOICES AND CONSEQUENCES

As illustrated in Fig. 3-2, electric energy is derived from various sources listed below, most of them from the sun directly or indirectly, except for the nuclear energy which dates back to the creation itself.

- Hydro
- Fossil Fuels: Coal, Natural Gas, Oil
- Nuclear
- Renewable: Wind, Solar, Biomass and Geothermal

There are environmental consequences of using energy; in fact, there is an environmental impact of all human activities. These consequences are listed below:

- Greenhouse Gases, primarily Carbon dioxide
- Sulfur Dioxide
- Nitrogen oxides
- Mercury
- Thermal Pollution

3-3 HYDRO POWER

This is one of the oldest forms for producing electricity. In hydro power plants, as shown in Fig. 3-3, water in a reservoir or a dam created out of a river is discharged through penstocks into turbines that spin generators and produce electricity. In such power plants, turbine efficiencies can be better than 93% [2].

Hydro power can be classified based on available head (drop in the river level): high, medium or low (run-of-river). Higher the head (H in Fig. 3-3), more is the potential energy that can be converted by the turbine into mechanical output. Because of the environmental impact and social implications that can be enormous, including uprooting of people, high and medium head hydro are generally not considered in the category of renewable energy, although technically they are. On the other hand, low-head (run-of-river) hydro, where the kinetic energy associated with flowing water is converted by a turbine into mechanical output, is considered renewable. As an example in a recent study, heads below 66 feet (20 m) were considered in the category of renewable energy. Hydro power plants can respond very quickly, in matter of a few seconds, by changing their output to meet the changes in the power demand.

Fig. 3-3 Hydro power (Source: www.bpa.gov).

3-4 FOSSIL-FUEL BASED POWER PLANTS

Fossil fuels are the main source of electric energy all over the world, except in a few countries such as hydro in Norway and nuclear in France. These fossil fuels are primarily in the following form:

- Coal
- Natural Gas and,
- Oil

Fossil fuels are derived from sun's energy by decaying vegetation and plants. In this sense, fossil fuels are also renewable but at a time scale that is much longer – hundreds of millions of years – as compared to the human existence. All the above sources of generation are discussed briefly in the following sections.

3-4-1   Coal-Fired Power Plants

As mentioned earlier, coal-fired power plants are the main source of electricity in most countries. United States is richly endowed with this resource with 30% of the world's total – enough to last hundreds of years. However, there are serious environmental consequences of burning coal, namely greenhouse gases as discussed later in this chapter. The available coal can be divided into the following categories where each type has its own characteristics in terms of the energy content and the resulting pollution: anthracite, bituminous, sub-bituminous, lignite and peat.

Coal is burnt using various coal-firing mechanisms with different efficiencies and carbon emission into the atmosphere: mechanical stokers, pulverized-coal firing, cyclone-furnace firing, fluidized-bed combustion, and gasification. Heat from burning of coal produces steam from water, which is used in the Rankine thermodynamic cycle, shown in Fig. 3-4, where water is used as a working fluid. Heat is added to the water at a high pressure in the boiler to produce steam, which expands through the turbine blades, and then is cooled in the condenser. Thermal efficiencies of such a cycle are typically in a 35-40 percent range, where for example, 9,000 BTU/kWh is typical, which corresponds to a conversion efficiency of approximately 38%.

In the above discussion of efficiencies, we should note that the limit of any thermal cycle efficiency is lower than that of a Carnot Cycle [3] efficiency η_c given below:

$$\eta_C = \frac{T_H - T_L}{T_H} \qquad (3\text{-}1)$$

where the temperatures are in Kelvin, T_H is the higher temperature at which the heat is added, and T_L is the lower temperature at which the heat is rejected.

Fig. 3-4 Rankine thermodynamic cycle in coal-fired power plants.

Coal-fired power plants have enormous environmental consequences as discussed later in this chapter, but the availability of coal at affordable cost makes it an attractive choice. Coal plants take a long time to bring on-line from cold start, and also to change their power output on demand, from one level to another, takes minutes.

3-4-2   Natural-Gas and Oil Power Plants

Natural gas is plentiful in certain regions of the world. Gas plants do not have the same environmental consequences as the coal-fired power plants such as mercury pollution, but the natural gas being a hydrocarbon-based fuel also contributes to the greenhouse gases. They are relatively inexpensive and quick to build and can have reasonable efficiencies as discussed below. Oil power plants are similar to gas-fired power plants in their operation and efficiencies.

3-4-2-1 Single-Cycle Gas Turbines

Single-cycle gas plants use Brayton thermodynamic cycle. Brayton thermodynamic cycle can take many different forms, simplest of which is shown in Fig. 3-5, where natural gas is burnt in the combustion chamber in the presence of compressed air and then expanded through the turbine blades in a manner similar to steam in the Rankine cycle.

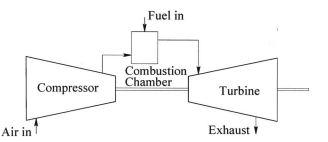

Fig. 3-5 Brayton thermodynamic cycle in natural-gas power plants.

In single-cycle gas-fired power plants, efficiencies are around 35 percent that are satisfactory where primary function is to supply peak loads.

3-4-2-2 Combined-Cycle Gas Turbines

In combine-cycle gas turbines, heat in the exhaust of the Brayton cycle mentioned above is recovered to operate another steam-based Rankine cycle and the efficiency can be boosted to be in a range of 55-60 percent. Because of high efficiencies, combined-cycle power plants can be base loaded, and sizes of such plants can be as high as 500 MW.

3-5 NUCLEAR POWER

As mentioned earlier, nuclear energy in matter dates back to the time of creation, the so called big bang, such that a gram of completely fissionable material can produce 1000 MW-Day of energy! A large nuclear plant can save 50,000 barrels of oil a day which at the present rate of above 60 dollars per barrel amounts to over 3 M$/day. Nuclear power doesn't contribute to greenhouse gases but it creates a serious problem of storing radioactive waste for generations to come. This is a problem that has not been resolved in the United States where there is a de facto moratorium on the construction of new nuclear power plants.

The nuclear process results in release of energy in a nuclear reactor which produces steam to spin a turbine and a generator connected to it, similar to that in coal-fired power plants using the Rankine thermodynamic cycle. Nuclear processes can be broadly classified into two categories which are briefly examined below.

3-5-1 Nuclear Fusion

Fusion is a thermonuclear reaction that is similar to the reaction that occurs incessantly on the sun where hydrogen atoms fuse together and release energy in the process. These atoms are at extremely high temperatures for this reaction to take place. In fusion reactors, two deuterium (H^2 or D) atoms fusing together result in a tritium (H^3 or T) atom, a proton (p), and in the process release 4 MeV of energy, as shown below, where 1 MeV of energy equals 4.44×10^{-20} kWh:

$$D + D \rightarrow T + p + 4\,Mev \qquad\qquad (3\text{-}2)$$

Unlike fission reactors discussed in the next section, fusion reactors would have a smaller radioactive waste problem. However, the plasma that consists of fusing atoms at millions of degree in temperature must be confined away from the reactor walls, and this problem is unlikely to be solved in the near future at a commercial scale, although another attempt is now beginning to be made [4].

3-5-2 Nuclear Fission Reactors

All large commercial nuclear reactors rely on the fission process. In this process, neutrons strike atoms of fissionable material like uranium, "splitting" them, and in the process releasing more neutrons to keep this chain reaction continuing and releasing energy. This reaction can be expressed as below:

$$_{92}U^{235} + {}_0n^1 \rightarrow {}_{54}Xe^{140} + {}_{38}Sr^{94} + 2\,{}_0n^1 + 196 \; Mev \qquad (3\text{-}3)$$

where subscripts correspond to the atomic number and superscripts to the atomic mass. The reaction above shows that a neutron striking a $_{92}U^{235}$ atom results in two other fission products, xenon $_{54}Xe^{140}$ and strontium $_{38}Sr^{94}$, two neutrons, and releases 196 MeV of energy. Resulting neutrons strike other uranium atoms and keep the chain reaction continuing in a controlled fashion.

In the fission process described above, the neutrons produced are at very high energy, which without being slowed would fail to strike other uranium atoms to keep the chain reaction going. Therefore, they must be "moderated", often by the coolant that transports heat and also acts as the "moderator". This chain reaction is controlled by control-rods that consist of, for example, boron that absorbs neutron and thus allows control over the rate at which the chain reaction is maintained. Generally, nuclear plants are base loaded, implying that they are operated at their rated capacity. In case of emergency, nuclear reactors can be shut down by releasing chemical shim that acts as a "poison" that "kills" the nuclear reaction. However, the use of chemical shim may result in the reactor to be inoperable for days that it takes to clean away its effect.

3-5-2-1 Pressurized Water Reactors (PWR)

In the past, a few boiling-water reactors (BWR), as shown in Fig. 3-6a, were built in addition to a few gas-cooled reactors (GCR). But most modern reactors are pressurized-water reactors (PWR). In PWRs, as shown in Fig. 3-6b, water under pressure that is keeps it from boiling acts as a coolant to transport heat and also as a moderator to continue the chain reaction. Using a heat exchanger, the secondary cycle results in its water to boil and the steam produced is used in a Rankine thermodynamic cycle, similar to that in coal-fired plants, to spin the turbine and the generator.

(a) (b)

Fig. 3-6 (a) BWR and (b) PWR reactors [5].

3-5-2-2 Pressurized Heavy Water Reactors (PHWR)

Natural uranium is composed of less than 1 percent of U^{235} and approximately 99 percent of U^{238}. In PWR and BWR reactors where natural water is used as the moderator, enriched uranium must be used so that it has a greater percentage of U^{235} compared to natural uranium. However, enriching uranium requires centrifuges which are extremely energy expensive and difficult to justify in the absence of a large weapons' program. Therefore in countries for example in Canada, CANDU reactors utilize natural uranium but use heavy water as the moderator and the coolant. Heavy water is derived from natural water in such a way it has the heavier isotope of hydrogen present. Except for this difference, otherwise, PHWRs, in principle, are similar to PWRs.

3-5-3-3 Fast Breeder Reactors

These reactors utilize plutonium and produce more nuclear fuel than they consume. Therefore, they can be self-sustaining, however, their extensive use of plutonium, a substance for making nuclear weapons, makes them an extremely risky proposition, particularly in this post-9/11 world. With its large Super-Phenix reactors, France has made the largest implementation of such breeder reactors.

3-6   RENEWABLE ENERGY

Renewable energy is a means of reducing the rate of pollution caused by fossil-fuel based power plants. Renewable sources include wind, solar, biomass, and others. Some of these are described briefly.

3-6-1   Wind Energy

Wind energy is an indirect manifestation of solar energy, caused by uneven heating of the earth's surface by the sun. Out of all renewable energies, wind has come a long way and still this potential is just beginning to be realized. Fig. 3-7 shows the wind potential by states in the United States, where there are several areas with good to excellent wind conditions.

In wind, the mass flow rate $\dot{m}$ in kg/s is

$$\dot{m} = \rho A V \qquad\qquad (3\text{-}4)$$

where ρ is the wind density in kg/m^3, A is the cross-sectional area in m^2 perpendicular to the wind velocity and V is the wind velocity in m/s.

Fig. 3-7 Wind-resource map of the United States [6].

Therefore, the power in wind is the rate of the kinetic energy of the wind stream:

$$P_{tot} = \frac{1}{2}\dot{m}V^2 = \frac{1}{2}\rho A V^3 \qquad\qquad (3\text{-}5)$$

which shows the highly nonlinear dependence of wind power on the cube of the wind velocity. All this power cannot be removed from the wind otherwise it will "pile up" behind the turbine; an impossibility. The power that can be derived is the total power times a coefficient of performance, C_p, that the ratio of the power available in the wind to that harnessed:

$$P_w = C_p P_{tot} = C_p \left(\frac{1}{2}\rho A V^3\right) \qquad\qquad (3\text{-}6)$$

where, a detailed derivation in [3] shows that in the limit, theoretically, $C_{p,\max} = 0.5926$. As wind approaches the plane in which the turbine blades are rotating, the pressure builds up and the velocity begins to go down. After the plane of the blades, which has a very short thickness, the pressure begins to decrease and equals the pressure that exists much before the windmill. However, the wind-stream velocity keeps going down and levels off at a value lower than the initial velocity, due to the energy extracted from it.

This characteristic C_p in Eq. 3-6 is a function of the tip-speed ratio λ, as plotted in Fig. 3-8 where

Blade Tip-Speed Ratio $\lambda = \dfrac{\omega_m r}{V}$ (3-7)

in which r is the radius of the turbine blades in m, and ω_m is the turbine rotational speed in rad/s, and V is the wind speed in m/s.

In practice, the maximum attainable value of C_p is generally around 0.45 at a pitch-angle of $\beta = 0$ degrees (this angle is zero when the blades are vertical to the wind direction). As shown in Fig. 3-8, for each blade pitch-angle β, C_p reaches a maximum at a particular value of the tip-speed ratio λ, which, for a given wind speed V, can be obtained by controlling the turbine rotational speed ω_m. The curves for various values of the pitch-angle β shows that the power harnessed from wind can be regulated by controlling the pitch-angle of the blades, and thus "spilling" some of the wind at very high wind speeds to prevent the power output from exceeding its design (rated) value.

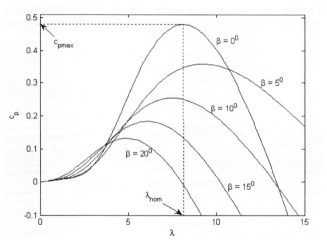

Fig. 3-8 c_p as a function of λ [7]; these would vary based on the turbine design.

3-6-1-1 Types of Generation Schemes in Windmills

Commonly used schemes for power generation in windmills require a gearing mechanism because the wind turbine rotates at very slow speeds, whereas the generator operates at a high speed close to the synchronous speed, which at the 60-Hz line frequency would be 1800 rpm for a 4-pole and 900 rpm for an 8-pole machine. Therefore, the nacelle contains a gearing mechanism that boosts up the turbine speed to drive the generator at a higher speed; need for a gearing mechanism is one of the inherent drawbacks of such schemes. There are proposal to use direct-drive (without gears) permanent magnet machines in very large sizes, however in practice, most windmills use gearing. This subsection describes various types of wind-generation schemes.

<u>Induction Generators, Directly Connected to the Grid</u>. As shown in Fig. 3-9, this is the simplest scheme, where a wind-turbine driven squirrel-cage induction generator is directly connected to the grid through a back-to-back connected thyristor-pair for soft-start. Therefore, it is least expensive and uses a rugged squirrel-cage rotor induction machine.

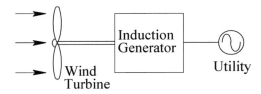

Fig. 3-9 Induction generator directly connected to the grid [8].

For the induction machine to operate in its generator mode, the rotor speed must be greater than the synchronous speed. The drawback of this scheme is that since the induction machine always operates very close to the synchronous speed, it is not possible to achieve the optimum C_p at all times, and hence is not optimum at low and high wind speeds compared to variable speed schemes described below. Another disadvantage of this scheme is that a squirrel-cage induction machine always operates at a lagging power factor (that is, it draws reactive power from the grid as an inductive-load would). Therefore, a separate source, for example shunt-connected capacitors are often needed to supply the reactive power to overcome the lagging power factor operation of the induction machine.

<u>Doubly-Fed, Wound-Rotor Induction Generators</u>. The scheme in Fig. 3-10 utilizes a wound-rotor induction machine where the stator is directly connected to the utility supply and the rotor is injected desired currents through a power-electronics interface, which is discussed in chapter 7. Typically, four-fifth of the power flows directly from the stator to the grid and only one-fifth of the power flows through the power electronics in the rotor circuit. The drawback of this scheme is that it uses a wound-rotor induction machine where the currents to the three-phase wound rotor are supplied through slip-rings and brushes which require maintenance. In spite of the fact that power electronics is expensive, since power electronics is rated only one-fifth of the system rating, therefore the overall cost is not much higher than the previous scheme. However, there are several distinct advantages over the previous scheme, as described below.

The scheme using a doubly-fed wound-rotor induction machine can typically operate in a range ±30% around the synchronous speed and hence it is able to capture more power at lower and higher wind speeds compared to the previous scheme because it can operate at above, as well as below, the synchronous speed. It can also supply reactive power, whereas in the previous scheme, the squirrel-cage induction machine only absorbs reactive power. Therefore, the scheme using a doubly-fed wound-rotor induction machine is quite popular in windmills being installed in the United States.

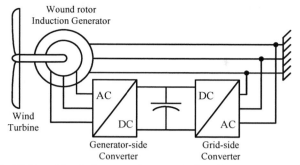

Fig. 3-10 Doubly-fed, wound-rotor induction generator [9].

Power Electronics Connected Generator. In the third scheme shown in Fig. 3-11, a squirrel-cage induction generator or a permanent-magnet generator is connected to the grid through a power electronics interface described in chapter 7. This interface consists of two converters. The converter at the generator-end supplies the reactive power excitation needed if it is an induction generator. Its frequency of operation is controlled to be optimum for the prevailing wind speed. The converter at the line-end is capable of absorbing or supplying reactive power in a continuous manner. This is the most flexible arrangement using a rugged squirrel-cage machine or a high-efficiency permanent-magnet generator, which can operate in a very wide wind-speed range and is the likely contender for the future arrangements as the cost of the power electronics interface, that must handle the entire power output of the system, is continuing to go down.

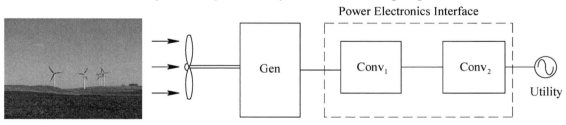

Fig. 3-11 Power Electronics connected generator [10].

3-6-1-2 Challenges in Harnessing Wind Energy

Wind power has enormous potential. North and South Dakotas alone can potentially supply two-thirds of the present electric energy needs of the United States. But wind power also has many challenges. Wind is variable and the power in it varies as the cube of the wind velocity. Therefore, it is difficult to use it as a conventional dispatchable source by Energy Control Centers. To overcome the dispatchability problem, research is being conducted in storage for example in flywheels for a short duration, supplemented by other generation, such as bio-diesel when wind dies down for longer periods. The other problem with wind resources is that they are located far away from load centers, and harnessing this energy would require new transmission lines to be built.

3-6-2 Photovoltaic Energy

As mentioned earlier, except for nuclear, all forms of energy resources are indirectly based on solar energy. Photovoltaic cells convert the energy in sun's rays directly into electricity. Solar energy is the ultimate in distributed resource, however, the cost of photovoltaic cells is a barrier that is preventing its economic feasibility and a breakthrough is awaited.

Photovoltaic cells consist of a *pn* junction where due to incident photons in the sun's rays cause excess electrons and holes to be generated above their normal thermal equilibrium. This causes a potential to be developed and if the external circuit is completed, it results in flow of electrons and thus the flow of current. The $v-i$ characteristic of a photovoltaic cell is as shown in Fig. 3-12, which shows that each cell produces an open-circuit voltage of approximately 0.6 V. The short-circuit current is limited and the power available is at its optimum value around the "knee" of the $v-i$ characteristic.

Fig. 3-12 PV cell characteristics [11].

In PV systems, the PV arrays (typically four of them connected in series) provide a voltage of 53-V to 90-V DC, which the power electronic system, as shown in Fig. 3-13, converts to 120V/60Hz sinusoidal voltage suitable for interfacing with the single-phase utility. A maximum-power-point tracking circuit in Fig. 3-13 allows these cells to be operated at this maximum-power point.

There are several types of photovoltaic cells, like mono-crystalline silicon with efficiency of 15-18 %, multi-crystalline silicon with efficiency of 13-18 %, and amorphous silicon with efficiency of 5-8 % . As mentioned earlier, the cost of any of these panels at present is economically prohibitive and a breakthrough is needed to make them feasible for power production, such as that using windmills.

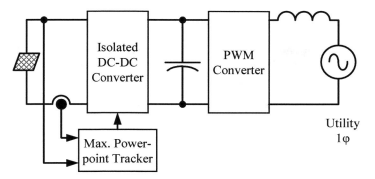

Fig. 3-13 Photovoltaic systems.

3-6-3   Fuel Cells

Lately, there has been a great deal of interest in, and effort being devoted to fuel cell systems. Fuel cells use hydrogen (and possibly other fuels) as the input and, through a chemical reaction, directly produce electricity with water and heat as byproducts. In fuel cells, hydrogen reacts with the catalyst to produce electrons and protons. Protons pass through a membrane. Electrons flow through the external circuit and combine with the protons and oxygen to produce water. Heat is generated in this process as a byproduct. Therefore they have none of the environmental consequences of the conventional fuels and also their efficiency can be as high as 60%.

Fuel-cell output is a dc voltage as shown in Fig. 3-14, and therefore the need for power electronics converters to interface with the utility is the same in fuel-cell systems as in photovoltaic systems.

Fig. 3-14 Fuel cell *v-i* relationship and cell power [12].

At present, fuel cells are not commercially competitive and there are several challenges to be overcome. It is not clear what would be the best way to produce and transport hydrogen. If some other fuel such as natural gas is used, what would be the economic feasibility of reformers that would be needed in conjunction with fuel cells? However, intense research is being conducted in the development of various fuel cells and some of them are listed here with expected percentage system efficiency in brackets: PEM (32%-40%), Alkaline (32%-45%), Phosphoric Acid (36%-45%),Molten Carbonate (43%-55%), Solid Oxide (43%-55%).

3-6-4   Biomass

There are various other sources for electrical generation under consideration. Biomass consists of biological material like agricultural waste, wood, and manure. Other possibilities are vegetable oil, ethanol from corn and other crops, and gas from anaerobic decomposition. Biomass includes refuse-derived fuel. Use of biomass and its derivatives for commercial power production is just beginning but significant effort is being put into this field.

3-7   DISTRIBUTED GENERATION (DG)

As mentioned in Chapter 1, utility landscape is changing and although in its infancy, there is growing use of distributed generation. This type of generation, as the name implies, is distributed and usually much smaller in power rating than the conventional powerplants. Therefore, distributed generation is often spurred by renewable resources such as windmills. In addition, there is a movement to generate electricity local to the load so to minimize the cost of transmission and distribution lines, and the power losses associated with them. Such distributed generation may be by micro-turbines and fuel cells that may be able to utilize natural gas through a reformer. One of the significant advantages of such distributed generation would be to utilize the heat produced as a byproduct of this generation, rather than "throwing" it away as is common in central powerplants, thus resulting in much higher energy efficiency in comparison. An ultimate achievement in distributed generation would be photovoltaic if the cost of PV cells were to decrease significantly.

3-8 ENVIRONMENTAL CONSEQUENCES AND REMEDIAL ACTIONS

3-8-1   Environmental Consequences

Burning of fossil fuels in power plants produces greenhouse gases, such as CO_2, that lead to climate change. The greenhouse effect of CO_2 is illustrated in Fig. 3-15. Similar to the glass panes of a greenhouse, as illustrated by Fig. 3-15, radiation from the sun in the form of ultraviolet light passes through the atmosphere, with some of it absorbed and some reflected back. The radiation that passes through is mostly absorbed by the earth, warming it. Heat is radiated back, but due to the low temperature of the earth's surface, this radiation is in the in the form of infrared. Like the glass in a greenhouse, greenhouse gases such as carbon dioxide and nitrous oxide in the atmosphere trap the infrared heat, so less is radiated through and back to space. This greenhouse effect is leading to climate change with disastrous consequences predicted.

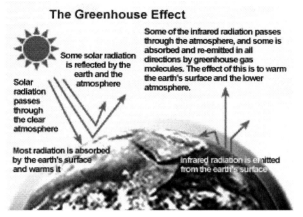

Fig. 3-15 Greenhouse effect [13].

There are other consequences as well. Burning of fossil fuels results in increased concentration of sulfur and nitrogen oxides in the atmosphere. These get converted into acid rain or acid snow with risk to health and aquatic life. Certain types of coal lead to mercury pollution that is extremely harmful to health and gets concentrated in fish, for example. Since the efficiency of thermodynamic cycle in fossil fuel plants is only around 40%, the rest of the energy goes directly into creating thermal pollution of the water that is used to cool it. This can have adverse consequences such as the growth of algae, etc.

3-8-2   Remedial Actions

These include flue-gas de-sulfurization, scrubbers for nitrogen oxides removal and electrostatic participators. Such remedies increase power plant costs and hence of the generated electricity. Carbon sequestering is also being investigated.

3-9   RESOURCE PLANNING

Choice of using available resources for generating electricity is based on various considerations: initial investment, cost of electricity, environmental considerations, etc, and utilities use a mix of resources, illustrated as an example in Fig. 3-16 [14]. These include coal, nuclear, gas and oil, renewables, and purchases from other utilities.

Fig. 3-16 Resource mix at XcelEnergy [14].

The cost of fuel for electricity in year 2005 in the United States is shown in Fig. 3-17 by months.

Fig. 3-17 Electric power industry fuel costs in the U.S. in 2005 [1].

Some of the facts and approximate figures for year 2007 for a utility in Minnesota are as follows:

- Coal-Fired Plants: These take 6-8 years to build and cost 2,000 dollars/kW. Their thermal efficiency is in a range of 33-37%. The startup time associated with coal plants is 6-8 hours. Including the fuel and all other costs, the electricity cost from such plants is 2.0-2.5 cents/kWh. (This cost is so low due to the availability of coal to this utility at cheap prices at the mine-mouth plant and the transmission of electricity over HVDC lines.)

- Single-Cycle Gas-Fired Plants: These take approximately a year to build and cost 500 dollars/kW. Their thermal efficiency is the same as the coal-fired plants, in a range of 33-37%. The startup time associated with gas plants is as little as 10 minutes and can be longer than 30 minutes. Including the fuel and all other costs, the electricity cost from such plants is 20 cents/kWh.

- Combined-Cycle Gas-Fired Plants: Compared to simple single-cycle gas plants their thermal efficiency can be twice as high, upwards of 60%. As a rule-of-thumb, if a plant is to be used for less than 20% of the time in a year, then the single-cycle gas turbine is selected. In a 20-60 percent range, a combined-cycle gas plant is used; any higher than 60% usage favors a base-loaded coal-fired plant. Including the fuel and all other costs, the electricity cost from such plants is around 10 cents/kWh.

- Wind Turbines: Wind has become a commercial resource with the cost of electricity approximately 4.5 cents/kWh with the Federal Production Tax Credits (PTC) and 6.4 cents/kWh without them.

It should be noted that photovoltaic on the utility-scale and wave energy have the potential to become economically feasible and research into these areas is aggressively being pursued.

REFERENCES

1. U.S. Department of Energy (www.eia.doe.gov).
2. Electric Utility Systems and Practices, 4th Edition by Homer M. Rustebakke (Editor), John Wiley & Sons, August 1983.
3. Powerplant Technology by M. M. El-Wakil, McGraw-Hill Companies, 1984.
4. Technology Review Magazine published by MIT, September 2005.
5. http://www.nrc.gov/reading-rm/basic-ref/students/reactors.html.
6. National Renewable Energy Lab (www.nrel.gov).
7. http://www.mathworks.com/access/helpdesk/help/toolbox/physmod/powersys/windturbine.html.
8. Electric Drives: An Integrative Approach by Ned Mohan, (www.mnpere.com).
9. Advanced Electric Drives by Ned Mohan, (www.mnpere.com).
10. First Course on Power Electronics by Ned Mohan (www.mnpere.com).
11. Power Electronics: Converters, Applications and Design, by N. Mohan, T. Undeland and W. P. Robbins, John Wiley & Sons, (www.wiley.com).
12. www.NETL.DOE.gov.
13. www.epa.gov/globalwarming/kids/greenhouse.html.
14. 2004 Environmental Report, www.xcelenergy.com.

PROBLEMS

3-1   What are the sources of electric energy?

3-2   What are the environmental consequences of using electric energy?

3-3   Describe hydro power plants.

3-4   Describe two nuclear processes and which one is used for commercial nuclear power production?

3-5   Describe different types of nuclear reactors.

3-6   Describe coal-fired power plants.

3-7   Describe gas-fired power plants.

3-8   What are the potential and the challenges associated with wind energy?

3-9   How does the wind-turbine efficiency depend on the tip-speed ratio and the pitch angle of the blades?

3-10   What the three most commonly-used generation schemes associated with harnessing wind energy?

3-11   What is the principle underlying the operation of PV cells?

3-12   What is the principle underlying the operation of fuel cells?

3-13   What is the greenhouse effect?

3-14   What are other environmental consequences of power production from using fossil fuels?

3-15   What are the present and potential remedies to minimize environmental impacts of using fossil fuels?

3-16   A U.S. Department of Energy report estimates that over 122 billion kWh/year can be saved in the manufacturing sector in the United States by using mature and cost-effective conservation technologies. Calculate (a) how many 1000-MW generating plants are needed to operate constantly to supply this wasted energy, and (b) the annual savings in dollars if the cost of electricity is 0.10 $/kWh.

3-17   Electricity generation in the U.S. in year 2000 was approximately 3.8×10^9 MW-hrs, 16% of which is used for heating, ventilating and air conditioning. Based on a DOE report, as much as 30% of the energy can be saved in such systems by using adjustable speed drives. On this basis, calculate the savings in energy per year and relate that to 1000-MW generating plants needed to operate constantly to supply this wasted energy.

3-18   The total amount of electricity that could potentially be generated from wind in the United States has been estimated at 10.8×10^9 MW-hrs annually. If one-tenth of this potential is developed, estimate the number of 2 MW windmills that would be required, assuming that on average a windmill produces only 25% of the energy that it is capable of.

3-19   In problem 3-18, if each 2 MW windmill has 20% of its output power flowing through the power electronics interface, estimate the total rating of these power electronics interfaces in kW.

3-20   Lighting in the U.S. consumes 19% of the generated electricity. Compact Fluorescent Lamps (CFLs) consume one-fourth of the power consumed by incandescent lamps for the same light output. Electricity generation in the U.S. in year 2000 was approximately 3.8×10^9 MW-hrs. Based on this information, estimate the savings in MW-hrs annually, assuming all lighting at present is by incandescent lamps, which are going to be replaced by CFLs.

3-21   Fuel-cell systems that also utilize the heat produced can achieve efficiencies approaching 80%, more than double of the gas-turbine based electrical generation. Assume that 25 million households produce an average of 5 kW. Calculate the percentage of electricity generated by these fuel-cell systems compared to the annual electricity generation in the U.S. of 3.8×10^9 MW-hrs.

3-22   Induction cooking based on power electronics is estimated to be 80% efficient compared to 55% for conventional electric cooking. If an average home consumes 2 kW-hrs daily using conventional electric cooking, and that 50 million households switch to induction cooking in the U.S., calculate the annual savings in electricity usage.

3-23   Assume the average energy density of sunlight to be 800 W/m^2 and the overall photovoltaic system efficiency to be 10%. Calculate the land area covered with photovoltaic cells needed to produce 1,000 MW, the size of a typical large central power plant.

3-24   In problem 3-23, the solar cells are distributed on top of roofs, each in area of 50 m^2. Calculate the number of homes needed to produce the same power.

CHAPTER 4

AC TRANSMISSION LINES AND UNDERGROUND CABLES

4-1 NEED FOR TRANSMISSION LINES AND CABLES

Electricity is often generated in areas that are remote to load centers like the metropolitan areas. Transmission lines form an important link in the power system structure to transport large amounts of electrical power with as little power loss as possible, keeping the system operating stably, and all this at a minimum cost. Transmission line access has become an important bottleneck in power systems operation today, with building of additional transmission lines becoming a serious hurdle to overcome. This is one of the challenges facing large-scale harnessing of wind energy, for example.

Most transmission systems consist of ac overhead transmission lines. Although we will mostly discuss overhead ac transmission lines, the analysis presented in this chapter applies to underground ac cables as well, as described briefly in this chapter, which are used near metropolitan areas.

There are several high voltage dc (HVDC) transmission systems that are also used to transport large amounts of power over long distances. Such systems are expected to be used more frequently. HVDC systems require power electronics converters and thus are discussed in a separate chapter along with other applications of power electronics in power systems.

4-2 OVERHEAD AC TRANSMISSION LINES

The discussion presented here applies to transmission as well as distribution lines, although the focus is on transmission lines. Transmission lines always consist of three phases at commonly used voltages of 115 kV, 230 kV, 345 kV, 500 kV and 765 kV. Voltages lower than 115 kV are generally considered for distribution. Voltages higher than 765 kV are being considered for long distance transmission.

A typical 500-kV transmission tower is shown in Fig. 4-1a. There are three phases (a, b and c) where each phase consists of three conductor bundles that are hung from the steel tower through insulators, as shown in Fig. 4-1b. The conductors with multiple stands of aluminum on the outside and steel at the core, as shown in Fig. 4-1c, are called Aluminum Conductors Steel Reinforced (ACSR). The current through the conductor primarily flows through the aluminum that has conductivity higher than seven times that of steel, which is used at the core to provide tensile strength and thus prevent these lines from excessive sagging in between the towers. Typically, there are approximately 5 towers per mile.

(a)

(b)

(c)

Fig. 4-1 500-kV transmission line (Source: University of Minnesota EMTP course).

Parameters of a transmission line depend on the voltage level for which it is designed since higher voltage lines require larger values of separation between conductors, height of the conductors, and their separation from the tower that is grounded. A proper clearance is needed to keep electric field strengths at the ground level under the transmission lines to be within the limit, which is specified to be 8 kV (rms)/m by the Minnesota Environmental Quality Board, for example.

4-2-1 Shield Wires, Bundling and Cost

Shield Wires:

As shown in Fig. 4-1a, shield wires are sometimes used to shield transmission-line phase conductors from being struck by lightening. These are also called ground wires, which are periodically grounded through the tower. Therefore, it is important to achieve as small a tower footing resistance as possible.

Bundling:

Bundled conductors are used, as shown in Fig. 4-1b, to minimize electric field strength at the conductor surface to avoid the corona effect discussed later in this chapter. According to [1], the maximum surface conductor gradient should be less than 16 kV/cm. Bundling of conductors also results in reducing the line series inductance and increasing the shunt capacitance, both of which are beneficial in loading of lines to higher power levels. However, conductor bundling results in higher cost and in increasing the clearance required from the tower [2]. At line voltages lower than 345 kV, most transmission lines consist of single conductors. At 345 kV, most transmission lines consist of bundled conductors, usually a two-conductor bundle at a spacing of 18 inches. At 500 kV, transmission lines use bundled conductors, such as a three-conductor bundle shown in Fig. 4-1b, with a spacing of 18 inches.

Cost:

Cost of such lines depends on a variety of factors but as a rough estimate, a 345-kV line costs range from 500,000 dollars per mile (1.6 km) in rural areas to over 2 million dollars per mile in urban areas of Minnesota, with an average of approximately 750,000 dollars per mile. Similar rough estimates are available for other transmission voltages.

4-3 TRANSPOSITION OF TRANSMISSION LINE PHASES

In the structure shown in Fig. 4-1a, the phases are arranged in a triangular fashion. In other structures, these phases may be all horizontal or all vertical as shown in Fig. 4-2a. It is clear from these arrangements that the electrical and magnetic couplings are not equal between the phases. For example in Fig. 4-2a, coupling between phases a and b would differ that between phases a and c. To make these three phases appear balanced, they are transposed as shown in Fig. 4-2b. This unbalance is not of much significance for short lines, for example less then 50 miles (80 km) in length. But in long lines, the length of the "barrel", equal to the three sections or one cycle of transposition as shown in Fig 4-2b, is recommended to be approximately 100 miles for a triangular configuration and smaller for horizontal or vertical arrangements [3]. In spite of the fact that the transmission lines are seldom transposed, we will assume the three phases to be perfectly balanced in our simplified analysis to follow.

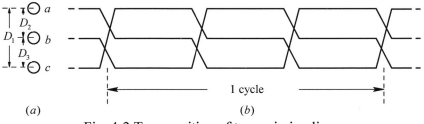

Fig. 4-2 Transposition of transmission lines.

4-4 TRANSMISSION LINES PARAMETERS

Transmission line resistances, inductances and capacitances are distributed all through the length of the line. Assuming the three phases to be balanced, we can easily calculate the transmission line parameters on a per-phase basis, as shown in Fig. 4-3 where the bottom conductor is neutral (in general, hypothetical) that carries no current in a perfectly balanced three-phase arrangement under a balanced sinusoidal steady state operation. For unbalanced arrangements including the effect of the ground plane and the shield wires, computer programs such as PSCAD/EMTDC [4] and EMTP are available that can also include frequency dependence of the transmission line parameters.

Fig. 4-3 Distributed parameter representation on a per-phase basis.

4-4-1   Resistance R

The resistance of a transmission line in per unit is designed to be small to minimize $I^2 R$ power losses. These losses go down as the conductor size is increased but the costs of conductors and towers go up. In the U.S., the Department of Energy estimates that approximately 9 percent of the generated electricity is lost in transmission and distribution. Therefore, it is important to keep the transmission line resistance small. In a bundled arrangement, it is the parallel resistance of the bundled conductors that is of consideration.

There are tables [2] that give the resistance at dc and 60 Hz frequency at various temperatures. ACSR conductors such as that shown in Fig. 4-1c are considered hollow as shown in Fig. 4-4a because the electrical resistance of the steel core is much higher than the outer aluminum strands.

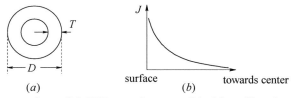

Fig. 4-4 (a) Cross-section of ACSR conductors, (b) skin-effect in a solid conductor.

Also the skin-effect phenomenon plays a role at 60-Hz (or 50-Hz) frequency. The line resistance R depends on the length of the conductor l, the resistivity of the material ρ (that increases with temperature), and inversely on the effective cross-sectional area A of the conductor through which the current flows:

$$R = \frac{\rho l}{A} \tag{4-1}$$

The effective area A in Eq. 4-1 depends on the frequency due to the skin effect, where the current at 60-Hz frequency is not uniformly distributed throughout the cross-section; rather it crowds towards the periphery of the conductor with a higher current-density J as shown in Fig. 4-4b for a *solid* conductor (it will be more uniform in a hollow conductor), and decreases exponentially such that at the skin-depth, the current density is a factor of $e(=2.718)$ smaller than that at the surface. The skin depth of a material at a frequency f is [5]

$$\delta = \sqrt{\frac{2\rho}{(2\pi f)\mu}} \tag{4-2}$$

which is calculated for aluminum in the example below.

▲ **Example 4-1**   In Fig. 4-4a, the conductor is aluminum with resistivity $\rho = 2.65 \, \mu\Omega - cm$. Calculate the skin-depth δ at 60-Hz frequency.

Solution   The permeability of aluminum can be consider to be that of free space, that is, $\mu = 4\pi \times 10^{-7} \, H/m$.   The resistivity is specified as $\rho = 2.65 \times 10^2 \, \mu\Omega - m$. Substituting these values in Eq. 4-2,

$$\delta = 18.75 \, mm \qquad\qquad\qquad\qquad\qquad\qquad ▲$$

Therefore, in ACSR conductors, the aluminum thickness T, as shown in Fig. 4-4a, is kept at the order of the skin depth and any further thickness of aluminum will essentially be a waste that will not result in decreasing the overall resistance to ac currents. In case of a type of ACSR conductor, called the Bunting conductor, shown in Fig. 4-4a, $T/D = 0.3748$, where $D = 1.302$ inches. Therefore, the skin effect results in a resistance only slightly higher at 60 Hz compared to at dc in such a "hollow" conductor, where the resistance at dc is listed as 0.0787 ohms/mile versus 0.0811 ohms/mile at 60 Hz, both at the temperature of $25^0 C$ [2].

4-4-2   Shunt Conductance G

In transmission lines, in addition to the power loss due to $I^2 R$ in the series resistance, there is a small loss due to the leakage current flowing thorough the insulator. This effect is amplified due to the corona effect where the surrounding air is ionized and a hissing sound can be heard in misty, foggy weather. The corona problem can be averted by increasing the conductor size and by the use of conductor bundling as discussed earlier [2]. These losses can be represented by putting a conductance G in shunt with the capacitance in Fig. 4-3, since such losses depend approximately on the square of the voltage. However, these losses are negligibly small, and thus in our analysis we will neglect the presence of G.

4-4-3   Series Inductance L

Fig. 4-5a shows a balanced three-phase transmission line with currents i_a, i_b, and i_c, which add up to zero under balanced conditions, that is, at any time

$$i_a + i_b + i_c = 0 \tag{4-3}$$

We will calculate the inductance of each phase, for example phase-a, as the ratio of the total flux linking it to its current. The total flux linking a phase conductor by the three currents can be obtained by superposition, and thus the per-phase inductance can be calculated as:

$$L_a = \frac{\lambda_{a,total}}{i_a} = \frac{1}{i_a}\left(\lambda_{a,i_a} + \lambda_{a,i_b} + \lambda_{a,i_c}\right) \tag{4-4}$$

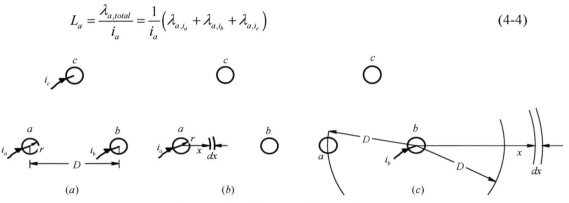

Fig. 4-5 Flux linkage with conductor-a.

Considering i_a by itself, as shown in Fig. 4-5b, by Ampere's law at a distance x from conductor-a,

$$H_x = \frac{i_a}{2\pi x} \qquad \text{and} \qquad B_x = \mu_0 H_x = \left(\frac{\mu_0}{2\pi x}\right)i_a \tag{4-5}$$

Therefore, the differential flux-linkage in a differential distance dx over a unit length along the conductor ($\ell = 1$) is

$$d\lambda_{x,i_a} = B_x \cdot dx = \left(\frac{\mu_0}{2\pi x}\right)i_a \cdot dx \tag{4-6}$$

Assuming the current in each conductor to be at the surface (a reasonable assumption, based on the discussion of the skin effect in calculating the line resistances), integrating x from the conductor radius to infinity,

$$\lambda_{a,i_a} = \int_r^\infty d\lambda_{x,i_a} = B_x \cdot dx = \left(\frac{\mu_0}{2\pi}\right) i_a \int_r^\infty \frac{1}{x} \cdot dx = \left(\frac{\mu_0}{2\pi}\right) i_a \ln \frac{\infty}{r} \qquad (4\text{-}7)$$

Next, we will calculate the mutual flux linking conductor-a due to i_b in conductor-b, as shown in Fig. 4-5c. Noting that $D \gg r$, the flux linking conductor-a due to i_b is between a distance of D and infinity. Therefore, using the procedure above and using Eq. 4-7,

$$\lambda_{a,i_b} = \left(\frac{\mu_0}{2\pi}\right) i_b \ln \frac{\infty}{D} \qquad (4\text{-}8)$$

Similarly, due to i_c

$$\lambda_{a,i_c} = \left(\frac{\mu_0}{2\pi}\right) i_c \ln \frac{\infty}{D} \qquad (4\text{-}9)$$

Therefore, adding the flux linkage components from Eqs 4-7 though 4-9,

$$\lambda_{a,total} = \lambda_{a,i_a} + \lambda_{a,i_b} + \lambda_{a,i_c} = \left(\frac{\mu_0}{2\pi}\right)\left[i_a \ln \frac{\infty}{r} + (i_b + i_c) \ln \frac{\infty}{D}\right] \qquad (4\text{-}10)$$

From Eq. 4-3, sum of i_b and i_c equals $(-i_a)$ in Eq. 4-10, which simplifies to

$$\lambda_{a,total} = \left(\frac{\mu_0}{2\pi}\right) i_a \ln \frac{D}{r} \qquad (4\text{-}11)$$

Therefore, from Eq. 4-4, the inductance L associated with each phase per-unit length is

$$L = \left(\frac{\mu_0}{2\pi}\right) \ln \frac{D}{r} \quad \text{(in H/m)} \qquad (4\text{-}12)$$

If the three conductors are at distances D_1, D_2, and D_3 with respect to each other, as shown in Fig. 4-2 but transposed, then the equivalent distance D (also known as the Geometric Mean Distance GMD) between them, for use in Eq. 4-12, can be calculated as

$$D = \sqrt[3]{D_1 D_2 D_3} \qquad (4\text{-}13)$$

In calculations above, it is assumed that the current of each conductor flows entirely at the surface. However, computer programs such as PSCAD/EMTDC can take into account the internal conductor inductance based on the current-density distribution internal to the conductor at a given frequency.

In bundled conductors, the inductance per-unit length is smaller, for example by a factor of 0.7 if a 3 conductor bundle is used with a spacing of 18 inches as shown in Fig. 4-1b [2]. This factor is approximately 0.8 in a 2-conductor bundle with a spacing of 18 inches.

4-4-4   Shunt Capacitance C

To calculate line capacitances, consider a charge q on a conductor, as shown in Fig. 4-6, that results in dielectric flux lines and the electric field intensity E. Considering a surface at a distance x from the conductor of unit length along the conductor. The surface area per-unit length, perpendicular to the field lines, is $(2\pi x)\times 1$. Therefore, the dielectric flux-density D and the electric field E can be calculated as

$$D = \frac{q}{(2\pi x)\times 1} \quad \text{and} \quad E = \frac{D}{\varepsilon_0} = \frac{q}{(2\pi x)\varepsilon_0} \tag{4-14}$$

where $\varepsilon_0 = 8.85\times 10^{-12}\,F/m$ is the permittivity of free space, and approximately the same for air.

Fig. 4-6 Electric field due to a charge.

Therefore, in Fig. 4-6, the voltage of point 1, with respect to point 2, that is v_{12}, is

$$v_{12} = -\int_{x_2}^{x_1} E(x)\cdot dx = \left(\frac{q}{2\pi\varepsilon_0}\right)\ln\frac{x_2}{x_1} \tag{4-15}$$

Considering three conductors at symmetrical distance D (not to be confused with the dielectric flux-density), as shown in Fig. 4-7a, we can calculate voltage v_{ab}, for example, by superposing the effects of q_a, q_b and q_c.

Fig. 4-7 Shunt capacitances.

From Eq. 4-15, where r the conductor radius,

$$v_{ab,q_a} = \left(\frac{q_a}{2\pi\varepsilon_0}\right)\ln\frac{D}{r} \tag{4-16}$$

Similarly, due to q_b

$$v_{ba,q_b} = \left(\frac{q_b}{2\pi\varepsilon_0}\right)\ln\frac{D}{r} = -v_{ab,q_b} \tag{4-17}$$

where $v_{ab,q_b} = -\left(\frac{q_b}{2\pi\varepsilon_0}\right)\ln\frac{D}{r}$.

Note that q_c, being equidistant from both the conductors a and b, does not produce any voltage between a and b. Therefore, from Eqs. 4-16 and 4-17,

$$v_{ab} = v_{ab,q_a} + v_{ab,q_b} = \frac{1}{2\pi\varepsilon_0}(q_a - q_b)\ln\frac{D}{r} \tag{4-18}$$

Considering a hypothetical neutral point n, as shown in Fig. 4-7b, and the capacitances C from each phase as indicated,

$$v_{ab} = v_{an} - v_{bn} = \frac{q_a}{C} - \frac{q_b}{C} = \frac{1}{C}(q_a - q_b) \tag{4-19}$$

Comparing Eqs. 4-18 and 4-19, the shunt capacitance per-unit length is

$$C = \frac{2\pi\varepsilon_0}{\ln\dfrac{D}{r}} \qquad \text{(in F/m)} \tag{4-20}$$

If the three conductors are at distances D_1, D_2 and D_3, as shown in Fig. 4-2, but transposed, then the equivalent distance (GMD) D between them, for use in Eq. 4-20, can be calculated as

$$D = \sqrt[3]{D_1 D_2 D_3} \tag{4-21}$$

In Eq. 4-20, it should be noted that the per-phase capacitance does not include the effect of ground and the presence of shield wires. This effect is included in [4].

In bundled conductors, the per unit shunt capacitance is larger by a factor of approximately 1.4 if a 3 conductor bundle is used with a spacing of 18 inches [2]. This factor is approximately 1.25 in a 2-conductor bundle with a spacing of 18 inches.

Typical values of transmission line parameters at various voltage levels are given in Table 4-1, where it is assumed that the conductors are arranged in 3-conductor bundles with spacing of 18 inches [6].

Table 4-1

Transmission Line Parameters with Bundled Conductors (except at 230 kV) at 60 Hz [2, 6]

Nominal Voltage	$R(\Omega/km)$	$\omega L(\Omega/km)$	$\omega C(\mu\mho/km)$
230 kV	0.055	0.489	3.373
345 kV	0.037	0.376	4.518
500 kV	0.029	0.326	5.220
765 kV	0.013	0.339	4.988

▲ **Example 4-2** Consider a 345-kV transmission line consists of 3L3 type towers shown in Fig. 4-8. This transmission system consists of a single-conductor per phase, which is a Bluebird ACSR conductor with a diameter of 1.762 inches. Ignoring the effect of ground, ground wires and conductor sags, calculate $\omega L(\Omega/km)$ and $\omega C(\mu\mho/km)$, and compare the results with those given in Table 4-1.

Fig. 4-8 A 345-kV, single-conductor per phase, transmission system.

Solution   The distances between conductors in Fig. 4-8 are 7.5 m, 7.5 m and 15 m, respectively. Therefore, from Eq. 4-21, the equivalent distance between them is $D = \sqrt[3]{7.5 \times 7.5 \times 15} = 9.45m$, and the radius is $r = 0.0224m$. Therefore at 60 Hz, from Eqs. 4-12 and 4-20, $\omega L = 0.456\Omega/km$ and $\omega C = 3.467\mu\mho/km$. These values are for a specific non-bundled conductor geometry, whereas the parameters in Table 4-1 are typical values for bundled conductors. Therefore, the values of inductances and capacitances calculated from Eqs. 4-12 and 4-20, modified by the factors to account for bundling mentioned earlier are in the "ballpark", whereas more accurate values are calculated using EMTDC in one of the homework problems.

▲

4-5   DISTRIBUTED-PARAMETER REPRESENTATION OF TRANSMISSION LINES

A three-phase transmission line, assumed to be perfectly transposed, can be treated on a per-phase basis, as shown in Fig. 4-9 under balanced operation.

Fig. 4-9 Distributed per-phase transmission line (G not shown).

With the distance x measured from the receiving end as shown in Fig. 4-9 in Laplace domain, at a distance x

$$\frac{\partial}{\partial x}V_x(s) = (sL + R)I_x(s,x) \tag{4-22}$$

Similarly, due to the current flowing through distributed shunt capacitance,

$$\frac{\partial}{\partial x}I_x(s) = (sC + G)V_x(s) \tag{4-23}$$

Partially differentiating Eq. 4-22 with respect to x and substituting into Eq. 4-23,

$$\frac{\partial^2}{\partial x^2}V_x(s) = (sL + R)(sC + G)V_x(s) = \gamma^2 V_x(s) \tag{4-24}$$

where,

$$\gamma = \sqrt{(sL + R)(sC + G)} = \alpha + j\beta \tag{4-25}$$

is the propagation constant where α and β are positive in values. Similarly, for the current,

$$\frac{\partial^2}{\partial x^2}I_x(s) = (sL + R)(sC + G)I_x(s) = \gamma^2 I_x(s) \tag{4-26}$$

We should note that under the assumption of perfect transposition that allows us to treat a three-phase transmission line on a per-phase basis, the voltage equation of Eq. 4-24 is independent of current, while the current equation of Eq. 4-26 is independent of voltage. From Eq. 4-24, its solution is of the form

$$V_x(s) = V_1 e^{\gamma x} + V_2 e^{-\gamma x} \tag{4-27}$$

where V_1 and V_2 are coefficients that will be calculated based on the boundary conditions. The current in Eq. 4-26 will have a solution of a similar form as Eq. 4-27. Differentiating Eq. 4-27 with respect to x,

$$\frac{\partial}{\partial x} V_x(s) = \gamma \left(V_1 e^{\gamma x} - V_2 e^{-\gamma x} \right) \tag{4-28}$$

Comparing Eq. 4-28 with Eq. 4-22,

$$I_x(s) = \left(V_1 e^{\gamma x} - V_2 e^{-\gamma x} \right) / Z_c \tag{4-29}$$

where Z_c is the surge impedance

$$Z_c = \sqrt{\frac{sL + R}{sC + G}} \tag{4-30}$$

Applying the boundary conditions in Eqs. 4-27 and 4-29, that is, at the receiving-end $x = 0$, $V_{x=0}(s) = V_R(s)$ and $I_{x=0}(s) = I_R(s)$

$$V_1 + V_2 = V_R(s) \quad \text{and} \quad V_1 - V_2 = Z_c I_R(s) \tag{4-31}$$

From Eq. 4-31,

$$V_1 = \frac{V_R(s) + Z_c I_R(s)}{2} \quad \text{and} \quad V_2 = \frac{V_R(s) - Z_c I_R(s)}{2} \tag{4-32}$$

Substituting from Eq. 4-32 into Eq. 4-27, recognizing $\dfrac{e^{\gamma x} + e^{-\gamma x}}{2} = \cosh \gamma x$ and

$\dfrac{e^{\gamma x} - e^{-\gamma x}}{2} = \sinh \gamma x$

$$V_x(s) = V_R(s) \cosh \gamma x + Z_c I_R(s) \sinh \gamma x \tag{4-33}$$

Similarly, from 4-32 into Eq. 4-29

$$I_x(s) = \frac{V_R(s)}{Z_c} \sinh \gamma x + I_R(s) \cosh \gamma x \tag{4-34}$$

4-6 SURGE IMPEDANCE Z_c AND THE SURGE IMPEDANCE LOADING (SIL)

In transmission lines, losses due to corona etc. are usually extremely small, hence it is reasonable to assume that the shunt conductance $G = 0$. Also, without any significant sacrifice of accuracy, the distributed transmission line resistance can be considered as a lumped element, resulting in the rest of the transmission line to be lossless, consisting of only distributed inductance and capacitance. In such a lossless line, the characteristic impedance Z_c, also called the surge impedance, given by Eq. 4-30, becomes a real value

$$Z_c = \sqrt{\frac{L}{C}} \tag{4-35}$$

and the propagation constant γ in Eq. 4-25 has no real part

$$\gamma = j\omega\sqrt{LC} = j\beta \tag{4-36}$$

where,

$$\beta = \omega\sqrt{LC} \tag{4-37}$$

In sinusoidal steady state, the Laplace operator $s = j\omega$, and hence we can make use of phasors in Fig. 4-10a, where a lossless transmission line is loaded by a resistance that equals Z_c. Assuming the receiving end voltage to be the reference phasor:

$$\overline{V}_R = V_R \angle 0^0 \quad \text{and} \quad \overline{I}_R = \frac{V_R}{Z_c} \angle 0^0 \tag{4-38}$$

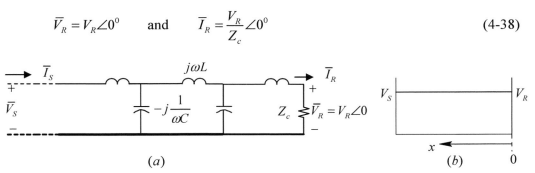

(a)   (b)

Fig. 4-10 Per-phase transmission line terminated with a resistance equal to Z_c.

Therefore, from Eqs. 4-33 and 4-38, recognizing that $\cosh jA = \cos A$ and $\sinh jA = j \sin A$

$$\overline{V}_x = V_R \left(\cos\beta x + j \sin\beta x \right) = V_R e^{j\beta x} \tag{4-39}$$

Similarly, from Eqs. 4-34 and 4-38,

$$\overline{I}_x = I_R \left(\cos \beta x + j \sin \beta x \right) = I_R e^{j\beta x} \tag{4-40}$$

The voltage equation given by Eq. 4-39 shows that the voltage magnitude has a flat profile, as shown in Fig. 4-10b, that is, it is the same magnitude everywhere on the line, only the angle increases with distance x. This loading is called the Surge Impedance Loading (SIL); the reactive power consumed by the line everywhere is the same as the reactive power produced:

$$\omega L I_x^2 = V_x^2 \omega C \tag{4-41}$$

which is true, since under SIL, from Eqs. 4-39 and 4-40, $V_x / I_x = Z_c$.

For a given voltage level, the characteristic impedance of a transmission line falls in a narrow range because the separation and the height of the conductors above ground depend on this voltage level. Table 4-2 shows the typical values for the surge impedance and the three-phase Surge Impedance Loading (SIL), where

$$SIL = \frac{V_{LL}^2}{Z_c} \tag{4-42}$$

Table 4-2
Surge Impedance and Three-Phase Surge Impedance Loading [2, 6]

Nominal Voltage	$Z_c(\Omega)$	$SIL(MW)$
230 kV	375	140 MW
345 kV	280	425 MW
500 kV	250	1000 MW
765 kV	255	2300 MW

From Table 4-2, it is clear that for a large transfer of power, for example 1,000 MW, calls for a high voltage line such as at 345 kV or 500 kV; otherwise many circuits in parallel will be needed.

▲ **Example 4-3**   For the 345-kV transmission line described in Example 4-2, calculate the surge impedance Z_c and the Surge Impedance Loading SIL. If the line is 100 km long and the line resistance is $0.031 \Omega / km$, calculate the percentage loss if the line is surge-impedance loaded.

Solution   In the single-conductor transmission line of Example 4-2, we calculated that $\omega L = 0.456 \Omega / km$ and $\omega C = 3.467 \, \mu \mho / km$. Therefore, from Eq. 4-35, $Z_c \approx 363 \Omega$ and from Eq. 4-42, $SIL = 328\,MW$. At surge-impedance loading of this transmission line, the per-phase current through the line is

$$I = \frac{345 \times 10^3 / \sqrt{3}}{Z_c} = 548.7\,A,\text{ and therefore the power loss as a percentage of } SIL$$

in this 100 km long line is,

$$\% I^2 R = 100 \times \frac{3 \times 548.7^2 \times (0.031 \times 100)}{328 \times 10^6} \approx 0.85\%. \qquad \blacktriangle$$

4-6-1 Line Loadability [6, 7]

The Surge Impedance Loading (SIL) provides a benchmark in terms of which the amount of maximum loading of a transmission line can be expressed. This loading is a function of the length of the transmission line so that certain constraints are met. This approximate loadability is a function of the line length. Short line less than 50 miles (80 km) in length can be loaded more than 3 times SIL, based on not exceeding the thermal limits. Medium length lines 50-150 miles in length (80-240 km) can be loaded to 1.5 to 3 times the SIL before the voltage drop across them exceeds more than 5%. Long lines in the 150-300 miles (240-480 km) range can be loaded to around the SIL because of the stability limit (discussed later in this book) so that the phase angle of the voltage between the two ends does not exceed 40 to 45 degrees. The loadability of medium and long length lines can be increased by providing series and shunt compensation discussed in the chapter dealing with stability. These results are summarized in the table below.

Table 4-3
Loadability of Transmission Lines [6]

Line Length (km)	Limiting Factor	Multiple of SIL
0 - 80	Thermal	> 3
80 - 240	5% Voltage Drop	1.5 - 3
240 - 480	Stability	1.0 – 1.5

4-7 LUMPED TRANSMISSION LINE MODELS IN STEADY STATE

In a balanced sinusoidal steady state, it is very useful to have per-phase model of transmission lines on the assumption that the three phases are perfectly transposed and applied voltages and currents are balanced and sinusoidal in steady state. These models can be classified based on line length as illustrated in the following sub-sections.

4-7-1   Long-Length Lines

In the distributed-parameter representation of the transmission line in the previous section, from Eqs. 4-33 and 4-34, at the sending end with $x = \ell$,

$$V_S(s) = V_R(s)\cosh\gamma\ell + Z_c I_R(s)\sinh\gamma\ell \qquad (4\text{-}43)$$

and

$$I_S(s) = \frac{V_R(s)}{2}\sinh\gamma\ell + I_R(s)\cosh\gamma\ell \qquad (4\text{-}44)$$

This transmission line can be represented by a two-port shown in Fig. 4-11, where, the symmetry is necessary from both ports due to the bilateral nature of the transmission line. To find Z_{series} and $Y_{shunt}/2$, the following procedure is followed: short-circuiting the receiving end results in $V_R(s) = 0$, and from Fig. 4-11 and Eq. 4-43

$$\left.\frac{V_S}{I_R}(s)\right|_{V_R(s)=0} = Z_{series} = Z_c\sinh\gamma\ell \qquad (4\text{-}45)$$

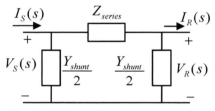

Fig. 4-11 Long line representation.

With the receiving end open-circuited in Fig. 4-11, $I_R(s) = 0$, and from Eq. 4-43

$$\left.\frac{V_S}{V_R}(s)\right|_{I_R(s)=0} = 1 + Z_{series}\frac{Y_{shunt}}{2} = \cosh\gamma\ell \qquad (4\text{-}46)$$

Therefore, from Eqs. 4-45 and 4-46

$$\frac{Y_{shunt}}{2} = \frac{1}{Z_c}\left(\frac{\cosh\gamma\ell - 1}{\sinh\gamma\ell}\right) \qquad (4\text{-}47)$$

From mathematical tables,

$$\frac{\cosh A - 1}{\sinh A} = \tanh\left(\frac{A}{2}\right) \qquad (4\text{-}48)$$

and therefore in Eq. 4-47

$$\frac{Y_{shunt}}{2} = \frac{\tanh\left(\dfrac{\gamma\ell}{2}\right)}{Z_c} \tag{4-49}$$

The per-phase equivalent circuit representation for long lines in phasor domain is similar to that in Fig. 4-11, and is shown in Fig. 4-12a.

$$(a) \qquad\qquad\qquad (b) \qquad\qquad\qquad (c)$$

Fig. 4-12 Per-phase transmission line representation based on length.

4-7-2   Medium-Length Lines

For lines less than 200 miles in length at 60 Hz frequency, it makes almost no difference to assume the transmission line resistance as a lumped value $R_{line}(=R\ell)$, rather than distributed. In addition, the shunt conductance can be neglected, with $G = 0$. Therefore, the rest of the line is lossless, and hence in Eq. 4-30, the characteristic impedance is real, $Z_c = \sqrt{L/C}$, as given by Eq. 4-35. In sinusoidal steady state with $s = j\omega$, as given by Eqs. 4-36 and 4-37, $\gamma = j\beta = j\omega\sqrt{LC}$ where $\beta = \omega\sqrt{LC}$. In Eq. 4-45, recognizing that $\sinh jA = j\sin A$,

$$Z_{series} = j\sqrt{\frac{L}{C}}\sin(\beta\ell) \tag{4-50}$$

Recognizing that for small values of $\beta\ell$, $\sin\beta\ell \simeq \beta\ell$ and making use of it in Eq. 4-50

$$Z_{series} = j\omega L_{line} \quad \text{where} \quad L_{line} = \ell L \tag{4-51}$$

Similarly in Eq. 4-49 (see homework problems)

$$\frac{Y_{shunt}}{2} = j\frac{\omega C_{line}}{2} \quad \text{where} \quad C_{line} = C\ell \tag{4-52}$$

The equivalent circuit for a medium length line simplifies as shown in Fig. 4-12b, where the series resistance is explicitly shown as a lumped element.

4-7-3   Short-Length Lines

In short lines less than 100 miles in length, the effect of capacitive vars is small compared to the system strength to provide Q and can often be neglected. This results in the simplified circuit shown in Fig. 4-12c with only the series impedance where the series resistance may even be neglected in some simplified studies.

4-8 CABLES [8]

As stated in [8], the underground transmission cable usage in the United States is very small: less than 1 percent of overhead line mileage. The highest underground cable voltage that is commonly used in the United States is 345 kV, and a large portion of this cable system is high-pressure fluid-filled pipe-type cable. Extruded dielectric cables are commonly used in the United States up to 230 kV, with up to 500 kV in service overseas. Underground transmission cable is generally more expensive than overhead lines. Because of all the variables (system design, route considerations, cable type, raceway type, etc.), it has to be determined case by case if underground transmission cable is a viable alternative. A rule of thumb is that underground transmission cable will cost from three to twenty times the cost of overhead line construction. As a result of the high cost, the use of high-voltage power cable for transmission and sub-transmission is generally limited to special applications caused by environmental and/or right-of-way restrictions. If underground transmission cable is going to be considered, an engineering study is required to properly evaluate the possible underground alternatives.

Underground cables are however used for power transfer in and around metropolitan areas due to lack of space for overhead transmission lines and for aesthetic reasons. Cables are also more reliable, not exposed to the elements of nature like the overhead transmission lines. For long distance bulk power transmission, cables are generally not used because of their cost compared to the overhead transmission lines, although new trenching technologies and cable materials may reduce this cost disadvantage.

Underground cables have much larger capacitance than the overhead transmission lines and hence their characteristic impedance Z_c is much smaller. However, in spite of lower values of Z_c and higher values of SIL, loading of cables is limited by the problem of getting rid of the dissipated heat. For underwater transmission, cables are used in dc systems for the following reason: because of the high capacitance of underground cables, operating at 60/50-Hz ac would require shunt reactors at periodic distances to compensate the capacitive charging currents. Such underwater compensation reactors are not feasible.

There are various types of cables in use: pipe-type oil filled cables, self-contained oil-filled cables with a single core, cross-linked cables with polyethylene insulation, and gas-insulated cables with compressed SF_6 gas [9]. One such type is shown in Fig. 4-13. Research is being done on superconducting cables as well. The modeling of cable parameters for power system studies is similar to those for overhead transmission lines.

4-18

Fig. 4-13 Underground cable.

REFERENCES

1. United States Department of Agriculture, Design Manual for High Voltage Transmission Lines, RUS BULLETIN 1724E-200.

2. Electric Power Research Institute (EPRI), *Transmission Line Reference Book: 345 kV and above*, 2nd edition.

3. Hermann W. Dommel, *EMTP Theory Book*, BPA, August 1986.

4. PSCAD/EMTDC, Manitoba HVDC Research Centre: www.hvdc.ca.

5. N. Mohan, T. Undeland and W.P. Robbins, *Power Electronics: Converters, Applications, and Design*, 3rd edition, Year 2003, John Wiley & Sons.

6. Prabha Kundur, *Power System Stability and Control*, McGraw Hill, 1994.

7. R. Dunlop et al, "Analytical Development of Loadability Characteristics for EHV and UHV Transmission Lines", IEEE Transaction on PAS, Vol PAS-98, No.2, March/April 1979.

8. United States Department of Agriculture, Rural Utilities Service, Design Guide for Rural Substations, RUS BULLETIN 1724E-300.

9. EPRI's *Underground Transmission Systems Reference Book*.

PROBLEMS

4-1   According to [1], the conductor surface gradient in a single-conductor per-phase transmission line can be calculated as follows:

$$g = \frac{kV_{LL}}{\sqrt{3}\, r \ln \dfrac{D}{r}}$$

where kV_{LL} is line-line voltage in kV, r is the conductor radius in cm, D is the geometric mean distance (GMD) of the phase conductors in cm, and g is the conductor surface gradient in kV/cm.

Calculate the conductor surface gradient for a 230 kV line (a) with Dove ACSR conductors for which $r = 1.18\,cm$, and (b) with Pheasant ACSR conductors for which $r = 1.755\,cm$. Assume that $D = 784.9\,cm$ in both cases.

4-2 According to [1], the conductor surface gradient in two-conductor bundle per-phase transmission line can be calculated as follows:

$$g = \frac{kV_{LL}(1 + 2r/s)}{2\sqrt{3}\,r \ln \dfrac{D}{\sqrt{rs}}}$$

where kV_{LL} is line-line voltage in kV, r is the conductor radius in cm, D is the geometric mean distance (GMD) of the phase conductors in cm, s is the separation between sub-conductors in cm, and g is the conductor surface gradient in kV/cm.

Calculate the conductor surface gradient for a 345 kV line with a two-conductor bundle per phase with Drake ACSR conductors for which $r = 1.407\,cm$. Assume that $D = 914\,cm$ and $s = 45.72\,cm\,(18\,inches)$.

4-3 The parameters for a 500-kV transmission system shown in Fig. 4-1 with bundled conductors are as follows: $Z_c = 258\,\Omega$ and $R = 1.76 \times 10^{-2}\,\Omega/km$. Calculate the value for the Surge Impedance Loading SIL and the percentage power loss in this transmission line if it is 300 km long and is loaded to its SIL.

4-4 The 500-kV line of the type in Problem 4-3 is a short-length line, 80 km long. It is loaded to three times its SIL. Calculate the power loss in this line as a percentage of its loading.

4-5 The 345-kV transmission line of the type described in Example 4-3 is 300-km long. Calculate the parameters for its model as a long-length line as shown in Fig. 4-12a. Compare these parameter values for the model in Fig. 4-12b that assumes it to be a medium-length line. Compare the percentage errors in assuming it to be a medium-length line.

4-6 Consider a 345-kV transmission line that has parameters similar to those described in Table 4-1. Assuming a $100\,MVA$ base, obtain its parameters in per unit.

4-7 Consider a 300-km long, 345-kV transmission line that has parameters similar to those described in Table 4-1. Assume its receiving-end voltage $V_R = 1.0\,pu$. Plot the voltage ratio V_s/V_R as a function of P_R/SIL, where P_R is the unity power factor load at the receiving-end. P_R/SIL varies in a range from 0 to 3.

4-8   Repeat Problem 4-7 if the load impedance has a power factor of (a) 0.9 lagging, and (b) 0.9 leading. Compare these results with a unity-power-factor loading.

4-9   Calculate the phase angle difference of voltages between the two ends of the line in Problem 4-7 that has unity-power-factor loading.

4-10   A 200 km long 345-kV line has the parameters given in Table 4-1. Neglect the resistance. Calculate the voltage profile along this line if it's loaded to (a) 1.5 times *SIL*, and (b) 0.75 times *SIL*, if both ends are held at the voltages of 1 per unit.

4-11   In Problem 4-10, calculate the reactive power at both ends under the two levels of loading.

4-12   In a 230-kV cable system, the surge impedance is 25 ohms and the charging MVA/km is 14.5. The resistance is 0.05 ohms/km. The cable length is 20 km. Both ends of this cable system are held at 1 per unit. Calculate the maximum loading, in terms of its *SIL*, if the power loss in this cable is not to exceed 5 percent of the power transferred.

EMTDC-based Problems

4-13   Calculate the parameters for the single-conductor per phase, 345-kV transmission line in Example 4-2, using the data file for this problem on the accompanying CD.

4-14   Calculate the parameters for the two-conductor bundle per phase, 345-kV transmission line, using the data file for this problem on the accompanying CD.

4-15   Calculate the parameters for the three-conductor bundle per phase, 500-kV transmission line, using the data file for this problem on the accompanying CD.

4-16   Obtain the results of Problem 4-11 in EMTDC using the data file for this problem on the accompanying CD.

CHAPTER 5

POWER FLOW IN POWER SYSTEM NETWORKS

5-1 INTRODUCTION

For planning purposes, it is important to know the power transfer capability of transmission lines to meet the anticipated load demand. It is also important to know the levels of power flow though various transmission lines under normal as well as under certain contingency outage conditions to maintain the continuity of service. Knowledge of power flows and voltage levels under normal operating conditions are also necessary in order to determine fault currents, if a line were to short-circuit for example, and the ensuing consequences on the transient stability of the system.

A Power Flow program, which determines this power flow is commonly used by all power companies for planning and operation purposes. These power flow calculations are usually performed on the bulk power system where the effect of the secondary underlying network is implicitly included.

Determining power flow requires measurements of certain power system conditions. Theoretically, if all the bus voltages in terms of their magnitudes and phase angles could be measured with confidence, then the power flow calculations could simply be carried out by solving the linear circuit in which voltages and branch impedances, including the load impedances, are all given, and there would be no need for the procedure outlined in this chapter.

However, utilities measure a combination of quantities such as voltage magnitude V, real power P, and the reactive power Q at various buses. (Many fault protection relays make these measurements anyway to perform their function, and this information gathered by them is utilized for power flow calculations.) The measured information is telemetered to a central operating station, often through dedicated microwave transmitters and receivers. This information has to be instantaneous, that is measured simultaneously in time. The system to acquire these measurements and to telemeter them to a Control Center is called SCADA (Supervisory Control and Data Acquisition) system. It is recognized that all the measurement transducers do not provide accurate information all the time. To overcome this problem, the system is over-measured by measuring more quantities than are required. Then, a State Estimator is used to throw away the "bad" and the redundant measurements on a probabilistic manner.

In this chapter, we will study the basic formulation of power-flow problem and discuss the most commonly used numerical solution method to carry it out. To simplify our discussion, we will assume a balanced three-phase system, and therefore only a per-phase representation is necessary.

Next, we will describe how the system is represented for this study. The transmission lines are represented by their pi-circuit modal with a series impedance $Z_{series}(= R + j\omega L)$ and a susceptance $B_{shunt}/2(= \omega C/2)$ at each end of the line. These are expressed in per unit at a common MVA and kV base. It is customary to use a three-phase 100 MVA base. Similarly, transformers are represented by their total leakage impedance expressed in per unit in terms of the common base, ignoring their exciting currents. Transformers are assumed to be at their nominal turns-ratio hence the turns-ratios do not enter into this per unit based calculations. Loads can be represented in a combination of different ways: by specifying their real and reactive powers (P and Q), as a constant-current source, or by their impedance that is treated as constant.

5-2 DESCRIPTION OF THE POWER SYSTEM

A power system under study can be considered as consisting of the following buses that are interconnected through transmission lines:

1. Load Buses where P and Q are specified. These are called PQ buses.
2. Generator buses where the voltage magnitude V and the power P are specified. These are called PV buses. If the upper and/or lower limits on the reactive power Q on a PV bus are specified and this limit is reached, then such a bus is treated as a PQ bus as if the reactive power is specified at that limit.
3. A Slack Bus which is essentially an "infinite" bus, where the voltage magnitude V is specified (normally 1 pu) and its phase angle is assumed zero as a reference angle. At this bus, P can be what it needs to be, based on the line losses, and hence it is called the slack bus which takes up the slack. Similarly, Q at this bus can be what it needs to be to hold the voltage at the specified value.
4. There are buses where there is no P and Q injection specified, and the voltage is also not specified. Often, these become necessary for including transformers.

These can be considered as a subset of PQ buses with specified injection of $P = 0$ and $Q = 0$.

5-3 EXAMPLE POWER SYSTEM

To illustrate power flow calculations, an extremely simple power system consisting of three buses is shown in Fig. 5-1. These three buses are connected through three 345-kV transmission lines 200 km, 150 km and 150 km long, as shown in Fig. 5-1. As listed in Table 4-1 of Chapter 4, these transmission lines with bundled conductors have the series reactance of 0.376 Ω/km at 60 Hz and the series resistance of 0.037 Ω/km. The shunt susceptance $B(=\omega C)$ is $4.5\,\mu\mho/km$.

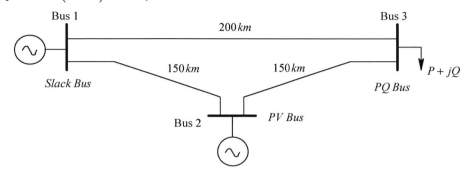

Fig. 5-1 A three-bus 345-kV example system.

To convert the actual quantities to per-unit, the voltage base is 345 kV (L-L). Following the convention, a common three-phase 100 MVA base is chosen. Therefore, the base impedance is

$$Z_{base} = \frac{kV_{base}^2(phase)}{MVA_{base}(1-\phi)} = \frac{kV_{base}^2(L-L)}{MVA_{base}(3-\phi)} = 1190.25\,\Omega \tag{5-1}$$

The base admittance $Y_{base} = 1/Z_{base}$. Based on these base impedance and base admittance, and the line lengths, the line parameters and their per-unit values are as given in Table 5-1 below.

Table 5-1 Per-Unit Values in the Example System

Line	Series Impedance Z in Ω (pu)	Total Susceptance B in $\mu\mho$ (pu)
1-2	$Z_{12} = (5.55 + j56.4)\Omega = (0.0047 + j0.0474)\,pu$	$B_{Total} = 675\,\mu\mho = (0.8034)\,pu$
1-3	$Z_{13} = (7.40 + j75.2)\Omega = (0.0062 + j0.0632)\,pu$	$B_{Total} = 900\,\mu\mho = (1.0712)\,pu$
2-3	$Z_{23} = (5.55 + j56.4)\Omega = (0.0047 + j0.0474)\,pu$	$B_{Total} = 675\,\mu\mho = (0.8034)\,pu$

5-4 BUILDING THE ADMITTANCE MATRIX

It is easiest to carry out the network solution in a nodal form, in comparison to writing loop equations which are more numerous. In writing the nodal equations, the current $\overline{I}_k$ is the current *injected* into a bus k, as shown in Fig. 5-2 for the example system of Fig. 5-1.

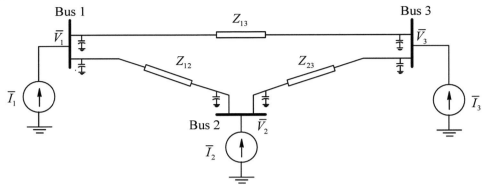

Fig. 5-2 Example system of Fig. 5-1 for assembling Y-bus matrix.

By Kirchhoff's current law, the current injection at bus k is related to the bus voltages as follows:

$$\overline{I}_k = \overline{V}_k Y_{kG} + \sum_{\substack{m \\ m \neq k}} \frac{\overline{V}_k - \overline{V}_m}{Z_{km}} \tag{5-2}$$

where Y_{kG} is the sum of the admittances connected at bus k to ground, and the second term consists of flows on all the lines connected to bus k, with the series impedance being Z_{km}, for example between buses k and m. Therefore,

$$\overline{I}_k = \overline{V}_k \left(Y_{kG} + \sum_{\substack{m \\ m \neq k}} \frac{1}{Z_{km}} \right) - \sum_{\substack{m \\ m \neq k}} \frac{\overline{V}_m}{Z_{km}} \tag{5-3}$$

In Eq. 5-3, the quantities within the brackets on the right-side are designated as

$$Y_{kk} = Y_{kG} + \sum_{\substack{m \\ m \neq k}} \frac{1}{Z_{km}}, \tag{5-4}$$

which is the self-admittance and is the sum of the admittances connected between bus-k and the other buses including ground. Similarly in Eq. 5-3, between buses k and m, the mutual admittance is

$$Y_{km} = -\frac{1}{Z_{km}} \qquad (5\text{-}5)$$

which is negative of the inverse of the series impedance between buses k and m. This procedure allows the formulation of the bus-admittance matrix $[Y]$ for an n-bus system as

$$
\begin{bmatrix} \overline{I}_1 \\ \overline{I}_2 \\ .. \\ .. \\ .. \\ \overline{I}_n \end{bmatrix} =
\begin{bmatrix}
Y_{11} & Y_{12} & .. & .. & .. & Y_{1n} \\
Y_{21} & Y_{22} & .. & .. & .. & Y_{2n} \\
.. & .. & .. & .. & .. & .. \\
.. & .. & .. & .. & .. & .. \\
.. & .. & .. & .. & .. & .. \\
Y_{n1} & Y_{n2} & .. & .. & .. & Y_{nn}
\end{bmatrix}
\begin{bmatrix} \overline{V}_1 \\ \overline{V}_2 \\ .. \\ .. \\ .. \\ \overline{V}_n \end{bmatrix}
\qquad (5\text{-}6)
$$

▲ **Example 5-1**   In the example system of Fig. 5-2, ignore all the shunt susceptances and assemble the bus-admittance matrix of the form in Eq. 5-6.

Solution   In the example system, in per unit,

$$Z_{12} = (0.0047 + j0.0474)\, pu, \; Z_{13} = (0.0062 + j0.0632)\, pu, \; Z_{23} = (0.0047 + j0.0474)\, pu\,.$$

Therefore,

$$
\begin{bmatrix} \overline{I}_1 \\ \overline{I}_2 \\ \overline{I}_3 \end{bmatrix} =
\begin{bmatrix}
3.5994 - j36.5773 & -2.0568 + j20.9013 & -1.5426 + j15.6760 \\
-2.0568 + j20.9013 & 4.1136 - j41.8027 & -2.0568 + j20.9013 \\
-1.5426 + j15.6760 & -2.0568 + j20.9013 & 3.5994 - j36.5773
\end{bmatrix}
\begin{bmatrix} \overline{V}_1 \\ \overline{V}_2 \\ \overline{V}_3 \end{bmatrix}
$$

▲

5-5 BASIC POWER FLOW EQUATIONS

In the network equation of Eq. 5-6, the current injections into buses are not specified explicitly. Rather, the injected real power P is specified at PV buses, and P and Q injections are specified at PQ buses as

$$P_k + jQ_k = \overline{V}_k \overline{I}_k^* \qquad (5\text{-}7)$$

From the nodal equation in Eq. 5-6,

$$\overline{I}_k = \sum_{m=1}^{n} Y_{km} \overline{V}_m \quad \text{where,} \; (Y_{km} = G_{km} + jB_{km}) \qquad (5\text{-}8)$$

From Eq. 5-8, recognizing that in terms of complex variables if $a = bc$, then $a^* = b^* c^*$,

$$\overline{I}_k^* = \sum_{m=1}^{n} Y_{km}^* \overline{V}_m^* = \sum_{m=1}^{n} (G_{km} - jB_{km})\overline{V}_m^* \qquad (5\text{-}9)$$

5-5

Substituting Eq. 5-9 into Eq. 5-7,

$$P_k + jQ_k = \overline{V}_k \overline{I}_k^* = \sum_{m=1}^{n}\left[(G_{km} - jB_{km})(\overline{V}_k \overline{V}_m^*)\right]$$ (5-10)

In Eq. 5-10, $\overline{V}_k \overline{V}_m^*$ can be written in the polar form as

$$\overline{V}_k \overline{V}_m^* = \left(V_k e^{j\theta_k}\right)\left(V_m e^{-j\theta_m}\right) = V_k V_m e^{j\theta_{km}} = V_k V_m \left(\cos\theta_{km} + j\sin\theta_{km}\right)$$ (5-11)

where, $\theta_{km} = \theta_k - \theta_m$.

Substituting Eq. 5-11 into Eq. 5-10 and separating real and imaginary parts (note that $\cos\theta_{kk} = 1$ and $\sin\theta_{kk} = 0$),

$$P_k = G_{kk}V_k^2 + V_k\sum_{\substack{m=1\\m\neq k}}^{n} V_m \left(G_{km}\cos\theta_{km} + B_{km}\sin\theta_{km}\right)$$ (5-12)

and

$$Q_k = -B_{kk}V_k^2 + V_k\sum_{\substack{m=1\\m\neq k}}^{n} V_m \left(G_{km}\sin\theta_{km} - B_{km}\cos\theta_{km}\right)$$ (5-13)

where the first terms on the right-side of Eqs. 5-12 and 5-13 correspond to $m = k$. In an n-bus system, let us specify the types of buses as follows: one slack bus, n_{PV} PV buses and n_{PQ} PQ buses such that

$$1 + n_{PV} + n_{PQ} = n$$ (5-14)

Therefore, $(n_{PV} + n_{PQ})$ equations are written where P are specified, and n_{PQ} equations are written where Q are specified. Therefore, there are a total of $(n_{PV} + 2n_{PQ})$ equations of the form similar to Eq. 5-12 or 5-13. Similarly, there are n_{PQ} unknown voltage magnitudes and $(n_{PV} + n_{PQ})$ unknown voltage phase angles. Therefore, out of a total of $2n$ voltage magnitudes and phase angles, there are a total of $(n_{PV} + 2n_{PQ})$ unknown variables to solve and as many equations.

There is no closed-form solution to Eqs. 5-12 and 5-13 that are nonlinear, thus we will use a trial-and-error approach. Using Taylor's series expansion, we will linearize them and use an iterative procedure called the Newton-Raphson method until the solution is reached. To do this, we can write Eqs. 5-12 and 5-13 as follows where P_k^{sp} and Q_k^{sp} are the specified values of injected real and reactive powers:

$$P_k^{sp} - P_k(V_1,...,V_n,\theta_1,...,\theta_n) = 0 \qquad\qquad \text{k} \ne S\text{lack Bus} \qquad\qquad (5\text{-}15)$$

and

$$Q_k^{sp} - Q_k(V_1,...,V_n,\theta_1,...,\theta_n) = 0 \qquad\qquad \text{k=}PQ \text{ Buses} \qquad\qquad (5\text{-}16)$$

5-6 NEWTON-RAPHSON PROCEDURE

For solving equations of the form given by Eqs. 5-15 and 5-16, the Newton-Raphson procedure has now become the commonly used approach due to its speed and the likelihood of conversion, and hence we will only focus on this procedure, recognizing that there are other procedures as well such as the Gauss-Seidel method. The Newton-Raphson procedure is explained by means of a simple nonlinear equation of the same form as Eqs. 5-15 and 5-16

$$c - f(x) = 0 \qquad\qquad (5\text{-}17)$$

where c is a constant, and $f(x)$ is a nonlinear function of a variable x :. In order to determine the value of x which satisfies Eq. 5-17, we will start with an initial guess $x^{(0)}$ which is not exactly the solution but close to it. A small adjustment Δx is needed so that $(x^{(0)} + \Delta x)$ comes closer to the actual solution, that is

$$c - f(x^{(0)} + \Delta x) \simeq 0 \qquad\qquad (5\text{-}18)$$

Using the Taylor series expansion, the function in Eq. 5-18 can be expressed as follows where the terms involving higher orders of Δx are ignored:

$$c - [f(x^{(0)}) + \left.\frac{\partial f}{\partial x}\right|_0 \Delta x] = 0 \qquad\qquad (5\text{-}19)$$

or

$$c - f(x^{(0)}) = \left.\frac{\partial f}{\partial x}\right|_0 \Delta x \qquad\qquad (5\text{-}20)$$

where the partial derivative is taken at $x = x^{(0)}$. The objective in Eq. 5-20 is to calculate the adjustment Δx, which can be calculated as

$$\Delta x = \frac{c - f(x^{(0)})}{\left.\dfrac{\partial f}{\partial x}\right|_0} \qquad\qquad (5\text{-}21)$$

This results in the new estimate of x,

$$x^{(1)} = x^{(0)} + \Delta x \qquad\qquad (5\text{-}22)$$

Now, similar to Eq. 5-21, the new correction to the estimate can be calculated as

$$\Delta x = \frac{c - f(x^{(1)})}{\left.\dfrac{\partial f}{\partial x}\right|_{1}}$$
(5-23)

where the partial derivative is taken at $x = x^{(1)}$. Therefore,

$$x^{(2)} = x^{(1)} + \Delta x$$
(5-24)

This process is repeated until the error $\varepsilon = |c - f(x)|$ is below a certain pre-specified error tolerance value and the convergence is assumed to have been reached such that the original equation, Eq. 5-17, is satisfied.

This Newton-Raphson procedure is illustrated by means of a simple example.

▲ **Example 5-2**   Consider a simple equation below

$$4 - x^2 = 0$$
(5-25)

where corresponding to Eq. 5-17, $c = 4$, and $f(x) = x^2$. Solve for x which satisfies Eq. 5-25 with an error ε below a tolerance of 0.0002.

Solution   The solution to this equation is obvious, that is, $x = 2$. However, to illustrate the Newton-Raphson procedure, the left-side of Eq. 5-25 is plotted in Fig. 5-3, as a function of x.

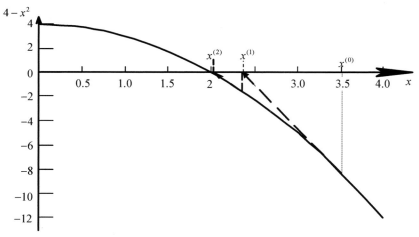

Fig. 5-3 Plot of $4 - x^2$ as a function of x.

For $f(x) = x^2$, $\dfrac{\partial f}{\partial x} = 2x$. Using this partial derivative and the initial guess as $x^{(0)} = 3.5$, from Eq. 5-21,

$$\Delta x = \frac{c - f(x^{(0)})}{\left.\dfrac{\partial f}{\partial x}\right|_0} = -1.17857, \quad x^{(1)} = x^{(0)} + \Delta x = 2.3214, \text{ and } \varepsilon = \left|4 - \left(x^{(1)}\right)^2\right| = 0.3214$$

Using $x^{(1)} = 2.3214$, from Eq. 5-23,

$$\Delta x = \frac{c - f(x^{(1)})}{\left.\dfrac{\partial f}{\partial x}\right|_1} = -0.29915, \quad x^{(2)} = x^{(1)} + \Delta x = 2.022, \text{ and } \varepsilon = \left|4 - \left(x^{(2)}\right)^2\right| = 0.022$$

Repeating this procedure,

$$\Delta x = \frac{c - f(x^{(2)})}{\left.\dfrac{\partial f}{\partial x}\right|_2} = -0.02188, \quad x^{(3)} = x^{(2)} + \Delta x = 2.000122, \quad \varepsilon = \left|4 - \left(x^{(3)}\right)^2\right| = 0.000122$$

The error $\varepsilon = 0.000122$ is now below the pre-specified tolerance and the conversion is achieved. ▲

5-7 SOLUTION OF POWER FLOW EQUATIONS USING N-R METHOD

Having looked at the basics of the Newton-Raphson procedure, we are ready to apply it to the power flow equations of 5-15 and 5-16. In Eqs. 5-12 and 5-13, P_k and Q_k are in terms of the estimates of voltage magnitudes and phase angles, some of which are unknown thus yet to be determined. Corrections are expressed by ΔV's and $\Delta \theta$'s. In order to evaluate the partial derivatives, we should recognize the following, noting that $\theta_{km} = \theta_k - \theta_m$:

$$\frac{\partial(\cos\theta_{km})}{\partial\theta_k} = -\sin\theta_{km} \; ; \quad \frac{\partial(\cos\theta_{km})}{\partial\theta_m} = \sin\theta_{km} \; ; \quad \frac{\partial(\sin\theta_{km})}{\partial\theta_k} = \cos\theta_{km} \; ; \quad \frac{\partial(\sin\theta_{km})}{\partial\theta_m} = -\cos\theta_{km}$$

Therefore, the partial derivates from Eq. 5-12 for the real power are as follows for bus k:

$$\frac{\partial P_k}{\partial\theta_k} = V_k \sum_{\substack{m=1 \\ m \neq k}}^{n} V_m \left(-G_{km}\sin\theta_{km} + B_{km}\cos\theta_{km}\right) \tag{5-26}$$

If m takes a value j in Eq. 5-12, then

$$\frac{\partial P_k}{\partial \theta_j} = V_k V_j \left(G_{kj} \sin \theta_{kj} - B_{kj} \cos \theta_{kj} \right) \qquad\qquad j \neq k \qquad\qquad (5\text{-}27)$$

$$\frac{\partial P_k}{\partial V_k} = 2 G_{kk} V_k + \sum_{\substack{m=1 \\ m \neq k}}^{n} V_m \left(G_{km} \cos \theta_{km} + B_{km} \sin \theta_{km} \right) \qquad\qquad (5\text{-}28)$$

If m takes a value j in Eq. 5-12, then

$$\frac{\partial P_k}{\partial V_j} = V_k \left(G_{kj} \cos \theta_{kj} + B_{kj} \sin \theta_{kj} \right) \qquad\qquad j \neq k \qquad\qquad (5\text{-}29)$$

Partial derivates from Eq. 5-13 for the reactive power are as follows for bus k :

$$\frac{\partial Q_k}{\partial \theta_k} = V_k \sum_{\substack{m=1 \\ m \neq k}}^{n} V_m \left(G_{km} \cos \theta_{km} + B_{km} \sin \theta_{km} \right) \qquad\qquad (5\text{-}30)$$

If m takes a value j in Eq. 5-13, then

$$\frac{\partial Q_k}{\partial \theta_j} = V_k V_j \left(-G_{kj} \cos \theta_{kj} - B_{kj} \sin \theta_{kj} \right) \qquad\qquad j \neq k \qquad\qquad (5\text{-}31)$$

$$\frac{\partial Q_k}{\partial V_k} = -2 B_{kk} V_k + \sum_{\substack{m=1 \\ m \neq k}}^{n} V_m \left(G_{km} \sin \theta_{km} - B_{km} \cos \theta_{km} \right) \qquad\qquad (5\text{-}32)$$

If m takes a value j in Eq. 5-13, then

$$\frac{\partial Q_k}{\partial V_j} = V_k \left(G_{kj} \sin \theta_{kj} - B_{kj} \cos \theta_{kj} \right) \qquad\qquad j \neq k \qquad\qquad (5\text{-}33)$$

Using the procedure outlined earlier leading to Eq. 5-20, and with P_k^{sp} and Q_k^{sp} as the specified values, the following matrix equation can be written in terms of vectors and sub-matrices as

$$\underbrace{\begin{bmatrix} P^{sp} - P \\ Q^{sp} - Q \end{bmatrix}}_{(2n_{PQ}+n_{PV}) \times 1} = \underbrace{\begin{bmatrix} \dfrac{\partial P}{\partial \theta} & \dfrac{\partial P}{\partial V} \\ \dfrac{\partial Q}{\partial \theta} & \dfrac{\partial Q}{\partial V} \end{bmatrix}}_{\substack{[J] \\ (2n_{PQ}+n_{PV}) \times (2n_{PQ}+n_{PV})}} \underbrace{\begin{bmatrix} \Delta\theta \\ \Delta V \end{bmatrix}}_{(2n_{PQ}+n_{PV}) \times 1} \qquad\qquad (5\text{-}34)$$

It should be noted that another row in Eq. 5-34 is added for each PV Bus that becomes a PQ Bus due to the its reactive power reaching one of its limits, if they were to be specified.

Convergence to the Correct Solution: The iterative N-R procedure is continued until all the mismatches in the left-side vector in Eq. 5-34 are less than the specified tolerance values, at which point it is assumed that the solution has converged to the correct values. Until the convergence is achieved, in each iterative step, the above matrix equation is solved for the needed corrections $\Delta\theta$'s and ΔV's. In a practical power network with thousands of buses, the Jacobian J is calculated using sparsity and optimal ordering techniques. This discussion is beyond the scope of this book and for the example system at hand, we will use the matrix inversion in Eq. 5-34 to calculate the correction terms in each iteration step as follows:

$$\begin{bmatrix} \Delta\theta \\ \Delta V \end{bmatrix} = [J]^{-1} \begin{bmatrix} P^{sp} - P \\ Q^{sp} - Q \end{bmatrix} \tag{5-35}$$

▲ **Example 5-3** In the example system of Fig. 5-1, ignore all the shunt susceptances. Bus-1 is a slack bus, Bus-2 is a PV bus and Bus-3 is a PQ bus. Using the N-R procedure described above, assemble the Jacobian matrix for the example power system.

Solution In this system, there are three buses with $n = 3$, $n_{PV} = 1$ and $n_{PQ} = 1$. There are three specified injected real/reactive powers (P_2^{sp}, P_3^{sp} and Q_3^{sp}) and three unknowns (θ_2, θ_3 and V_3) related to the bus voltages. Therefore, the correction terms in Eq. 5-34 are of the following form:

$$\begin{bmatrix} P_2^{sp} - P_2 \\ P_3^{sp} - P_3 \\ Q_3^{sp} - Q_3 \end{bmatrix} = \underbrace{\begin{bmatrix} \dfrac{\partial P_2}{\partial \theta_2} & \dfrac{\partial P_2}{\partial \theta_3} & \dfrac{\partial P_2}{\partial V_3} \\ \dfrac{\partial P_3}{\partial \theta_2} & \dfrac{\partial P_3}{\partial \theta_3} & \dfrac{\partial P_3}{\partial V_3} \\ \dfrac{\partial Q_3}{\partial \theta_2} & \dfrac{\partial Q_3}{\partial \theta_3} & \dfrac{\partial Q_3}{\partial V_3} \end{bmatrix}}_{J} \begin{bmatrix} \Delta\theta_2 \\ \Delta\theta_3 \\ \Delta V_3 \end{bmatrix} \tag{5-36}$$

To assemble the Jacobian matrix J of Eq. 5-36, the bus values of k, j, and m in the equations related to the N-R procedure can be recognized for each element as shown in Table 5-2 below:

Table 5-2 Buses Related to the Jacobian Matrix of Eq. 5-36

Eq. 5-26	Eq. 5-27	Eq. 5-29
$\dfrac{\partial P_2}{\partial \theta_2}: k=2;\ m=1,3$	$\dfrac{\partial P_2}{\partial \theta_3}: k=2;\ j=3$	$\dfrac{\partial P_2}{\partial V_3}: k=2;\ j=3$
Eq. 5-27	Eq. 5-26	Eq. 5-28
$\dfrac{\partial P_3}{\partial \theta_2}: k=3;\ j=2$	$\dfrac{\partial P_3}{\partial \theta_3}: k=3;\ m=1,2$	$\dfrac{\partial P_3}{\partial V_3}: k=3;\ m=1,2$
Eq. 5-31	Eq. 5-30	Eq. 5-32
$\dfrac{\partial Q_3}{\partial \theta_2}: k=3;\ j=2$	$\dfrac{\partial Q_3}{\partial \theta_3}: k=3;\ m=1,2$	$\dfrac{\partial Q_3}{\partial V_3}: k=3;\ m=1,2$

Equations for the above Jacobian elements are as follows:

$$J(1,1) = V_2 V_1 \left(-G_{21} \sin\theta_{21} + B_{21} \cos\theta_{21} \right) + V_2 V_3 \left(-G_{23}\sin\theta_{23} + B_{23}\cos\theta_{23} \right) \qquad (5\text{-}37)$$

$$J(1,2) = V_2 V_3 \left(G_{23}\sin\theta_{23} - B_{23}\cos\theta_{23} \right) \qquad (5\text{-}38)$$

$$J(1,3) = V_2 \left(G_{23}\cos\theta_{23} + B_{23}\sin\theta_{23} \right) \qquad (5\text{-}39)$$

$$J(2,1) = V_3 V_2 \left(G_{32}\sin\theta_{32} - B_{32}\cos\theta_{32} \right) \qquad (5\text{-}40)$$

$$J(2,2) = V_3 V_1 \left(-G_{31}\sin\theta_{31} + B_{31}\cos\theta_{31} \right) + V_3 V_2 \left(-G_{32}\sin\theta_{32} + B_{32}\cos\theta_{32} \right) \qquad (5\text{-}41)$$

$$J(2,3) = 2G_{33}V_3 + V_1 \left(G_{31}\cos\theta_{31} + B_{31}\sin\theta_{31} \right) + V_2 \left(G_{32}\cos\theta_{32} + B_{32}\sin\theta_{32} \right) \qquad (5\text{-}42)$$

$$J(3,1) = V_3 V_2 \left(-G_{32}\cos\theta_{32} - B_{32}\sin\theta_{32} \right) \qquad (5\text{-}43)$$

$$J(3,2) = V_3 V_1 \left(G_{31}\cos\theta_{31} + B_{31}\sin\theta_{31} \right) + V_3 V_2 \left(G_{32}\cos\theta_{32} + B_{32}\sin\theta_{32} \right) \qquad (5\text{-}44)$$

$$J(3,3) = -2B_{33}V_3 + V_1 \left(G_{31}\sin\theta_{31} - B_{31}\cos\theta_{31} \right) + V_2 \left(G_{32}\sin\theta_{32} - B_{32}\cos\theta_{32} \right) \qquad (5\text{-}45)$$

▲

▲ **Example 5-4** In the example system of Fig. 5-1, ignore all the shunt susceptances. Bus-1 is a slack bus with $V_1 = 1.0\,pu$ and $\theta_1 = 0$. Bus-2 is a PV bus with $V_2 = 1.05\,pu$

and $P_2^{sp} = 2.0 \, pu$. Bus-3 is a PQ bus with injections of $P_3^{sp} = -5.0 \, pu$ and $Q_3^{sp} = -1.0 \, pu$. Using the N-R procedure described above, the Jacobian matrix was assembled in Example 5-3. Using that in the N-R procedure, calculate the power flow on all three lines in this example power system.

Solution   The MATLAB program for this example is included on the accompanying CD-ROM and the results are as follows:

After the N-R procedure has converged, the Jacobian matrix is as follows:

$$J = \begin{bmatrix} 43.42 & -21.56 & 0.4237 \\ -21.07 & 35.99 & -1.5913 \\ 0.414 & -8.44 & 34.75 \end{bmatrix}$$

The bus voltages are as follows:

$$\bar{V}_1 = 1\angle 0^0 \, pu, \; \bar{V}_2 = 1.05\angle\text{-}2.07^0 \, pu, \; \bar{V}_3 = 0.978\angle\text{-}8.79^0 \, pu$$

At Bus 1, $P_{1\text{-}2} + jQ_{1\text{-}2} = (0.69 - j1.11) \, pu$

At Bus 1, $P_{1\text{-}3} + jQ_{1\text{-}3} = (2.39 + j0.29) \, pu$

At Bus 2, $P_{2\text{-}3} + jQ_{2\text{-}3} = (2.68 + j1.48) \, pu$

The power and reactive powers supplied by the generators at buses 1 and 2 are as follows:

$$P_1 + jQ_1 = (3.08 - j0.82) \, pu \text{ and } P_2 + jQ_2 = (2.0 \quad + j2.67) \, pu.$$

These results are graphically shown in Fig. 5-4.

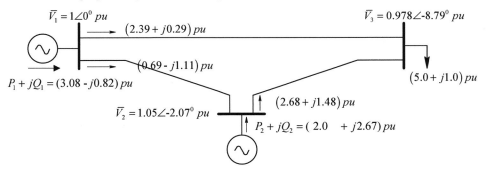

Fig. 5-4 Power-Flow results of Example 5-4.

▲

5-8 FAST DECOUPLED N-R METHOD FOR POWER FLOW

In power systems, generally reactive powers $Q's$ influence the voltage magnitudes, and the real powers $P's$ influence the phase angle $\theta's$. Therefore, the solution using the

Newton-Raphson method can be considerably simplified by including only the couplings mentioned above, and ignoring the $\partial P / \partial V$ and $\partial Q / \partial \theta$ terms in the Jacobian of Eq. 5-36. Thus,

$$\left[P^{sp} - P \right] = \left[\frac{\partial P}{\partial \theta} \right] [\Delta \theta] \tag{5-46}$$

$$\left[Q^{sp} - Q \right] = \left[\frac{\partial Q}{\partial V} \right] [\Delta V] \tag{5-47}$$

These two equations are much faster to solve than the coupled set of equations in full Newton-Raphson procedure. Further simplifications can be made such that the elements of the Jacobian matrices of Eqs. 5-46 and 5-47 are constants and hence do not need to be calculated at every iteration, unlike the scenario in the full N-R method [1]. This technique can be very useful for calculating power flow for contingencies where the speed of calculations is of primary importance, even if the accuracy is somewhat sacrificed compared to the full N-R method.

5-9 SENSITIVITY ANALYSIS

The fast-decoupled formulation of section 5-8 also shows that these equations can be used for sensitivity analysis, for example to determine where to install a reactive power supplying device to control the bus voltage magnitude. This can be seen by rewriting Eq. 5-47 as

$$[\Delta Q] = \left[\frac{\partial Q}{\partial V} \right] [\Delta V] \tag{5-48}$$

Thus,

$$[\Delta V] = \left[\frac{\partial Q}{\partial V} \right]^{-1} [\Delta Q] \tag{5-49}$$

Eq. 5-49 demonstrates the sensitivity of various bus voltage magnitudes to the incremental change in reactive power at a selected bus.

5-10   REACHING THE BUS VAR LIMIT

As discussed in Chapter 9, synchronous generators have limits on the amount of reactive power (var) they can supply. Certain buses may contain additional devices to supply vars but such devices also have their limits. Therefore, in a power-flow condition, if the demand of vars at any PV bus reaches its limit, then that bus voltage can be held at its specified magnitude, and thus must be treated as the PQ bus.

As an example, in the 3-bus system shown in Fig. 5-1, bus-2 is a PV bus. If the vars needed from the generator at this bus reach the limit, then bus-2 must be treated as a PQ bus. Therefore, Eq. 5-36 without the limit is modified as follows, where $Q_2^{\lim}$ is the var limit at bus-2 and a column and a row, shown in bold, must be added to the Jacobian matrix:

$$
\begin{bmatrix} P_2^{sp} - P_2 \\ P_3^{sp} - P_3 \\ Q_3^{sp} - Q_3 \\ \boldsymbol{Q_2^{\lim} - Q_2} \end{bmatrix} = \underbrace{\begin{bmatrix} \dfrac{\partial P_2}{\partial \theta_2} & \dfrac{\partial P_2}{\partial \theta_3} & \dfrac{\partial P_2}{\partial V_3} & \dfrac{\partial \boldsymbol{P_2}}{\partial \boldsymbol{V_2}} \\[2ex] \dfrac{\partial P_3}{\partial \theta_2} & \dfrac{\partial P_3}{\partial \theta_3} & \dfrac{\partial P_3}{\partial V_3} & \dfrac{\partial \boldsymbol{P_3}}{\partial \boldsymbol{V_2}} \\[2ex] \dfrac{\partial Q_3}{\partial \theta_2} & \dfrac{\partial Q_3}{\partial \theta_3} & \dfrac{\partial Q_3}{\partial V_3} & \dfrac{\partial \boldsymbol{Q_3}}{\partial \boldsymbol{V_2}} \\[2ex] \dfrac{\partial \boldsymbol{Q_2}}{\partial \boldsymbol{\theta_2}} & \dfrac{\partial \boldsymbol{Q_2}}{\partial \boldsymbol{\theta_3}} & \dfrac{\partial \boldsymbol{Q_2}}{\partial \boldsymbol{V_3}} & \dfrac{\partial \boldsymbol{Q_2}}{\partial \boldsymbol{V_2}} \end{bmatrix}}_{J} \begin{bmatrix} \Delta \theta_2 \\ \Delta \theta_3 \\ \Delta V_3 \\ \boldsymbol{\Delta V_2} \end{bmatrix}
\tag{5-50}
$$

In an n-bus case, similar modifications are needed at all PV buses that reach their var limits and must be treated as PQ buses.

REFERENCES

1. Prabha Kundur, *Power System Stability and Control*, McGraw-Hill, 1994.
2. Paul Anderson, Analysis of Faulted Power Systems, IEEE Press, 1995.
3. Power World Computer Program (www.powerworld.com).
4. G.T. Heydt, *Computer Analysis Methods for Power Systems*, Stars in a Circle Publications, 1996.
5. A. Burgen, V. Vittal, *Power Systems Analysis*, 2nd edition, Prentice Hall, 1999.
6. W. D. Stevenson, *Elements of Power System Analysis*, 4th edition, McGraw-Hill, 1982.

PROBLEMS

5-1 In Example 5-1, include the line susceptances and construct the bus-admittance Y matrix.

5-2 Include the line susceptances in Example 5-4 and compare the results with the solution ignoring them.

5-3 In Example 5-4, ignore the $\partial P / \partial V$ and $\partial Q / \partial \theta$ terms in the Jacobian matrix for a decoupled N-R solution, and compare results and the iterations needed with the full N-R procedure.

5-4 In Example 5-4, calculate the sensitivity of reactive power to voltage at Bus 3. Compare the result of using this sensitivity analysis, to injecting 1.0 pu reactive power at bus-3 in the N-R solution of Example 5-4 and computing the increase in bus-3 voltage.

5-5   In Example 5-4, demonstrate the effect of reducing reactive power demand at Bus 3 to zero on the Bus-3 voltage.

5-6   In Example 5-4, demonstrate the effect of series compensation in line 1-2 in the example 3-bus system of Fig. 5-1 on the line power flows and bus voltages, where the series reactance of the line is reduced by 50% by inserting a capacitor in series with the line 1-2.

PowerWorld-Based Problems:

5-7   Compare the MATLAB results in Example 5-4 by using the data for this problem on the accompanying CD.

5-8   In Problem 5-7, include the line susceptances and compare the results with those of Problem 5-2.

5-9   Compare the results of series compensation with that of Problem 5-6.

5-10 In the system of Example 5-4, the capability to supply vars at bus-2 is limited to 2 pu. Recalculate the power flow.

CHAPTER 6

TRANSFORMERS IN POWER SYSTEMS

6-1 INTRODUCTION

Transformers are absolutely essential in making large-scale power transfer feasible over long distances. The primary role of transformers is to change the voltage level. For example, generation in power systems, primarily by synchronous generators, takes place at around 20-kV level. However, it is too low a voltage to transmit economically significant amount of power over long distances. Therefore, transmission voltages of 230 kV, 345 kV and 500 kV are common and some are as high as 765 kV. At the load-end, these voltages are stepped-down to manageable and safe levels such as 120/240 V single-phase in residential usage. Another reason for using transformers in many applications is to provide electrical isolation for safety purposes. Transformers are also needed for converters used in high voltage dc transmission systems, as discussed in chapter 7.

Typically in power systems, voltages get transformed approximately 5 times between generation and the delivery to the ultimate users. Hence, the total installed MVA ratings of transformers are 5 times larger than that of generators.

6-2 BASIC PRINCIPLES OF TRANSFORMER OPERATION

A transformer consists of two or more tightly-coupled windings where almost all of the flux produced by one winding links the other windings. To understand the operating principles of transformers, consider a single coil, also called a winding of N_1 turns, as shown in Fig. 6-1a.

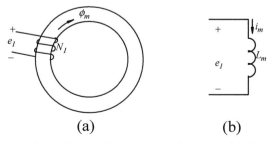

(a)   (b)

Fig. 6-1 Principle of transformers, beginning with just one coil.

Initially, we will assume that the resistance and the leakage inductance of this winding are both zero; assuming zero leakage flux implies that all of the flux produced by this winding is confined to the core. Applying a time-varying voltage e_1 to this winding results in a flux $\phi_m(t)$. From Faraday's Law:

$$e_1(t) = N_1 \frac{d\phi_m}{dt} \tag{6-1}$$

where $\phi_m(t)$ is completely dictated by the time-integral of the applied voltage, as given below (where it is assumed that the flux in the winding is initially zero):

$$\phi_m(t) = \frac{1}{N_1} \int_0^t e_1(\tau) \cdot d\tau \tag{6-2}$$

6-2-1   Transformer Exciting Current

Transformers use Ferromagnetic materials that guide magnetic flux lines and, due to their high permeability, require small ampere-turns (a small current for a given number of turns) to produce the desired flux density. These materials exhibit the multi-valued nonlinear behavior shown by their *B-H* characteristics in Fig. 6-2a.

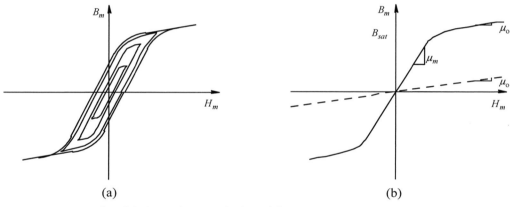

(a)   (b)

Fig. 6-2 B-H characteristics of ferromagnetic materials.

Imagine that the toroid in Fig. 6-1a consists of a ferromagnetic material such as silicon steel. If the current through the coil is slowly varied in a sinusoidal manner with time, the corresponding H-field will cause one of the hysteresis loops shown in Fig. 6-2a to be traced. Completing the loop once results in a net dissipation of energy within the material, causing power loss referred as the hysteresis loss. Increasing the peak value of the sinusoidally-varying *H*-field will result in a bigger hysteresis loop. Joining the peaks of the hysteresis loops, we can approximate the *B-H* characteristic by the single curve shown in Fig. 6-2b. In Fig. 6-2b, the linear relationship (with a constant μ_m) is approximately valid until the "knee" of the curve is reached, beyond which the material begins to saturate. Ferromagnetic materials are often operated up to a maximum flux density, slightly above the "knee" of 1.6 *T* to 1.8 *T*, beyond which many more ampere-turns are required to increase flux-density only slightly. In the saturated region, the incremental permeability of the magnetic material approaches μ_o, as shown by the slope of the curve in Fig. 6-2b.

In the B-H curve of the magnetic material in Fig. 6-2b, in accordance with the Faraday's law, B_m is proportional to the flux-linkage $\lambda_m (= N_1 \phi_m)$ of the coil, and in accordance with the Ampere's law, H_m is proportional to the magnetizing current i_m drawn by the coil to establish this flux. Therefore, B-H plot in Fig. 6-2b is in terms of λ_m and i_m. In the linear region with a constant slope μ_m, this linear relationship between λ_m and i_m can be expressed by a magnetizing inductance L_m

$$L_m = \frac{\lambda_m}{i_m} \tag{6-3}$$

The current $i_m(t)$ drawn to establish this flux depends on the magnetizing inductance L_m of the winding, as depicted in Fig. 6-1b. With a sinusoidal voltage applied to the winding as $e_1 = \sqrt{2} E_1 (rms) \cos \omega t$, the core flux from Eq. 6-2 is $\phi_m = \hat{\phi}_m \sin \omega t$. In the phasor domain, the relationship between these two, in accordance with the Faraday's law can be expressed as

$$\sqrt{2} E_1 (rms) = (2\pi f) N_1 \hat{\phi}_m \tag{6-4}$$

or,

$$\hat{\phi}_m \simeq \frac{E_1 (rms)}{4.44 N_1 f} \tag{6-5}$$

which clearly shows that exceeding the applied voltage $E_1 (rms)$ above its rated value will cause the maximum flux $\hat{\phi}_m$ to enter the saturation region in Fig. 6-2b, resulting in excessive magnetizing current to be drawn. In the saturation region, the magnetizing current drawn is also distorted, with a significant amount of the third-harmonic component.

In modern power transformers of large kVA ratings, the magnetizing currents in their normal operating region are very small, for example, well below 0.2 percent of the rated current at the 100% rated voltage.

6-2-2 Voltage Transformation

A second winding of N_2 turns is now placed on the core, as shown in Fig. 6-3a. A voltage is induced in the second winding due to the flux $\phi_m(t)$ linking it.

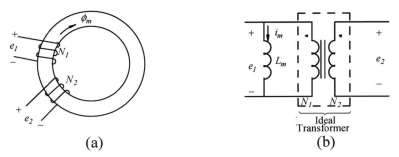

(a)   (b)

Fig. 6-3 Transformer with the open-circuited second coil.

From Faraday's Law,

$$e_2(t) = N_2 \frac{d\phi_m}{dt} \tag{6-6}$$

Eqs. 6-1 and 6-6 show that in each winding, the volts-per-turn are the same due to the same $d\phi_m / dt$:

$$\frac{e_1(t)}{N_1} = \frac{e_2(t)}{N_2} \tag{6-7}$$

We can represent the relationship of Eq. 6-7 in Fig. 6-3b by means of a hypothetical circuit component called the "ideal transformer," which relates the voltages in the two windings by the turns-ratio N_1 / N_2 on an instantaneous basis or in terms of phasors in sinusoidal steady state (shown in brackets):

$$\frac{e_1(t)}{e_2(t)} = \frac{N_1}{N_2} \qquad \text{and} \qquad \left(\frac{\overline{E}_1}{\overline{E}_2} = \frac{N_1}{N_2} \right) \tag{6-8}$$

The dots in Fig. 6-3b convey the information that the winding voltages will be of the same polarity at the dotted terminals with respect to their undotted terminals. For example, if ϕ_m is increasing with time, the voltages at both dotted terminals will be positive with respect to the corresponding undotted terminals. The advantage of using this dot convention is that the winding orientations on the core need not be shown in detail.

A load such an R-L combination is now connected across the secondary winding, as shown in Fig. 6-4a. A current $i_2(t)$ will now flow through the load. The resulting ampere-turns $N_2 i_2$ will tend to change the core flux ϕ_m but *cannot* because $\phi_m(t)$ is completely dictated by the applied voltage $e_1(t)$, as given in Eq. 6-2. Therefore, additional current i_2' in Fig. 6-4b is drawn by winding 1 in order to compensate (or nullify) $N_2 i_2$, such that $N_1 i_2' = N_2 i_2$. This is,

$$\frac{i_2'(t)}{i_2(t)} = \frac{N_2}{N_1} \qquad \text{and} \qquad \left(\frac{\overline{I}_2'}{\overline{I}_2} = \frac{N_2}{N_1}\right) \tag{6-9}$$

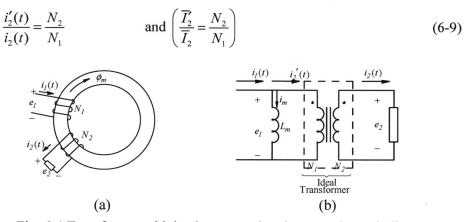

(a)   (b)

Fig. 6-4 Transformer with load connected to the secondary winding.

This is the second property of the "ideal transformer." Thus, the total current drawn from the terminals of winding 1 is

$$i_1(t) = i_m(t) + i_2'(t) \qquad \text{and} \qquad \left(\overline{I}_1 = \overline{I}_m + \overline{I}_2'\right) \tag{6-10}$$

6-2-3   Transformer Equivalent Circuit

In Fig. 6-4b, the resistance and the leakage inductance associated with winding 2 appear in series with the R-L load. Therefore, the induced voltage e_2 differs from the voltage v_2 at the winding terminals by the voltage drop across the winding resistance and the leakage reactance as depicted in Fig. 6-5 in the phasor domain. Similarly, the applied voltage v_1 differs from the emf e_1 (induced by the time-rate of change of the flux ϕ_m) in Fig. 6-4b by the voltage drop across the resistance and the leakage inductance of winding 1, represented in Fig. 6-5 in the phasor-domain.

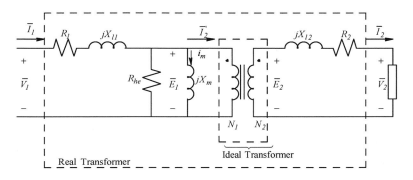

Fig. 6-5 Transformer equivalent circuit including leakage impedances and core losses.

6-2-4 Core Losses

The loss due to the hysteresis-loop in the *B-H* characteristic of the magnetic material was discussed earlier. Another source of core loss is due to eddy currents. All magnetic materials have a finite electrical resistivity (ideally, it should be infinite). By Faraday's voltage induction law, time-varying fluxes induce voltages in the core, which result in circulating (eddy) currents within the core to oppose these flux changes (and partially neutralize them).

In Fig. 6-6a, an increasing flux ϕ will set up many current loops (due to induced voltages that oppose the change in core flux), which result in losses. The primary means of limiting the eddy-current losses is to make the core out of steel laminations which are insulated from each other by means of thin layers of varnish, as shown in Fig. 6-6b.

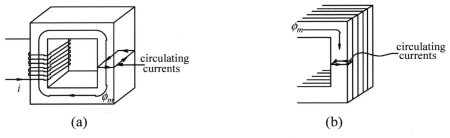

(a)   (b)

Fig. 6-6 Eddy currents in the transformer core.

A few laminations are shown to illustrate how insulated laminations reduce eddy-current losses. Because of the insulation between laminations, the current is forced to flow in much smaller loops within each lamination. Laminating the core reduces the flux and the induced voltage more than it reduces the effective resistance to the currents within a lamination, thus reducing the overall losses. For 50- or 60-*Hz* operation, lamination thicknesses are typically 0.2 to 1 mm. We can model core losses due to hysteresis and eddy currents by connecting a resistance R_{he} in parallel with X_m, as shown in Fig. 6-5. In large modern transformers, core losses are well below 0.1 percent of the transformer kVA rating.

6-2-5 Equivalent Circuit Parameters

In order to utilize the transformer equivalent circuit of Fig. 6-14, we need the values of its various parameters. These specifications are generally provided by the manufacturers of power transformers. These can also be obtained using short-circuit and open-circuit tests. In the open-circuit test, the rated voltage is applied to the low-voltage winding, keeping the high-side open-circuited. This allows the magnetizing reactance and the core-loss equivalent resistance to be estimated. In the short-circuit test, the low-voltage winding is short-circuited and a reduced voltage is applied to the high-voltage winding that results in the rated current. This allows the leakage impedances in the transformer equivalent circuit to be estimated. A detailed discussion of the open-circuit and the short-circuit tests can be found in any of the basic books dealing with transformers.

6-3 SIMPLIFIED TRANSFORMER MODEL

Consider the equivalent circuit of a real transformer, shown in Fig. 6-5. In many power system studies, the excitation current, which is the sum of the magnetizing current and the core-loss current components, is neglected resulting in the simplified model shown in Fig. 6-7. In this model, the subscript p refers to the primary winding and s to the secondary winding. Z_p and Z_s are the leakage impedances of the primary and the secondary windings, and the turns-ratio $n = n_s / n_p$.

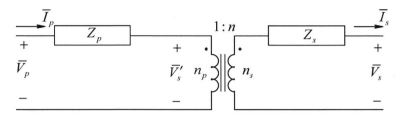

Fig. 6-7 Simplified transformer model.

6-3-1 Transferring Leakage Impedances across the Ideal Transformer Portion

In the simplified model of Fig. 6-7, if the secondary-winding terminals are hypothetically short-circuited, then related by the ideal transformer turns-ratio, $\overline{V}_s = 0$ and

$$\overline{V}'_s = \frac{Z_s \overline{I}_s}{n} \qquad \text{(under short circuit)} \qquad (6\text{-}11)$$

Also related by the ideal transformer turns-ratio, $\overline{I}_s = \overline{I}_p / n$. Substituting for $\overline{I}_s$ in Eq. 6-11,

$$\overline{V}'_s = \left(\frac{Z_s}{n^2}\right)\overline{I}_p \qquad \text{(under short circuit)} \qquad (6\text{-}12)$$

In Fig. 6-7,

$$\overline{V}_p = \overline{V}'_s + Z_p \overline{I}_p \qquad (6\text{-}13)$$

and therefore, from the primary-winding terminals under this hypothetical short-circuit, the impedance "seen" from the primary side is $\overline{V}_p / \overline{I}_p$, which is

$$Z_{ps} = Z_p + \left(Z_s / n^2\right) \qquad (6\text{-}14a)$$

as shown in Fig. 6-8a. Similarly, if the primary-winding leakage impedance is transferred to the secondary winding, then

$$Z_{sp} = Z_s + \left(n^2 Z_p\right),$$
(6-14b)

as shown in Fig. 6-8b.

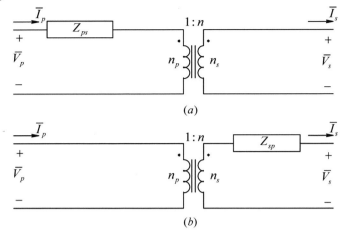

(a)

(b)

Fig. 6-8 Transferring leakage impedances across the ideal transformer of the model.

6-4   PER-UNIT REPRESENTATION

Most power system studies such as power flow, transient analysis and short-circuit fault calculations are carried out in terms of per-unit. In a transformer, the rated voltages and currents on each side are considered as the base values. Since the voltages and currents on the two sides are related by the turns-ratio, the MVA base, product of the voltage and current bases, is the same on each side. In terms of base values, the base impedance magnitudes $Z_{p,base}$ and $Z_{s,base}$ are

$$Z_{p,base} = V_{p,rated} / I_{p,rated} \qquad \text{and} \qquad Z_{s,base} = V_{s,rated} / I_{s,rated}$$
(6-15)

The magnitudes of voltage and currents associated with the ideal transformer in Fig. 6-7 are related as follows:

$$\frac{V_{p,rated}}{V_{s,rated}} = \frac{1}{n} \qquad \text{and} \qquad \frac{I_{p,rated}}{I_{s,rated}} = n$$
(6-16)

Therefore, the base impedance magnitudes on the two sides, given by Eq. 6-15, are related as

$$\frac{Z_{p,base}}{Z_{s,base}} = \left(\frac{1}{n}\right)^2$$
(6-17)

Using these base values, all the parameters and the variables in Figs. 6-8a and b can be expressed in per unit as the ratio of their base values, as shown by a common equivalent circuit of Fig. 6-p, where $Z_{tr}(pu)$ is the transformer per-unit leakage impedance, equal to $Z_{ps}(pu)$ and $Z_{sp}(pu)$:

$$Z_{tr}(\text{pu}) = \underbrace{Z_{ps}(\text{pu})}_{\left(=\frac{Z_{ps}}{Z_{p,base}}\right)} = \underbrace{Z_{sp}(\text{pu})}_{\left(=\frac{Z_{sp}}{Z_{s,base}}\right)} \qquad (6\text{-}18)$$

In Fig. 6-9, the primary and secondary winding currents are equal in per unit, that is, $\overline{I}_p(\text{pu}) = \overline{I}_s(\text{pu}) = \overline{I}(\text{pu})$, and the voltages on the two sides differ by the voltage drop across the leakage impedance.

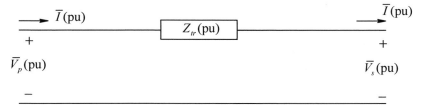

Fig. 6-9 Transformer equivalent circuit in per unit (pu).

In three-phase power systems, transformer windings are connected in a wye or a delta arrangement as shown in Fig. 6-10. The example below shows their per-phase representation in per-unit assuming that the primary-side and the secondary-side windings are connected as wye-wye or delta-delta. If one side is wye-connected and the other-side delta-connected, then there is a phase-shift of 30^0 which must be taken into account, as discussed later on.

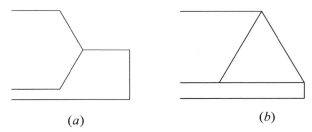

(a) (b)

Fig. 6-10 Winding connections in a three-phase system.

▲ **Example 6-1** Consider that the transmission line between buses "1" and "3" in the example power system is at 500 kV and two 345/500 kV transformers are used at both ends, as shown in the one-line diagram of Fig. 6-11. In the per-unit study, if the system base voltage is 345 kV, then the line impedance and the transformer leakage impedances are all calculated on the 345-kV voltage base, and 100 MVA base. The transmission line series impedance parameters are given in Table 4-1 of Chapter 4. Neglect line susceptances. Each of the transformers has a leakage reactance of 0.2 pu on the 345-kV and 1000-MA base.

Fig. 6-11 Including nominal-voltage transformers in per-unit.

Calculate the per-unit series impedance of the transmission line between buses 1 and 3 for the power flow study as discussed in Chapter 5.

Solution The 500-kV transmission line is 200-km long. Using the parameter values given in Table 4-1, and using the base impedance $Z_{base} = 1190.25\,\Omega$ calculated in Eq. 9-1, the series impedance of the line is $Z_{Line} = (5.6 + j65.0)\,\Omega = (0.0047 + j0.0546)\,pu$. The total leakage reactance of the two transformers is 0.4 pu on a 345-kV, 1000-MV base. In a 3-phase system,

$$Z_{base}(\Omega) = \frac{kV_{base}^2(\text{L-L})}{MVA_{base}(\text{3-phase})} \tag{6-19}$$

which shows the base impedance is inversely proportional to the base MVA. Therefore, on the system base, the combined transformer leakage impedances, specified originally on their own MVA base, can be calculated as

$$Z_{pu}(\text{new}) = Z_{pu}(\text{original}) \times \frac{MVA_{base}(\text{new})}{MVA_{base}(\text{original})} \tag{6-20}$$

Therefore, using 100-MVA as the new base and 1000 MVA as the original base in Eq. 6-20, the combined transformer leakage reactance is 0.04 pu. Therefore, adding it to Z_{Line}, the series impedance between buses 1 and 3 is

$$Z_{13} = (0.0047 + j0.0946)\,pu. \qquad\qquad \blacktriangle$$

6-5 TRANSFORMER EFFICIENCIES AND LEAKAGE REACTANCES

Power transformers are designed to minimize power losses within them. These consist of the I^2R losses, also called the copper losses, in the windings, and the core losses. Core losses are mostly independent of the transformer loading, where as the losses in windings depend on the square of the transformer loading. The energy efficiency of a transformer, in fact of any apparatus, is defined as follows, where the output power equals the input power minus the losses:

$$\%\text{Efficiency}=100\times\frac{P_{output}}{P_{input}}=100\times\left(1-\frac{P_{losses}}{P_{input}}\right) \tag{6-21}$$

Generally, transformer efficiencies are at their maximum at a load when the core losses and the winding losses are equal to each other. In large power transformers, these efficiencies are generally in excess of 99.5%.

For achieving high efficiencies in transformers, their winding resistances are generally well below 0.5% or 0.05 pu. Therefore, their leakage impedances are dominated by the leakage reactances, which depend of the voltage class of transformers. These leakage reactances are approximately in the following ranges: 7-10 percent in 69-kV transformers, 8-12 percent in 115-kV transformers, and 11-16 percent in 230-kV transformers. In 345-kV and 500-kV transformers, these reactances are 20 percent or even larger.

6-6   REGULATION IN TRANSFORMERS

Large values of leakage reactances are helpful in reducing currents during power system faults like short-circuits on transmission lines to which these transformers are connected. However, for a constant input voltage applied, the output voltage of a transformer changes, based on the transformer loading, due to the voltage drop across its leakage impedance. This is called *Regulation*, which is the change in output voltage, expressed as the percentage of the rated output voltage, if the rated output kVA load, at a specified power factor, is reduced to zero load. From Fig. 6-9, assuming the leakage impedance to be purely reactive:

$$\overline{V}_s(pu)=\overline{V}_P(pu)-jX_{tr}(pu)\overline{I}(pu) \tag{6-22}$$

It can be observed from Eq. 6-22 that lower the power-factor (lagging) of the load, larger the change in the output voltage and hence larger the regulation.

6-6-1   Transformers Tap-Changing For Voltage Control

By tap-changing in transformers, it is possible to adjust the output voltage magnitude. In such cases, the principle is the same as in any transformer except of the turns-ratio. It is possible to change taps under load, and such arrangements, called Load Tap Changers (LTC) are described in detail in [1]. Tap-changing is usually accomplished using auto-transformers discussed in the next section. Tap-changing can be included in power flow studies, as illustrated by a homework problem using *PowerWorld*.

6-7   AUTO-TRANSFORMERS

Auto-transformers are very frequently used in power systems for transforming voltages where electrical isolation is not necessary, and for tap-changing. In this analysis, we will assume an ideal transformer, neglecting the leakage impedances and the excitation current. Therefore, all the voltages and the currents are of the same phase respectively, hence they are represented by their magnitudes alone for convenience, rather than as phasors.

In the two-winding arrangement shown in Fig. 6-12a, in terms of the rated voltage and the rated current associated with each winding, the transformer rating is

$$\text{Two-Winding Transformer Rating} = V_1 I_1 = V_2 I_2 \qquad (6\text{-}23)$$

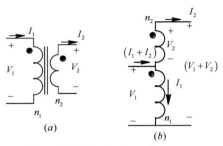

Fig. 6-12 Auto-transformer.

In the autotransformer arrangement shown in Fig. 6-12b, these two winding are connected in series. With V_1 applied to the low-side on the left, the high-side voltage is $(V_1 + V_2)$, as shown in Fig. 6-12b. The high-side is rated at I_2 without overloading any of the windings, and at this condition, from Kirchhoff's current law, the current on the low-side is $(I_1 + I_2)$. The product of the high-side voltage and current ratings is (using the product on the low-side will yield similar results) the auto-transformer rating, that is, the volt-amperes that can be transferred through it:

$$\text{Auto-Transformer Capability} = (V_1 + V_2) I_2 \qquad (6\text{-}24)$$

Comparing Eqs. 6-23 and 6-24, the ratings of the two arrangements are related as

$$\text{Auto-Transformer Capability} = \left(1 + \frac{V_1}{V_2}\right) \times \text{Two-Winding Transformer Rating} \qquad (6\text{-}25)$$

Since the two-Winding transformer rating equals the system VA transfer capability, VA rating of auto-transformer needs be as follows:

$$\text{Auto-Transformer Rating} = \text{System VA Transfer Requirement} \div \left(1 + \frac{V_1}{V_2}\right) \qquad (6\text{-}26)$$

From Fig. 6-12b, expressing the factor in Eq. 6-26 in terms of the high-side voltage V_H and the low-side voltage V_L

$$\text{Auto-Transformer Rating} = \left(1 - \frac{V_L}{V_H}\right) \times \text{System VA Transfer Requirement} \qquad (6\text{-}27)$$

In systems where the high-side and the low-side voltages are not far apart, the rating of an auto-transformer needed can be much smaller, as illustrated by an example below.

▲ **Example 6-2** In a system, 1 MVA have to be transferred with the low-side voltage of 22 kV and the high-side voltage of 33 kV. Calculate the kVA rating of an auto-transformer to satisfy these requirements.

Solution From Eq. 6-51, the auto-transformer rating is 333 kVA. ▲

The example above shows that only a 333 kVA auto-transformer will suffice, which otherwise would require a 1,000 kVA conventional two-winding transformer. Therefore, an auto-transformer will be physically smaller and less costly. Efficiencies of auto-transformers are higher than their two-winding counterparts, whereas their leakage reactances are comparatively smaller. The main disadvantage of auto-transformers is that there is no electrical (galvanic) isolation between the two sides, however it is not always needed. Hence, auto-transformers are very often used in power systems.

6-8 PHASE-SHIFT INTRODUCED BY TRANSFORMERS

Primarily, there are two ways that phase shift in voltages is introduced by the transformer connections in three-phase power systems. One of them is when transformers are connected in wye on one- side and delta on the other-side, as is a commonly practice, there is a phase shift of 30^0 in voltages between the two sides. The other reason is where controllable phase-shift is introduced on purpose, in order to regulate the power flow through the transmission line to which the transformer is connected. We will look at both of these cases.

6-8-1 Phase-Shift in Δ-Y Transformers

Transformers connected in Δ-Y-, as shown in Fig. 6-13a, result in a 30^0 phase-shift that is shown by the phasor diagram of Fig. 6-13b. In order to boost the voltages produced by the generators, the low-voltage sides are connected in a delta and the high-voltage sides are connected in a grounded wye. On the Δ-connected side, the terminal voltages, although isolated from ground, can be visualized by hypothetically connecting very large, but equal, resistances from each terminal to ground. Thus, $\overline{V}_A$ is the terminal-A voltage with respect to ground. As shown in Fig. 6-13b, $\overline{V}_A$ leads $\overline{V}_a$ by 30^0 and the magnitude of the two voltages can be related as follows:

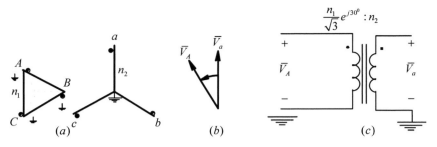

Fig. 6-13 Phase-shift in Δ-Y connected transformers.

$$V_{AC} = \frac{n_2}{n_1} V_a \text{ and thus,} \quad V_A = \frac{1}{\sqrt{3}} \frac{n_2}{n_1} V_a \tag{6-28}$$

Based on Eq. 6-28, the per-phase equivalent circuit is as shown in Fig. 6-13c.

6-8-2 Phase-Angle Control

As discussed in Chapter 2, power flow between two ac systems depends on $\sin\delta$, where δ is difference of the phase angles between the two. Fig. 6-14a shows a phase-regulating transformer arrangement for achieving a phase shift.

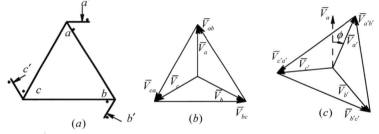

Fig. 6-14 Transformer for phase-angle control.

Phasor diagram of the incoming voltages $a-b-c$ is shown in Fig. 6-14b and of the outgoing voltages $a'-b'-c'$ in Fig. 6-14c, which show that the outgoing voltages are advanced by an angle ϕ with respect to the incoming voltages. The sliders in Fig. 6-14a represent finite taps.

6-9 THREE-WINDING TRANSFORMERS

Often in power system transformers and auto-transformers, an isolated third winding is added to which capacitors or power-electronics-based apparatus to supply reactive power to support the system voltage are connected. The Δ-connected tertiary winding is usually of a low voltage rating, and of a much lower kVA rating. The purpose of the tertiary winding is to provide a path for the zero-sequence currents to circulate, as discussed in the chapter on transmission-line faults, and to connect devices to supply reactive power.

The operating principle of the three-winding transformers is an extension of the two-winding transformers discussed earlier. Often, an autotransformer arrangement is used between the high-side and the low-side, and a tertiary winding is added and connected, as shown in Fig. 6-15a. These can be represented as shown in Fig. 6-15b.

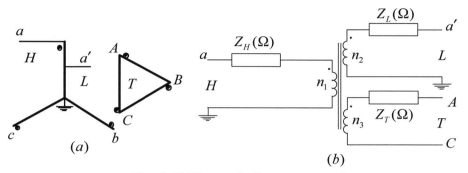

Fig. 6-15 Three-winding auto-transformer.

6-10   THREE-PHASE TRANSFORMERS

As discussed earlier, power transformers consists of three phases, where separate single-phase transformers discussed earlier may be connected in a Y or a Δ arrangement. In contrast, in a three-phase transformer, all the windings are placed on a common core, thus resulting in reduced core cost. The decision on the type of transformer to purchase depends on such factors as initial installed cost, maintenance costs, operating cost (efficiency), reliability, etc. Three-phase units have lower construction and maintenance costs and can be built to the same efficiency ratings as single-phase units. The initial cost of a three-phase transformer is usually approximately one-third less than four single-phase units. Additionally, the exposure of three-phase units to long outages can be minimized system-wide by designing the electrical system with sufficient transmission and distribution capacity to backup transformer failures. Also many electrical systems have mobile substations and emergency spare transformers to backup failures [3].

In extra-high voltage systems at high power levels, single-phase transformers are used. The reason has to do with the size of the three-phase transformers at these levels makes their transportation from the manufacturing site to the installation site difficult. For unique requirements it may be economical to have emergency spare single phase transformers (one-third of the total rating) rather than having spare three-phase transformers [3].

Three-phase transformers are either a shell or a core type. In balanced three-phase operation, the equivalent circuit of a three-phase transformer either type, on a per-phase basis, is similar to that of single-phase transformers. Only under unbalanced operation, such as during unsymmetrical faults, the difference between these three-phase transformer types appears, which is discussed with short-circuit faults.

6-11 REPRESENTING TRANSFORMERS WITH OFF-NOMINAL TURNS RATIOS, TAPS AND PHASE-SHIFT

As shown by Example 6-1, if a transformer with nominal turns-ratio and without phase-shift is encountered, then it can be simply represented by its leakage impedance. For transformers with off-nominal turns-ratio, taps and phase-shift, special consideration must be given. Fig. 6-16 shows a general representation where the voltage transformation is by $1:t$, where t is a real number in case of off-nominal turns-ratio and a complex number in case of a phase-shifter; Z_ℓ is the leakage impedance and $Y_\ell = 1/Z_\ell$.

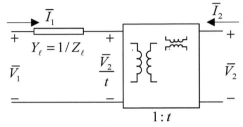

Fig. 6-16 General representation of an auto-transformer and a phase-shifter.

Considering the leakage impedance separately, the voltage transformation across the ideal-transformer portion is as shown in Fig. 6-16 and the sum of the complex powers into it must be equal to zero so that

$$\frac{\overline{V}_2}{t}\overline{I}_1^* = -\overline{V}_2\overline{I}_2^* \tag{6-29}$$

In Fig. 6-16,

$$\overline{I}_1 = \left(\overline{V}_1 - \frac{\overline{V}_2}{t}\right)Y_\ell \tag{6-30}$$

From Eqs. 6-29 and 6-30, and recognizing that $tt^* = |t|^2$

$$\overline{I}_2 = -\frac{\overline{I}_1}{t^*} = -\overline{V}_1\frac{Y_\ell}{t^*} + \overline{V}_2\frac{Y_\ell}{|t|^2} \tag{6-31}$$

From Eqs. 6-30 and 6-31,

$$\begin{bmatrix} \overline{I}_1 \\ \overline{I}_2 \end{bmatrix} = \begin{bmatrix} Y_\ell & -\dfrac{Y_\ell}{t} \\ -\dfrac{Y_\ell}{t^*} & \dfrac{Y_\ell}{|t|^2} \end{bmatrix} \begin{bmatrix} \overline{V}_1 \\ \overline{V}_2 \end{bmatrix} \qquad (6\text{-}32)$$

This nodal representation is similar to the one discussed in Chapter 5 for representing the system for power flow studies. It is discussed below, separately in auto-transformers and phase-shifters.

6-11-1 Off-Nominal Turns-Ratios and Taps

The per-unit representation of transformers with off-nominal turns-ratio and taps (without phase shift) is by a transformer with a turns-ratio $1:t$ where t is real in Fig. 6-17a. Using Eqs. 5-4 and 5-5 of the Power Flow study in Chapter 5, Eq. 6-32 can be represented by a pi-circuit as shown in Fig. 6-17b, where $t^* = t$ since t is real. Therefore, from Eq. 5-5, the series admittance Y_s in the pi-circuit of Fig. 6-17b is $Y_{12}(=Y_{21})$. From Eq. 5-4, the shunt admittances Y_1 and Y_2 in Fig. 6-17b can be calculated as shown.

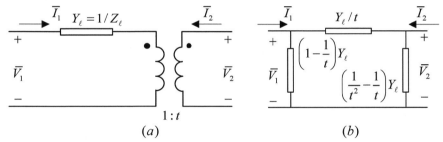

Fig. 6-17 Transformer with an off-nominal turns-ratio or taps in per unit; t is real.

▲ **Example 6-3** In the transformer of Fig. 6-18a in per unit, the leakage impedance $Z_\ell = j0.1\,pu$. The turns-ratio $t = 1.1$ in per-unit in order to boost the voltage at side-2. Calculate the parameters in the pi-circuit of Fig. 6-18b for use in power-flow programs.

Fig. 6-18 Transformer of Example 6-3.

Solution   In this example, $Y_\ell = 1/Z_\ell = -j10\,pu$. In the pi-circuit, $Y_1 = -j0.909\,pu$, where the susceptance value is negative, implying it is inductive. $Y_2 = j0.826\,pu$, where the susceptance value is positive, implying it is capacitive. The corresponding pi-circuit model is shown in Fig. 6-18b, which clearly shows how the LC circuit results in higher V_2 than V_1 in magnitude.   ▲

6-11-2 Representing Transformer Phase-Shift

In a phase-shift transformer arrangement, t in the Y-matrix of Eq. 6-32 is complex. Therefore, $Y_{12} \neq Y_{21}$. As a consequence, a transformer with a complex turns-ratio cannot be represented by a pi-circuit; rather, it calls for an admittance matrix of Eq. 6-32 to be used in the power flow studies.

REFERENCES

1. Prabha Kundur, *Power System Stability and Control*, McGraw Hill, 1994.
2. Electrical Transmission and Distribution Reference Book, Westinghouse Electric Corporation, 1950.
3. P. Anderson, Analysis of Faulted Power Systems, June 1995, Wiley-IEEE Press.
4. RUS Bulletin 1724E-300.

PROBLEMS

6-1   A transformer is designed to step down the applied voltage of 2400 V (rms) to 240 V (rms) at 60 Hz. Calculate the maximum rms voltage that can be applied to the high-side of this transformer without exceeding the rated flux density in the core if this transformer is supplied by a frequency of 50 Hz.

6-2   Assume the transformer in Fig. 6-4a to be ideal. Winding 1 is applied a sinusoidal voltage in steady state with $\overline{V}_1 = 120V\angle 0^o$ at a frequency f=60 Hz. $N_1/N_2 = 3$. The load on winding 2 is a series combination of R and L with $Z_L = (5 + j3)\Omega$. Calculate the current drawn from the voltage source.

6-3   Consider an ideal transformer, neglecting the winding resistances, leakage inductances, and the core loss. $N_1/N_2 = 3$. For a voltage of 120 V (rms) at a frequency of 60 Hz applied to winding 1, the magnetizing current is 1.0 A (rms). If a load of 1.1 Ω at a power factor of 0.866 (lagging) is connected to the secondary winding, calculate $\overline{I}_1$.

6-4   A 2400/240-V, 60-Hz transformer has the following parameters in the equivalent circuit of Fig. 6-5: the high-side leakage impedance is $(1.2 + j\,2.0)\,\Omega$, the low-side leakage impedance is $(0.012 + j\,0.02)\,\Omega$, and X_m at the high-side is 1800 Ω. Neglect R_{he}. Calculate the input voltage if the output voltage is 240 V (rms) and supplying a load of 1.5 Ω at a power factor of 0.9 (lagging).

6-18

6-5 Calculate the equivalent-circuit parameters of a transformer, if the following open-circuit and short-circuit test data is given for a 60-*Hz*, 50-*kVA*, 2400:240-*V* distribution transformer:

open-circuit test with high-side open: $V_{OC} = 240$ V, $I_{OC} = 5.0$ A, $P_{OC} = 400$ W,

short-circuit test with low-side shorted: $V_{SC} = 90$ V, $I_{SC} = 20$ A, $P_{SC} = 700W$.

6-6 Three two-winding transformers are grounded Y-Δ connected to 230 kV on the Y-side and to 34.5 kV on the Δ-side. The combined three-phase rating of these transformers is 200 MVA. The per-unit reactance is 11% on the basis of the transformer rating. Calculate the rated values of voltage and currents, and X_{ps} and X_{sp} (in Ω) in Figs. 6-8a and b.

6-7 In a transformer, the leakage reactance is 9% on the basis of its rating. What will be its percent value if, simultaneously the voltage-base is doubled and the MVA-base is halved.

6-8 Efficiency in a power transformer is 98.6% when loaded such that its core losses equal the copper losses. Calculate the per unit resistance of this transformer.

6-9 Using Fig. 6-9, calculate $\bar{V}_p$ in per unit, if $\bar{V}_s(\text{pu}) = 1\angle 0^0$, rated $\bar{I}(\text{pu}) = 1\angle -30^0$, and $X_{tr} = 11\%$. Draw the relationship between these calculated variables by a phasor diagram.

6-10 The % Regulation for a transformer is defined as

$$\% \text{ Regulation} = 100 \times \frac{V_{\text{no-load}} - V_{\text{rated}}}{V_{\text{rated}}},$$

where V_{rated} is the voltage at the rated kVA loading at the specified power load. Calculate the % regulation for the transformer in Problem 6-9.

6-11 Calculate the Regulation in problem 6-10, if the rated $\bar{I}(\text{pu}) = 1\angle 0^0$. Compare this value with that in problem 6-10.

6-12 Derive the expression for the full-load Regulation, where θ is the power factor angle, which is taken as positive when the current lags the voltage, and X_{tr} is in per-unit.

6-13 In Example 6-2, the auto-transformer is loaded to its rated MVA at unity power factor. Calculate all voltages and currents in the auto-transformer in Fig. 6-12b.

6-14 In Example 6-2, if a two-winding transformer is selected, the efficiency of the two-winding transformer is 99.1%. If the same transformer is connected as an auto-transformer, calculate its efficiency based on the MVA rating that it is capable of. Assume a unity power factor of operation in both cases.

6-15 In a Y-Δ connected transformer as shown in Fig. 6-13a, show all the phase and line-line voltages on both sides of the transformer, similar to Fig. 6-13b. The line-to-line voltage on Y-side is 230 kV and on the Δ-side 34.5 kV. Assume the phase angle $\overline{V}_a$ to 90^0.

6-16 In problem 6-15, the wye-connected load on the Δ-side is purely resistive and the load-current amplitude is 1 pu. Draw the currents within the Δ windings and those drawn from the Y-side in per-unit.

Transformers in PSCAD/EMTDC:

6-17 Obtain the transformer waveforms, as described on the accompanying CD.

Including Transformers in Power Flow Studies using *PowerWorld*:

6-18 The power flow in a 3-bus example power system is calculated using MATLAB in Example 5-4. Repeat this using *PowerWorld*, where include an auto-transformer in this example for voltage regulation, as described in the accompanying CD, and calculate the results of the power flow study.

6-19 The power flow in a 3-bus example power system is calculated using MATLAB in Example 5-4. Repeat this using *PowerWorld*, where include a phase-shifting transformer in this example for controlling power flow, as described in the accompanying CD, and calculate the results of the power flow study.

CHAPTER 7

HIGH VOLTAGE DC (HVDC) TRANSMISSION SYSTEMS

7-1   INTRODUCTION

For transmitting large amounts of power over long distances, for example from a remote source to a load center far away, a high voltage DC (HVDC) system can be more economical than an ac transmission system. In other words, an HVDC system should be considered for point-to-point transmission. For underwater transmission through cables, HVDC is almost always the preferred choice. Lately, for stability reasons, back-to-back HVDC systems (without any transmission lines) are built for transferring of power between two ac systems where an ac-link will not be stable. More such back-to-back systems are expected to be used in the future.

7-2   POWER SEMICONDUCTOR DEVICES AND THEIR CAPABILITIES [1]

These applications are made feasible by power semiconductor devices, whose symbols are shown in Fig. 7-1a. The power handling capabilities and switching speeds of these devices are indicated in Fig. 7-1b.

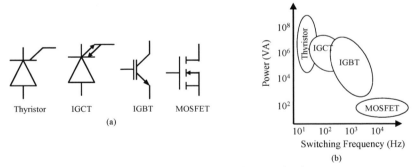

Fig. 7-1 Power semiconductor devices.

All these devices allow current flow only in their forward direction (the intrinsic anti-parallel diode of MOSFETs can be explained separately). Transistors (intrinsically or by design) can block only the forward polarity voltage, whereas thyristors block both forward and reverse polarity voltages. Diodes are uncontrolled devices, which conduct current in the forward direction and block a reverse voltage. At very high power levels, integrated-gate controlled thyristors (IGCTs), which have evolved from the gate-turn-off thyristors, are sometimes used. Thyristors are semi-controlled devices that can switch-on at the desired instant in their forward-blocking state, but cannot be switched off from their gate and hence rely on the circuit in which they are connected to switch them off. However, thyristors are available in very large voltage and current ratings. Fig. 7-2a shows the ratings of various high power semiconductors in use, and Fig. 7-2b shows the voltage and current ratings needed in various applications. There is a great deal of research being carried out in SiC-based devices which are highly suited for applications at high power in power systems.

(a)   (b)

Figure 7-2 Power semiconductor devices: (a) ratings (source: Siemens), (b) various applications (source: ABB).

7-3 HVDC TRANSMISSION SYSTEMS

HVDC systems are represented by a one-line diagram of Fig. 7-3 where the ac voltage at the sending-end is stepped up and supplied to a converter acting as a <u>rectifier</u> that converts ac into dc, and the power is transmitted over an HVDC transmission line. At the receiving end, there is another converter acting as an <u>inverter</u> that converters dc into ac that can be stepped down to the voltage level of the receiving-end system. The direction of the power flow can be reversible, thus reversing the role of the two converters. Fig. 7-4 shows two types of HVDC systems: (a) a current-link system that uses thyristors and (b) a voltage-link system that uses switches such as IGBTs. Both of these systems are discussed in this chapter.

AC_1 AC_2

Fig. 7-3 HVDC system – one-line diagram.

AC1   AC2   AC1   AC2

(a)   (b)

Fig. 7-4 HVDC systems: (a) Current-Link, and (b) Voltage-Link.

7-4   Current-Link HVDC Systems

Fig. 7-5 shows the HVDC projects in North America, most of which, except for a few exceptions use the current-link system. Many such projects exist around the world.

Fig. 7-5 HVDC projects, mostly current-link systems, in North America [source: ABB]

The block diagram of a current-link HVDC system is shown in Fig. 7-6. It consists of two poles: positive and negative with respect to ground. Each pole consists of two thyristors converters which are supplied through a $Y-Y$ and a $Y-\Delta$ arrangement of transformers to introduce a 30^0 phase shift between the two voltage sets, as discussed in the transformer chapter. In this current-link system, the transmission line inductance on the dc-side is usually supplemented by some extra inductance in series as shown in Fig. 7-6 by the smoothing reactor. Since the current in the dc-link cannot change instantaneously because of these inductances, hence the name current-link. Each pole at the sending-end and the receiving-end consists of converters consisting of thyristors which are sometimes referred to by their trade name of silicone-controlled rectifiers (SCRs). The characteristic of these converters is explored further in the following sub-section.

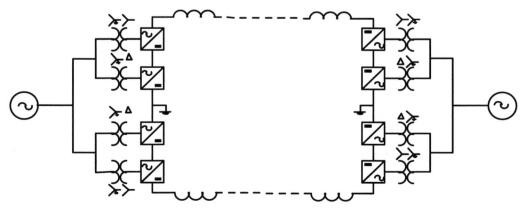

Fig. 7-6 Block diagram of a current-link HVDC system.

7-4-1 Thyristor Converters

We are familiar with diodes which block a negative polarity voltage and no current can flow in the reverse direction. Diodes begin to conduct current in the forward direction when a forward polarity voltage appears across them, with only a small voltage drop of the order a volt or two across them. These are represented by a symbol as shown in Fig. 7-7a by an anode (A), a cathode (K) and a gate terminal (G). Unlike diodes, thyristors are a four layer device as shown in Fig. 7-7b.

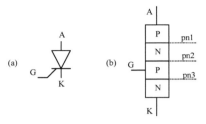

Fig. 7-7 Thyristors.

Similar to diodes, thyristors also conduct current only in the forward direction and block negative polarity voltage but unlike diodes, they can also block a forward-polarity voltage from conducting current as illustrated below.

Consider a primitive circuit to convert ac into dc as shown in Fig. 7-8a with a thyristor in series with an R-L load.

Fig. 7-8 Thyristor circuit with a resistive load and a series inductance.

As shown in Fig. 7-8b, beginning at $\omega t = 0$ during the positive-half-cycle of the input voltage, a forward voltage appears across the thyristor (anode A is positive with respect to cathode K), and if the thyristor were a diode, a current would begin to flow in this circuit at $\omega t = 0$. This instant, at which current would begin to flow if it were a diode, is referred to as the instant of natural conduction. With the thyristor blocking the forward voltage, the start of conduction can be controlled (delayed) with respect to $\omega t = 0$ by a delay angle α at which instant a current pulse to the gate of the thyristor is applied. Once in the conducting state, the thyristor latches on and behaves like a diode with a very small voltage drop of the order of 1 to 2 volts across it (we will idealize it as zero), and the R-L load voltage v_d equals v_s, as shown in Fig. 7-8b.

The current waveform in Fig. 7-8b shows that due to the inductor in series, the current through the thyristor keeps flowing for an interval into the negative half-cycle of the input voltage, coming to zero and staying at zero, not being able to reverse in direction due to the thyristor property, during the remainder of this half-cycle,. In the next voltage cycle, the current conduction again depends on the instant during the positive half-cycle at which the gate pulse is applied. By controlling the delay angle (or the phase control as it is often referred), we can control the average voltage v_d across the R-L load. This principle can be extended to the practical circuits discussed below.

In HVDC systems, each converter uses six thyristors, as shown in Fig. 7-9a. To explain the principle of converter operation, it is initially assumed that the converter is supplied by ideal three-phase voltage sources as shown in Fig. 7-9b, thyristors are drawn by a top group and a bottom group, and the dc-side is represented by a dc current-source I_d.

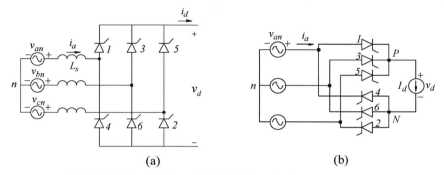

(a)   (b)

Fig. 7-9 Three-phase Full-Bridge thyristor converter.

Initially we will assume that the thyristors in Fig. 7-9b are replaced by diodes. Diodes represent thyristor operation with the delay angle $\alpha = 0^0$, and therefore replacing thyristors by diodes, we will be able to calculate the dc-side voltage for $\alpha = 0^0$. Assuming diodes in Fig. 7-9b, in the top-group, all the diodes have their cathodes connected together and therefore only the diode with its anode connected to the highest phase voltage conducts and the other two become reverse-biased. In the bottom-group, all diodes have their anodes connected together, and therefore only the diode with its cathode connected to the lowest voltages conducts and the other two get reverse-biased. The waveforms at Points P and N, with respect to the source-neutral are shown in Fig. 7-10a, where the dc-side voltage:

$$v_d = v_{Pn} - v_{Nn} \qquad (7\text{-}1)$$

is a line-line voltage within each 60^0 interval and is plotted in Fig. 7-10b. The average dc-side voltage with $\alpha = 0$ can be calculated from the waveforms in Fig. 7-10b by considering a 60^0 ($\pi/3$ rad) interval with which the waveforms repeat, where $\sqrt{2}V_{LL}$ is the peak value of the line-line input voltage as shown in Fig. 7-10b:

$$V_{do} = \frac{1}{\pi/3} \int_{-\pi/6}^{\pi/6} \sqrt{2}V_{LL} \cos\omega t \cdot d(\omega t) = \frac{3\sqrt{2}}{\pi} V_{LL} \qquad (7\text{-}2)$$

This average voltage is indicated by the straight line as V_{do} in Fig. 7-10b, where the subscript "o" refers to $\alpha = 0$. The line current waveforms are shown in Fig. 7-10c, where for example $i_a = I_d$ during the interval when phase-a has the highest voltage, and diode 1 connected to it is conducting. Similarly, $i_a = -I_d$ during the interval when phase-a has the lowest voltage, and diode 4 connected to it is conducting.

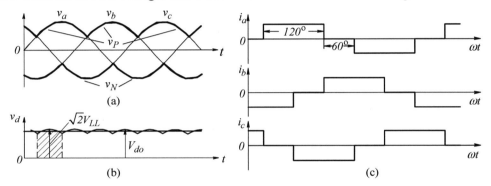

Fig. 7-10 Waveforms in a three-phase rectifier with $L_s = 0$ and $\alpha = 0$.

Delaying the gate pulses to the thyristors by an angle α measured with respect to their instants of natural conductions (the instant of natural conduction for a thyristor is the instant at which the current through it would begin to flow if α were to be zero), the waveforms are shown in Fig. 7-11.

In the dc-side output voltage waveforms, the area A_α corresponds to "loss" in units of volt-radians due to delaying the gate pulses by α every $\pi/3$ radian. Assuming the time-origin as shown in Fig. 7-11 at the instant at which the phase voltage waveforms for phases a and c cross, the line-line voltage v_{ac} waveform can be expressed as $\sqrt{2}V_{LL} \sin\omega t$. Therefore from Fig. 7-11, the drop ΔV_α in the average dc-side voltage can be calculated as

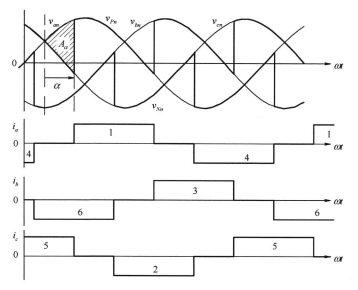

Fig. 7-11 Waveforms with $L_s = 0$.

$$\Delta V_\alpha = \frac{1}{\pi/3}\underbrace{\int_0^\alpha \sqrt{2}V_{LL}\sin\omega t \cdot d(\omega t)}_{A_\alpha} = \frac{3\sqrt{2}}{\pi}V_{LL}(1-\cos\alpha) \qquad (7\text{-}3)$$

Therefore, using Eqs. 7-2 and 7-3, the average value of the dc-side voltage can be controlled by the delay angle as

$$V_{d\alpha} = V_{do} - \Delta V_\alpha = \frac{3\sqrt{2}}{\pi}V_{LL}\cos\alpha \qquad (7\text{-}4)$$

which, as shown by Eq. 7-4, is positive for α between 0 and 90^0, hence the converter is said to operate as a *Rectifier*, whereas for α beyond 90^0, $V_{d\alpha}$ becomes negative and the converter operates as an *Inverter*.

▲ **Example 7-1** Three-phase thyristor converter of Fig. 7-9b is operating in its inverter mode with $\alpha = 150^0$. Draw waveforms similar to Fig. 7-11 for this operating condition.

Solution   These waveforms for $\alpha = 150^0$ in the inverter mode are shown in Fig. 7-12. On the dc-side, the waveform of the voltage v_{Pn} is negative and that of v_{Nn} is positive. Therefore, the dc-side voltage $v_{PN}(= v_{Pn} - v_{Nn})$ and its average values are negative in the inverter-mode of operation. Since the dc-side current is in the same direction, the flow of power is from the dc-side to the ac-side. On the ac-side, phase-current waveforms are shifted (lagging) by $\alpha = 150^0$, compare to the waveforms corresponding to $\alpha = 0$.

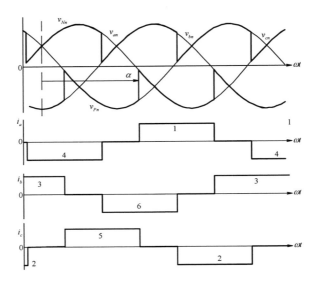

Fig. 7-12 Waveforms in the inverter mode.

▲

As shown in Fig. 7-13a, for $\alpha < 90^0$, the converter operates as a rectifier and the power flow, as shown in Fig. 7-13b, from the ac-side to the dc-side. The opposite is true in the inverter mode with $\alpha > 90^0$. In the inverter mode, the delay angle is limited to approximately 160^0 as shown in Fig. 7-13a, due to the commutation angle required to safely commutate current from one thyristor to the next, as discussed below.

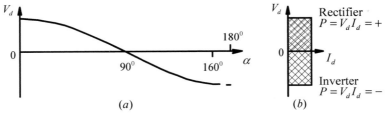

Fig. 7-13 Average dc-side voltage as a function of α.

In the idealized case with $L_s = 0$, the ac-side currents commutate instantly from one thyristor to another, as shown by the current waveforms in Fig. 7-11. However, in the presence of the ac-side inductance L_s, it takes a finite interval u during which the current commutates from one thyristor to another, as shown in Fig. 7-14. During this commutation interval u, from α to $\alpha + u$ for example, the instantaneous dc voltage is reduced due to the voltage drop across the inductance in series with the thyristor to which the current is commutating from 0 to $(+I_d)$. Therefore, the average dc output voltage is reduced by an additional area A_u every $\pi / 3$ radian as shown in Fig. 7-14, where

$$A_u = \int_{\alpha}^{\alpha+u} v_L \, d(\omega t) = \omega L_s \int_0^{I_d} di_s = \omega L_s I_d \qquad (7\text{-}5)$$

and therefore an additional voltage drop due to the presence of L_s is

$$\Delta V_u = \frac{A_u}{\pi/3} = \frac{3}{\pi} \omega L_s I_d \qquad (7\text{-}6)$$

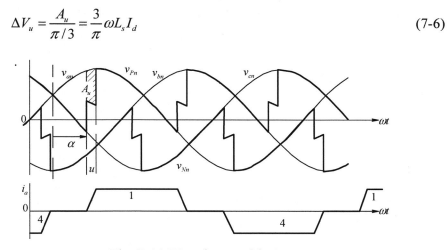

Fig. 7-14 Waveforms with L_s.

Therefore, the dc-side output voltage can be written as

$$V_d = V_{d\alpha} - \Delta V_u \qquad (7\text{-}7)$$

Substituting results from Eqs. 7-4 and 7-6 into Eq. 7-7

$$V_d = \frac{3\sqrt{2}}{\pi} V_{LL} \cos \alpha - \frac{3}{\pi} \omega L_s I_d \qquad (7\text{-}8)$$

It is useful to note that in Fig. 7-14, the bounded area below A_u is the same as A_u, since the voltage output on dc-side of the top group of thyristors under consideration is average of the two phase voltages involved in the current commutation. Therefore from Fig. 7-14, Eq. 7-8 can also be written as

$$V_d = \frac{3\sqrt{2}}{\pi} V_{LL} \cos(\alpha+u) + \frac{3}{\pi} \omega L_s I_d \qquad (7\text{-}9)$$

Considering the ac-side of the converter, the current for example in phase-a can be approximated as a trapezoid staring at an angle $(\pi/6+\alpha)$ rads and rising linearly from $-I_d$ to $+I_d$ during the commutation angle u. The fundamental component i_{a1} of the phase current lags behind the phase voltage approximately by an angle $\phi_1 (= \alpha + u/2)$, as shown in Fig. 7-15a in the rectifier mode, and in Fig. 7-15b in the inverter mode. The power factor, always lagging, is as follows:

$$\text{Power Factor (PF)} = \cos(\alpha + u/2) \qquad (7\text{-}10)$$

and the three-phase reactive power consumed by the converter is given as

$$Q_{3\phi} = 3V_a I_{a1} \sin(\alpha + u/2) \qquad (7\text{-}11)$$

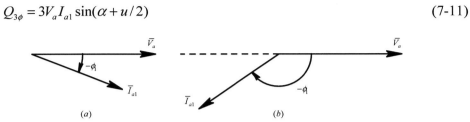

Fig. 7-15 Power-factor angle.

In the waveforms of Fig. 7-11, there are six pulses, each with an interval of $60^0 (\pi/3$ rad), every line-frequency cycle, and hence the converters for which these waveforms are drawn are called six-pulse converters. In most HVDC converter, in each pole, a 30^0 phase-shift is introduced by the $Y-Y$ and the $Y-\Delta$ transformer arrangements, as shown by the one-line diagram in Fig. 7-16.

Fig. 7-16 HVDC CU project; see the accompanying CD for better resolution.

Each converter draws current with a six-pulse waveform as shown in Fig. 7-17a by $i_a(Y-Y)$ and $i_a(Y-Y)$. But the sum of these two currents, i_a, drawn from the utility has a 12-pulse waveform that has much lower ripple content than the six-pulse waveform. Similarly, the dc-side voltage waveforms of the two converters, v_{d1} and v_{d2}, in a pole sum up to a 12-pulse waveform v_d that has a much less ripple riding on the dc voltage, as compared to the six-pulse waveform. In spite of this reduction in ripple (or harmonics of the fundamental as they are called), filters are placed at the ac-side for the harmonics in the current and on the dc-side for the harmonics in the voltage, as shown in the one-line diagram of Fig. 7-16, in an actual project so that these harmonic currents and voltages do not interfere with the power system operation,

(a)   (b)

Fig. 7-17 Six-pulse and 12-pulse current and voltage waveforms [2].

7-4-2   Power Flow in Current-Link Systems

Considering one of the poles, for example the positive pole in Fig. 7-16, the two terminals are shown in Fig. 7-18a where R_d is the resistance of the dc-link inductance.

Fig. 7-18 A pole of an HVDC system.

Since each terminal consists of two six-pulse thyristor converter as discussed previously,

$$V_{d1} = 2 \times \left[\frac{3\sqrt{2}}{\pi} V_{LL1} \cos\alpha_1 - \frac{3}{\pi}\omega L_{s1} I_d \right]$$ (7-12)

and

$$V_{d2} = 2 \times \left[\frac{3\sqrt{2}}{\pi} V_{LL2} \cos\alpha_2 - \frac{3}{\pi} \omega L_{s2} I_d \right] \qquad (7\text{-}13)$$

Note that in Fig. 7-18, the dc voltage of each terminal is defined as having a positive polarity where the current leaves. By controlling the delay angles α_1 and α_2 in a range from $0°$ to $160°$ as discussed previously, the average voltage, the average current, and the average power in the system of Fig. 7-18 can be controlled, where the current flow through the dc-link can be expressed as

$$I_d = \frac{V_{d1} + V_{d2}}{R_d} \qquad (7\text{-}14)$$

where the dc-link resistance R_d is generally very small. In such a system, for the power flow from system 1 to system 2, V_{d2} is made negative by controlling α_2 such that it operates as an inverter and establishes the voltage of the dc-link. Converter 1 is operated as a rectifier at a delay angle α_1 such that it controls the current in the dc-link. The converse is true for these two converters if the power is to flow from system 2 to system 1. Generally in an inverter, the delay angle α is controlled so that the sum of the delay angle α and the commutation interval u remains constant and results in a constant Extinction Angle γ which is defined as follows:

$$\gamma = 180° - (\alpha + u) \qquad (7\text{-}15)$$

This extinction angle is kept constant at a minimum value of usually $15°$ to $20°$. Substituting Eq. 7-15 into Eq. 7-13, and making use of Eq. 7-9

$$V_{d2} = 2 \times \left[-\frac{3\sqrt{2}}{\pi} V_{LL2} \cos\gamma_{min} + \frac{3}{\pi} \omega L_{s2} I_d \right] \qquad (7\text{-}16)$$

Using Eqs. 7-16 and 7-14

$$V_{d1} = 2 \times \frac{3\sqrt{2}}{\pi} V_{LL2} \cos\gamma_{min} - \underbrace{\left(\frac{6}{\pi} \omega L_{s2} - R_d \right)}_{positive} I_d \qquad (7\text{-}17)$$

The quantity within the "( )" in Eq. 7-17 is generally positive. Therefore with converter 2 operating at a constant minimum extinction angle γ_{min}, the voltage V_{d1} given by Eq. 7-17 is plotted in Fig. 7-19 as a function of the dc-link current I_d. Converter 1 is operating as a rectifier with its delay angle controlled to maintain the dc-link current at its reference value $I_{d,ref}$. Therefore, the intersection of the inverter and the rectifier characteristics establishes the operating point in terms of the voltage and the current in a HVDC system, as shown in Fig. 7-19.

Fig. 7-19 Control of an HVDC system [3].

7-4-3 Improvements in Current-Link Systems

Recently, there are systems introduced which use active filters, compared to passive filters, to improve the system performance while reducing the space needed to install them. Also, there are systems introduced which consist of capacitors in series between the converter transformers and the converter bridges. These offer several advantages as described in [4-6].

7-5 Voltage-Link HVDC Systems

One of the limitations of the current-link system is that both the converters, regardless of their mode of operation, rectifier or inverter, require reactive power from the ac system. This limitation can be overcome, as in a recent example shown in Fig. 7-20.

Fig. 7-20 Voltage-link, Cross Sound Cable HVDC Project [source: ABB].

In the block diagram of such a system repeated in Fig. 7-21, each converter can either absorb or supply reactive power in a controllable manner.

Fig. 7-21 Block diagram of voltage-link HVDC system.

Unlike in current-link systems, in the voltage-link system, there is a capacitor on the dc-side of the converter in parallel that appears as a voltage port and hence the converters in such a system are also called voltage-source converters. One such converter between dc and three-phase ac is shown by its block diagram in Fig. 7-22a. On a per-phase basis, this converter on the ac side appears as a voltage source as shown in Fig. 7-22b, interfacing the utility voltage source through a small inductance that may be the internal inductance of the utility system.

Fig. 7-22 Block diagram of a voltage-link converter and the phasor diagram.

The utility voltage can be assumed to be of constant amplitude with the reference phase angle of zero. Therefore in the circuit of Fig. 7-22b

$$\overline{V}_{conv} = \overline{V}_{bus} + jX_L\overline{I}_L \qquad (7\text{-}18)$$

The per-phase voltage synthesized by the converter can be controlled to be at the line-frequency, of the desired magnitude and phase. As the phasor diagram of Fig. 7-22c shows, the resulting current can be of the desired amplitude and phase and hence controlling the power in direction and magnitude, and reactive power in magnitude absorbed or supplied by the converter.

To synthesize these three-phase voltages, let us assume that we have three ideal transformers available with continuously variable turns-ratios, as shown in Fig. 7-23a. We will soon see that these ideal transformers are functional representations of the switch-mode converter that is required. We will focusing on only one of the three phases as shown in Fig. 7-23b, others being identical in functionality, where from practical considerations, d_a is restricted to be in a range $0 \le d_a \le 1$. With this restriction, v_{aN} cannot become negative and therefore a dc offset of half the dc-bus voltage, $0.5V_d$, is introduced so that around this offset, the desired output voltage v_a, with respect to the output neutral, can become both positive and negative in a sinusoidal manner.

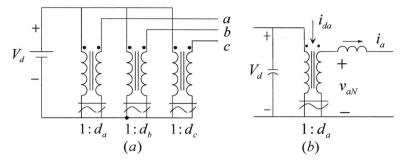

Fig. 7-23 Synthesis of sinusoidal voltages.

Therefore,

$$v_{aN} = 0.5V_d + \underbrace{\hat{V}_a \sin \omega t}_{v_a} \tag{7-19}$$

as shown in Fig. 7-23 In this ideal transformer of Fig. 7-23b, $v_{aN} = d_a V_d$ and hence the voltage in Eq. 7-19 can be obtained by varying the turns-ratio $1:d_a$ with time as follows, as shown in Fig. 7-24

$$d_a = 0.5 + \hat{d}_a \sin \omega t \tag{7-20}$$

where

$$\hat{V}_a = \hat{d}_a V_d \tag{7-21}$$

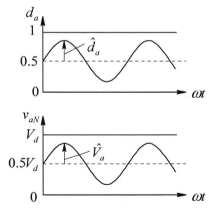

Fig. 7-24 Sinusoidal variation of turns-ratio d_a.

In Fig. 7-25a, all three phase output voltages are shown and the waveforms for plotted in Fig. 7-25b. In these outputs, the dc offsets (actually, these common-mode voltages need not be dc so long as they are the same in all three phases) are cancelled out from line-to-line voltages and hence can be ignored in consideration of the output voltages. It can be noted by Fig. 7-25b that by introducing the common-mode voltages of $V_d/2$ in series with each phase, the maximum ac voltage magnitude is $\hat{V}_a = V_d/2$. As explained in [1], it is possible to modulate the common-mode voltage, rather than keeping it to $V_d/2$, and thus get the line-line voltage peak to equal V_d at the limit. This increases the output voltage capability of such a converter by approximately 15%.

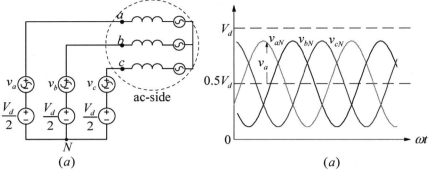

Fig. 7-25 Three-phase synthesis.

Next we will study how this ideal transformer functionality is obtained. As shown in Fig 7-26a, a bi-positional switch within a two-port, a voltage-port on the dc-side and a current-port on the ac side, is used. This switch can be considered ideal, either up or down for a switching signal q_a of 1 or zero, respectively. In reality, such a switch can be constructed as shown in Fig. 7-26b using two diodes and two IGBTs which are provided complimentary gate signals, q_a and q_a^-.

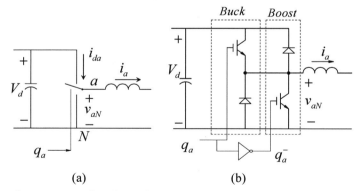

Fig. 7-26 Realization of the ideal transformer functionality.

In this bi-positional switch, when $q_a = 1$ and the upper IGBT is on and the lower one off, and the current through the output inductor can flow in either direction, through the upper IGBT if positive or through the upper diode if negative. In either of these cases, the potential of point "a" is the same as that of the upper dc-bus and $v_{aN}(sw) = V_d$. Similarly,

$q_a = 0$ results in $q_a^- = 1$ and the output current will flow either through the bottom diode or the bottom IGBT and hence $v_{aN}(sw) = 0$. Thus, the switching function q_a makes the switch operate as a bi-positional switch, either up or down.

<u>PWM</u>. We will operate this switch at a high frequency, two or three orders of magnitude higher than the fundamental frequency to be synthesized. For example in synthesizing 60 Hz, the switching frequency f_s may be 6 kHz that is 100 time higher. This results in the output waveform shown in Fig. 7-27a over one switching cycle $T_s (= 1/f_s)$, where the switching frequency f_s is kept constant. It shows that the output voltage has an average value that can be written as

$$\underbrace{v_{aN}}_{average} = d_a V_d \tag{7-22}$$

where,

$$d_a = \frac{T_{up}}{T_s} \tag{7-23}$$

In Eqs. 7-22 and 7-23, T_{up} and d_a can be continuously varied with time, sinusoidally with a dc offset, as discussed earlier, so that the average voltage given by Eq. 7-22 the same as obtained by the ideal transformer representation.

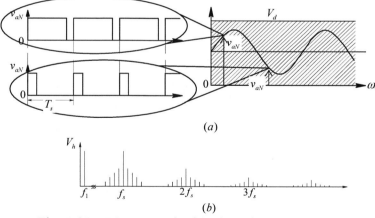

(a)

(b)

Fig. 7-27 PWM to synthesize sinusoidal waveform.

It should be recognized that in the output voltage, in addition to the desired average value Eq. 7-22, there are unwanted switching harmonics as shown in Fig. 7-27b at and around the multiples of the switching frequency, appearing as side bands at and around harmonic h where,

$$h = k_1 f_s \pm k_2 f_0 \tag{7-24}$$

The design of converters must take these harmonics into account and provide for adequate filtering so that they do not impact the ac system to which this converter is connected.

As explained earlier on a per-phase basis, the current phasor can be controlled anywhere with respect to ac-system voltage and thus the power flow can be in either direction and the reactive power can be absorbed or supplied as needed. Thus in the block diagram of a voltage-link HVDC system in Fig. 7-21, ignoring losses, $P_1 = P_2$, but Q_1 and Q_2 are totally independent of each other in magnitude and direction, each can be lagging or leading, and can help with the voltage stability as discussed in the stability chapter.

Use of the voltage-link HVDC converter concept is discussed for several other applications: in Chapter 3 in the rotor circuit of doubly-fed induction generators commonly used in windmills, for efficiently controlling the speed of induction motors discussed in Chapter 8, and for reactive power control in devices such as STATCOM and UPFC discussed in a later chapter dealing with the voltage stability in power systems.

REFERENCES

1. N. Mohan, *First Course on Power Electronics*, 2005 edition, MNPERE (www.MNPERE.com).
2. N. Mohan, T. Undeland and W.P. Robbins, *Power Electronics: Converters, Applications, and Design*, 3rd edition, Year 2003, John Wiley & Sons.
3. E. W. Kimbark, Direct Current Transmission, vol. 1, Wiley –Interscience, New York, 1971.
4. G. Balzer, H. Müller, Capacitor Commutated Converters For High Power HVDC Transmission, Seventh International Conference on AC-DC Power Transmission, London, UK, 28 - 30 November 2001.
5. M. Meisingset, A. Golé, A Comparison Of Conventional And Capacitor Commutated converters Based On Steady-State And Dynamic Considerations, Seventh International Conference on AC-DC Power Transmission, London, UK, 28 - 30 November 2001.
6. ABB Website (www.ABB.com)

PROBLEMS

7-1   In a three-phase thyristor converter, $V_{LL} = 460V(rms)$ at $60Hz$, and $L_s = 5mH$. The delay angle $\alpha = 30^0$. This converter is supplying $5kW$ of power. The dc-side current i_d can be assumed purely dc. (a) Calculate the commutation angle u, (b) Draw the waveforms for the converter variables: phase voltages, phase currents, v_{Pn}, v_{Nn} and v_d, and (c) Assuming that the currents through the

7-2 In Fig. 7-9a, assume $L_s = 0$ and $V_{LL} = 480V\,(rms)$ at a frequency of 60 Hz. The delay angle $\alpha = 0^0$. It is supplying a power of 10 kW. Calculate and plot the waveforms similar to those in Fig. 7-10.

7-3 Repeat Problem 7-2 if the delay angle $\alpha = 45^0$.

7-4 Repeat Problem 7-2 if the delay angle $\alpha = 145^0$.

7-5 Repeat Problem 7-2 if in Problem 7-2 the ac-side inductance L_s is such that the commutation angle $u = 10^0$.

7-6 Repeat Problem 7-2 if the delay angle $\alpha = 45^0$ and the ac-side inductance L_s is such that the commutation angle $u = 10^0$.

7-7 Repeat Problem 7-2 if the delay angle $\alpha = 145^0$ and the ac-side inductance L_s is such that the commutation angle $u = 10^0$. Note that the power flow is from the dc-side to the ac-side.

7-8 Calculate the reactive power consumed by the converter and the power factor angle in Problem 7-5.

7-9 Calculate the reactive power consumed by the converter and the power factor angle in Problem 7-6.

7-10 Calculate the reactive power consumed by the converter and the power factor angle in Problem 7-7. Note that the power flow is from the dc-side to the ac-side.

7-11 In the block diagram of Fig. 7-18, for both three-phase converters, $V_{d0} = 480kV$. The dc-side current is $I_d = 1kA$. Converter 2 operating as an inverter establishes the dc-link voltage such that $V_{d2} = -425kV$. $R_d = 10.0\Omega$. The drop in dc voltage due to commutation overlap in each converter is $10kV$. In dc steady state, calculate the following angles: α_1, α_2, u_1 and u_2.

7-12 In Problem 7-11, calculate the reactive power drawn by each converter. Assume that the currents through the thyristors increase/decrease linearly during commutations.

7-13 In a voltage-link converter, the dc-bus voltage V_d and the three-phase voltages to be synthesized are given. (a) Write the expressions for v_{aN}, v_{bN}, and v_{cN}, and (b) Write the expressions for d_a, d_b, and d_c

7-14 In Fig. 7-22, $\overline{V}_{bus} = 1\angle 0\,pu$ and $X_L = 0.1\,pu$. Calculate $\overline{V}_{conv}$ in order to supply 1 pu power at V_{bus} with (a) $Q = 0.5\,pu$, and (b) $Q = -0.5\,pu$.

Problems using PSCAD/EMTDC:

7-15   Analyze a primitive thyristor circuit, as described on the accompanying CD.

7-16   Obtain the waveforms in a 6-pulse diode rectifier described on the CD accompanying this book.

7-17   Obtain the waveforms in a 12-pulse diode rectifier described on the CD accompanying this book.

7-18   Obtain the waveforms in a 6-pulse thyristor converter operating in a rectifier-mode, as described on the accompanying CD.

7-19   Obtain the waveforms in a 12-pulse thyristor converter operating in a rectifier-mode, as described on the accompanying CD.

7-20   Obtain the waveforms in a 6-pulse inverter, as described on the accompanying CD.

7-21   Obtain the waveforms in a 12-pulse inverter, as described on the accompanying CD.

Including an HVDC Line in Power Flow Studies using *PowerWorld*:

7-22   Include an HVDC transmission system, as described on the accompanying CD, in the three-bus example power system.

CHAPTER 8

Distribution System, Loads and Power Quality

8-1   INTRODUCTION

In this chapter, we will briefly examine the distribution system, the nature of prominent types of loads and the power quality considerations to keep the power supply voltage sinusoidal at the rated voltage and line frequency.

8-2 DISTRIBUTION SYSTEMS

With the exception of distributed generation (DG) in the future, electricity today is normally generated remotely to the load centers and is transported through transmission lines at high, extra-high and even at ultra-high voltages.   Electricity from this transmission network is passed on to the sub-transmission network at voltages from 230 kV down to 35 kV. Some utilities consider this sub-transmission network to be part of the distribution system, while others consider only the network below 35 kV to be the distribution system.   As stated in the chapter on transmission lines, approximately 9 percent of the electricity in the United States is dissipated in transmission and distribution systems, most of it in the later.   Most industrial, commercial and residential loads are supplied at much lower voltages than 34.5 kV, with the primary voltages in a range of 34.5 kV (19.92 kV per-phase) down to 12 kV (6.93 kV per-phase), and the secondary voltages at 480/277 V, three-phase, four-wire and 120/240-V single-phase.   Other secondary voltages are at 208/120 V, 480 V and 600 V [1].

For residential loads, distribution substations supply single-phase distribution lines for various communities at voltages such as 13.8 kV.   These voltages are stepped down locally to supply a set of houses at $\pm 120V$ as shown in Fig. 8-1. At the entrance of a house, the neutral is grounded, and from the central breaker, a set of circuits, each with its own circuit breaker, are supplied by the $+120V$ line conductor and the neutral, whereas the other set is supplied by the $-120V$ line conductor and the neutral.

The ground conductor is carried along with each circuit to three-prong outlets, one for the line conductor, second for the neutral and the third for the ground conductor that is connected to the chassis of the load, for example a toaster. The reason for carrying along the ground conductor is elimination of shock hazard. Normally there is no current flow through the ground conductor and it remains at ground potential, whereas the neutral conductor can rise above the ground potential due to current flow through its impedance. It should be noted that only a current of $5\,mA$ is needed through the human heart to make it go into ventricular defibrillation. Outlets in more shock-susceptible areas with wet surfaces are equipped with Ground Fault Interrupters (GFIs) that measure the difference between the current on the line conductor to that returning on the neutral conductor. The difference between the two currents indicates a fault to ground, and the GFI triggers the associated circuit breaker to be tripped.

Fig. 8-1 Residential distribution system.

8-3   POWER SYSTEM LOADS

Power systems are designed to serve industrial, commercial and residential loads. A plot of the power demand on a utility, as a function of the time-of-day is plotted in Fig. 8-2a as an example. The waveform of this load curve may be different for weekday as compared to weekends that reflects shutdown of factories and commercial shops. The area underneath the plot in Fig. 8-2a represents energy that the utility must supply in a 24-hour period, where as the peak of this waveform is the peak load that the utility must supply by its own generation or by purchasing power from other utilities. The ratio between the kilowatt-hours represented underneath the load curve in Fig. 8-2a and the kilowatt-hours that would be necessary to generate if the load were constant at its peak value over the entire 24-hour period is called the *load factor*. The annual load-duration curve of Fig. 8-2b shows that the load is at or 90% above its peak value for only a small percentage of the time in a year.

Fig. 8-2 System load.

Ideally, utilities would desire load factor to be unity but in reality it is far less than that. The reason for desiring the load factor of unity has to do with the fact that the peak power is expensive to generate or to purchase from other utilities. It taxes the transmission system capacity and results in extra power losses. Some utilities have been very successful in increasing the load factor on their system by giving incentives to customers to shift their loads to off-peak periods by offering lower electricity rates at off-peak periods. Others have used energy storage in the form of pumped-hydro, for example, where, during off-peak periods, water is pumped from a lower reservoir up to a higher reservoir to generate electricity during peak periods. Somewhat along this line, utilities invest considerable sums of money in load forecasting over the next 24 hours to make purchasing agreements and to commit units to meet the expected load demand. Accurate forecasting of load results in considerable savings.

8-3-1 Nature of Power System Loads

Fig. 8-3a shows the percentage of electricity consumed by the industrial, commercial and residential sectors in the United States, whereas Fig. 8-3b shows electricity consumed by various types of loads.

Fig. 8-3 Utility loads.

Most utilities serve a variety of such loads. Industrial loads mainly depend on the type of industry, whereas the commercial and residential loads generally consist of the following in a variety of mixes:

- Electrical heating
- Lighting (incandescent and fluorescent)
- Motor loads to drive compressors for heating, ventilating, and air conditioning (HVAC)
- Power electronics based compressor loads and compact fluorescent lighting (CFL)

Each of these loads behaves differently for changes in the voltage magnitude and frequency. Generally, frequency does not vary appreciably in a large interconnected system such as that in North America (unless a phenomena called "islanding" occurs) to be concerned. However, the voltage sensitivity of loads must be included in calculating power flow and stability. Utilities estimate the mix of loads on their system, and knowing how each load behaves, the load aggregate is modeled in various studies by a combination of constant impedance, constant power and constant current representations.

Voltage sensitivities $a(=\partial P/\partial V)$ to real power and $b(=\partial Q/\partial V)$ to reactive power of various loads can be approximated as follows, and are summarized below in a tabular form:

- *Electric Heating:* These loads are resistive. Therefore their power factor equals unity; $a = 2$ and $b = 0$.

- *Incandescent Lighting*: Being resistive, their power factor is unity. Because the filament resistance is nonlinear, $a = 1.5$ and $b = 0$.

- *Fluorescent Lighting*: These use magnetic ballasts and their power factor is approximated at 0.9. It is reported that for such loads, $a = 1$ and $b = 1$.

- *Motor Loads*: Single-phase motors are used in smaller power ratings and three-phase motors in larger power ratings. Their power factor can be approximated in a range of 0.8 to 0.9. Their sensitivities to voltages depend of the type of load being driven, the fan-type or the compressor-type, because of the variation of the torque required by the load as a function of speed. Motor sensitivities are reported to be in a range of $a = 0.05-0.5$ and $b = 1-3$.

- *Modern Power-Electronics Based Loads*: Modern and future power-electronics based loads, that are increasingly being used, are nonlinear; they continue to draw the same power even if the input voltage were to change slightly in its magnitude and frequency, as discussed in this section. They can be designed with power-factor-corrected (PFC) interface that results in essentially a unity power factor. In such loads, ideally, it is possibly to get $a = 0$ and $b = 0$. Structure of these loads is described in further detail below.

Table 8-1 Power Factor and Voltage Sensitivity of Power Systems Load

Type of Load	Power Factor	$a = \partial P/\partial V$	$b = \partial Q/\partial V$
Electric Heating	1.0	2.0	0
Incandescent Lighting	1.0	1.5	0
Fluorescent Lighting	0.9	1.0	1.0
Motor Loads	0.8 – 0.9	0.05 – 0.5	1.0 – 3.0
Modern Power-Electronics based Loads	1.0	0	0

8-3-1-1 Power-Electronics Based Loads

The trend in power system loads is that they are increasingly being supplied through power electronics interface. Doing so increases the overall system efficiency, in some cases as much as 30 percent for example in heat pump systems [2], and hence has large energy conservation potential. In most cases, these loads are supplied by a voltage-link system, discussed in connection with HVDC transmission systems, as shown in Fig. 8-4.

Fig. 8-4 Voltage-link-system for modern and future power-electronics based loads.

A great deal of lighting load is shifting to compact fluorescent lamps (CFLs) where a power-electronics interface shown in Fig. 8-4 is needed to produce a high-frequency ac in the range of 30 kHz to 40 kHz at which these lamps operate most efficiently. CFLs, compared to incandescent lamps are approximately 4 times more efficient. That is, to provide the same illumination, they consume only one-fourth the electricity, hence amount to huge savings. In spite of their high initial cost, they are being used in increasing numbers, even in developing countries.

Fig. 8-5 shows the per-phase steady state equivalent circuit of a three-phase induction motor. Conventionally, the speed ω_m of such motors has been controlled by reducing the magnitude V_a of the applied voltage, without changing its frequency, that is, by keeping the synchronous speed ω_{syn} unchanged. Operating at large values of slip speed ω_{slip}, which equals $(\omega_{syn} - \omega_m)$, causes large power losses in the rotor circuit, resulting in very low energy efficiency of operation.

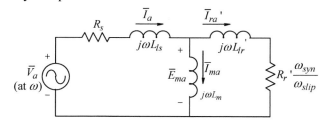

Fig. 8-5 Per-phase, steady state equivalent circuit of a three-phase induction motor.

Speed of induction-motor loads can be adjusted efficiently by a power electronics interface of Fig. 8-4 that produces three-phase output voltages whose amplitude and frequency can be controlled, independent of each other. By controlling the frequency of the voltages being applied to an induction motor, provided the voltage magnitude is also controlled to result in the rated air gap flux within the motor, the motor torque-speed characteristics can be plotted as shown in Fig. 8-6.

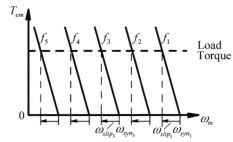

Fig. 8-6 Torque-speed characteristic of induction motor at various applied frequencies.

Each frequency of applied voltage results in the corresponding synchronous speed ω_{syn} from which the slip speed ω_{slip} is measured. Assuming a constant-torque load characteristic as shown dotted in Fig. 8-6, the operating speed can be varied continuously by continuously varying the applied frequency. At each operating point, the slip speed, measured with respect to its corresponding synchronous speed, remains small, and hence the energy efficiency remains high.

In applications mentioned earlier where a regulated dc power supply is needed, the voltage link system of Fig. 8-4 is used, as shown by the block diagram of Fig. 8-7, to produce high-frequency ac, which is stepped down in voltage by a high-frequency transformer and then rectified to produce a regulated dc output. The transformer operates at a high frequency in a range of 200 kHz to 300 kHz and hence can be made much smaller than a line-frequency transformer of the similar VA rating. Efficiency of such switch-mode dc power supplies approach 90% which is almost double of those associated with linear power supplies.

Fig. 8-7 Switch-mode dc power supply.

In developed countries with high cost of electricity, most of the compressor-loads such as air-conditioners and heat pumps are supplied through the power electronics interface of Fig. 8-4. Studies have shown that by adjusting the compressor speed to match the thermal load, as much as 30% savings in electricity can be achieved, as compared to the conventional on/off cycling approach. Similarly, in pump-driven systems to adjust flow-rate, controlling the pump speed by using the power-electronics interface of Fig. 8-4, considerable improvement in the overall system efficiency can be obtained as compared to the use of throttling valve. A report by DOE [3] estimates that if all the pump-driven systems were controlled using power electronics, a mature technology now, enough energy can be saved annually to equal that used by the state of New York!

Power electronics based loads are often nonlinear in the sense they often continue to draw the same power irrespective of change in the input voltage in a small range. If these power electronics based loads are not designed appropriately, they draw distorted (non-sinusoidal) currents from the utility source and hence can degrade the quality of power as discussed in the next section. However, it is possible to design power electronics interface of Fig 8-4 with current shaping circuits, often called power-factor-correction (PFC) circuits [4], so that the current drawn from the utility is sinusoidal and at a unity power factor.

8-4   POWER QUALITY CONSIDERATIONS

It is important to customers that the power they receive from their utility is of acceptable quality. These power quality considerations can be classified into the following categories:

- Continuity of Service
- Magnitude of Voltage
- Voltage Waveform

In an interconnected system such as that in North America, the frequency of voltage supply is seldom of concern and therefore is not mentioned above. We will discuss each of the above considerations in the following sub-sections.

8-4-1   Continuity of Service

Most serious power quality issue is the lack of the continuity of service. Utilities do their best to ensure it because a service disruption also means a loss of revenue for them. Interconnected systems, as one of their benefits, improve the continuity of service. If a part of the power system goes down for whatever reason, an interconnected system has a better chance of supplying power through an alternative route.

8-4-1-1 Uninterruptible Power Supplies (UPS)

To further improve this continuity for critical loads such as some computers and medical equipment, uninterruptible power supplies (UPS) are used that store energy in chemical batteries, and also in flywheels in the form of inertial energy, within the voltage-link system shown in Fig. 8-8.

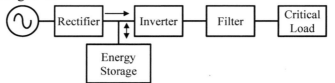

Fig. 8-8 Uninterruptible power supply.

8-4-1-2 Solid State Transfer Switches

On a larger scale for an entire industrial plant itself, it is possible to make use of two feeders if they are derived from different systems, as shown in Fig. 8-9. One of the feeders is used as the primary feeder that normally supplies power to the load. In case of a fault on this feeder, solid state transfer switches, made up of thyristors or IGBTs, switch the load to the alternate feeder within a few milliseconds and hence maintain the continuity of service. This action, of course, assumes that the same fault, in all probability far away, does not affect both feeders.

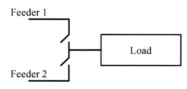

Fig. 8-9 Alternate feeder.

8-4-2   Voltage Magnitude

Power system loads prefer that the voltage magnitude be at its specified nominal value. Fig. 8-10 from CBEMA (Computer and Business Equipment Manufacturers Association) shows the extent of voltage fluctuations that can be tolerated for various lengths of time.

Fig. 8-10 CBEMA curve.

Utilities try to maintain voltage supply within a range such as ±5% of the nominal voltage. However under fault conditions, even far away, and heavy or very light loading of transmission lines can cause voltages to be outside the normal range in one or more phases. To maintain this voltage in magnitude, equipment such as Dynamic Voltage Restorers (DVR) is used. As shown in the block diagram form in Fig. 8-11, utilizing a voltage link system, DVRs inject a voltage in series with the utility supply to bring the voltage at the consumer-end to within the acceptable range.

Fig. 8-11 Dynamic Voltage Restorer (DVR).

On a larger scale, in distribution substations, voltage regulators and transformers with load-tap changing (LTC) automatically try to regulate the supply voltage. According to [5], both three-phase and single-phase voltage regulators are used in distribution substations to regulate the load-side voltage. Substation regulators are one of the primary means, along with load-tap-changing power transformers, shunt capacitors, and distribution line regulators, for maintaining a proper level of voltage at a customer's service entrance. A very important function of substation voltage regulation is to correct for supply voltage variation. With the proper use of the control settings and line drop compensation, regulators can correct for load variations as well. A properly applied and controlled voltage regulator not only keeps the voltage at a customer's service entrance within approved limits but also minimizes the range of voltage swing between light and heavy load periods [5].

Fig. 8-12 Three-Phase Voltage Regulator (Courtesy of Siemens) [5].

According to [5] In large distribution substations, the choice of three-phase regulators (see Fig. 8-12) may be based on costs or on the availability of single-phase regulators of the required size. Three-phase regulators require somewhat less space than three single-phase regulators; however, this is not generally a major factor in selection [5].

According to [5] Load-tap-changing power transformers are becoming more common in distribution substations. They consist essentially of a three-phase regulator built into a three-phase power transformer. The relative cost of this combination compared to a separate transformer and either three-phase or single-phase regulators varies depending on the size of the substation. Aside from the base cost of the equipment, the LTC method generally will result in a saving in space, bus work, and supporting structures. Because their controls sense only one phase of a three-phase circuit and since some unbalance may be expected among the phases, the voltage correction of three-phase regulators and LTC transformers will be less precise than that of single-phase regulators [5].

This problem of voltage outside the normal range can be mitigated by reactive power control using a power-electronics based device such as a Static Compensator, known as STATCOM, shown in Fig. 8-13 as a block diagram. A STATCOM acts as a continually-adjustable reactor, which can draw either inductive or capacitive volt-amperes (vars) within its designed rating, to regulate the bus voltage. STATCOMs are further explained in the chapter dealing with the voltage stability.

Fig. 8-13 STATCOM [4].

8-4-3   Voltage Waveform

Most of the load equipment in use is designed assuming a sinusoidal voltage waveform. Any distortion in this voltage waveform can cause loads such as induction motors to draw distorted (non-sinusoidal) currents which can result in loss of efficiency, overheating and may cause some loads to fail. As mentioned earlier, power-electronics based loads, if not designed with this consideration, would draw distorted currents and would cause the supply voltage, due to its internal impedance, to become distorted and hence cause problems to other adjacent loads.

8-4-3-1 Distortion and Power Factor

To quantify distortion in the current drawn by power electronic systems, it is necessary to define certain indices.

As a base case, consider the linear $R - L$ load shown in Fig. 8-14a which is supplied by a sinusoidal source in steady state. The voltage and current phasors are shown in Fig. 8-14b, where ϕ is the angle by which the current lags the voltage.

Figure 8-14 Voltage and current phasors in simple *R-L* circuit.

The voltage and current phasors are shown in Fig. 8-14b, where ϕ is the angle by which the current lags the voltage. Using rms values for the voltage and current magnitudes, the average power supplied by the source is

$$P = V_s I_s \cos\phi \qquad\qquad (8\text{-}1)$$

The power factor (*PF*) at which power is drawn is defined as the ratio of the real average power P to the product of the rms voltage and the rms current:

$$PF = \frac{P}{V_s I_s} = \cos\phi \qquad \text{(using Eq. 8-1)} \qquad\qquad (8\text{-}2)$$

where $V_s I_s$ is the apparent power. the For a given voltage, from Eq. 8-2, the rms current drawn is

$$I_s = \frac{P}{V_s \cdot PF} \qquad\qquad (8\text{-}3)$$

This shows that the power factor *PF* and the current I_s are inversely proportional. The current flows through the utility distribution lines, transformers, and so on, causing losses in their resistances. This is the reason why utilities prefer unity power factor loads that draw power at the minimum value of the rms current.

8-4-3-2 RMS Value of Distorted Current and the Total Harmonic Distortion (*THD*)

The sinusoidal current drawn by the linear load in Fig. 8-14 has zero distortion. However, power electronic systems without a power-factor-corrected (PFC) front-end draw currents with a distorted waveform such as that shown by $i_s(t)$ in Fig. 8-15a. The utility voltage $v_s(t)$ is assumed sinusoidal. The following analysis is general, applying to the utility supply that is either single-phase or three-phase, in which case the analysis is on a per-phase basis.

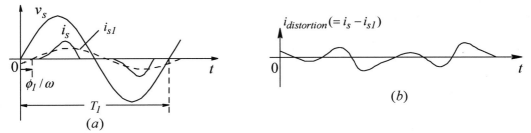

Figure 8-15 Current drawn by power electronics equipment without PFC.

The current waveform $i_s(t)$ in Fig. 8-15a repeats with a time-period T_1. By Fourier analysis of this repetitive waveform, we can compute its fundamental frequency ($= 1/T_1$) component $i_{s1}(t)$, shown dotted in Fig. 8-15a. The distortion component $i_{distortion}(t)$ in the input current is the difference between $i_s(t)$ and the fundamental-frequency component $i_{s1}(t)$:

$$i_{distortion}(t) = i_s(t) - i_{s1}(t) \tag{8-4}$$

where $i_{distortion}(t)$ using Eq. 8-4 is plotted in Fig. 8-15b. This distortion component consists of components at frequencies that are the multiples of the fundamental frequency.

To obtain the rms value of $i_s(t)$ in Fig. 8-15a, we will apply the basic definition of rms:

$$I_s = \sqrt{\frac{1}{T_1} \int_{T_1} i_s^2(t) \cdot dt} \tag{8-5}$$

Using Eq. 8-4,

$$i_s^2(t) = i_{s1}^2(t) + i_{distortion}^2(t) + 2i_{s1}(t) \times i_{distortion}(t) \tag{8-6}$$

In a repetitive waveform, the integral of the products of the two harmonic components (including the fundamental) at unequal frequencies, over the repetition time-period, equals zero:

$$\int_{T_1} g_{h_1}(t) \cdot g_{h_2}(t) \cdot dt = 0 \qquad h_1 \neq h_2 \tag{8-7}$$

Therefore, substituting Eq. 8-6 into Eq. 8-5, and making use of Eq. 8-7 that implies that the integral of the third term on the right side of Eq. 8-6 equals zero,

$$I_s = \sqrt{\underbrace{\frac{1}{T_1}\int_{T_1} i_{s1}^2(t)\cdot dt}_{I_{s1}^2} + \underbrace{\frac{1}{T_1}\int_{T_1} i_{distortion}^2(t)\cdot dt}_{I_{s1}^2} + 0} \qquad (8\text{-}8)$$

or,

$$I_s = \sqrt{I_{s1}^2 + I_{distortion}^2} \qquad (8\text{-}9)$$

where the rms values of the fundamental-frequency component and the distortion component are as follows:

$$I_{s1} = \sqrt{\frac{1}{T_1}\int_{T_1} i_{s1}^2(t)\cdot dt} \qquad (8\text{-}10)$$

and

$$I_{distortion} = \sqrt{\frac{1}{T_1}\int_{T_1} i_{distortion}^2(t)\cdot dt} \qquad (8\text{-}11)$$

Based on the rms values of the fundamental and the distortion components in the input current $i_s(t)$, a distortion index called the Total Harmonic Distortion (*THD*) is defined in percentage as follows:

$$\%\,THD = 100\times\frac{I_{distortion}}{I_{s1}} \qquad (8\text{-}12)$$

Using Eq. 8-9 into Eq. 8-12,

$$\%\,THD = 100\times\frac{\sqrt{I_s^2 - I_{s1}^2}}{I_{s1}} \qquad (8\text{-}13)$$

The rms value of the distortion component can be obtained based on the harmonic components (except the fundamental) as follows using Eq. 8-7:

$$I_{distortion} = \sqrt{\sum_{h=2}^{\infty} I_{sh}^2} \qquad (8\text{-}14)$$

where I_{sh} is the rms value of the harmonic component "h".

8-4-3-3 Obtaining Harmonic Components by Fourier Analysis

By Fourier analysis, any distorted (non-sinusoidal) waveform $g(t)$ that is repetitive with a fundamental frequency f_1, for example i_s in Fig. 8-15a, can be expressed as a sum of sinusoidal components at the fundament and its multiples (harmonic) frequencies:

$$g(t) = G_0 + \sum_{h=1}^{\infty} g_h(t) = G_0 + \sum_{h=1}^{\infty} \{a_h \cos(h\omega t) + b_h \sin(h\omega t)\} \qquad (8\text{-}15)$$

where the average value G_0 is dc

$$G_0 = \frac{1}{2\pi} \int_0^{2\pi} g(t) \cdot d(\omega t) \qquad (8\text{-}16)$$

The sinusoidal waveforms in Eq. 8-15 at the fundamental frequency f_1 ($h=1$) and the harmonic components at frequencies h times f_1 can be expressed as the sum of their cosine and sine components

$$a_h = \frac{1}{\pi} \int_0^{2\pi} g(t) \cos(h\omega t) d(\omega t) \quad h = 1, 2, \ldots, \infty \qquad (8\text{-}17)$$

$$b_h = \frac{1}{\pi} \int_0^{2\pi} g(t) \sin(h\omega t) d(\omega t) \quad h = 1, 2, \ldots, \infty \qquad (8\text{-}18)$$

The cosine and the sine components above, given by Eqs. 8-17 and 8-18, can be combined and written as a phasor in terms of its rms value

$$\bar{G}_h = G_h \angle \phi_h \qquad (8\text{-}19)$$

where the rms magnitude in terms of the peak values a_h and b_h equals

$$G_h = \frac{\sqrt{a_h^2 + b_h^2}}{2} \qquad (8\text{-}20)$$

and the phase ϕ_h can be expressed as

$$\tan \phi_h = \frac{-b_h}{a_h} \qquad (8\text{-}21)$$

It can be shown that the rms value of the distorted function $g(t)$ can be expressed in terms of its average and the sinusoidal components as

$$G = \sqrt{G_0^2 + \sum_{h=1}^{\infty} G_h^2} \qquad (8\text{-}22)$$

In Fourier analysis, by appropriate selection of the time origin, it is often possible to make the sine or the cosine components in Eq. 8-15, thus considerably simplifying the analysis, as illustrated by a simple example below.

▲ **Example 8-1** A current i_s of square waveform is shown in Fig. 8-16a. Calculate and plot its fundamental frequency component and its distortion component. What is the *%THD* associated with this waveform?

Solution From Fourier analysis, by choosing the time origin as shown in Fig. 8-16a, $i_s(t)$ in Fig. 8-16a can be expressed as

$$i_s = \frac{4}{\pi} I (\sin \omega_1 t + \frac{1}{3} \sin 3\omega_1 t + \frac{1}{5} \sin 5\omega_1 t + \frac{1}{7} \sin 7\omega_1 t + ...) \qquad (8\text{-}23)$$

The fundamental frequency component and the distortion component are plotted in Figs. 8-16b and 8-16c.

From Fig. 8-16a, it is obvious that the rms value I_s of the square waveform is equal to I. In the Fourier expression of Eq. 8-23, and the rms value of the fundamental-frequency component is

$$I_{s1} = \frac{(4/\pi)}{\sqrt{2}} I = 0.9I \ .$$

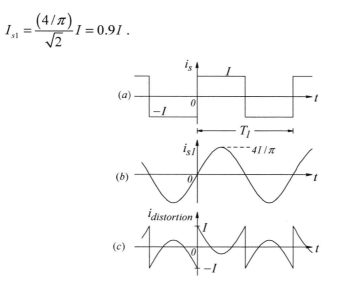

Figure 8-16 Example 8-1.

Therefore, the distortion component can be calculated from Eq. 8-9 as

$$I_{distortion} = \sqrt{I_s^2 - I_{s1}^2} = \sqrt{I^2 - (0.9I)^2} = 0.436 I \ .$$

Therefore, using the definition of *THD*,

$$\% THD = 100 \times \frac{I_{distortion}}{I_{s1}} = 100 \times \frac{0.436 I}{0.9 I} = 48.4\% \ .$$

▲

8-4-3-4 The Displacement Power Factor (*DPF*) and Power Factor (*PF*)

Next, we will consider the power factor at which power is drawn by a load with a distorted current waveform such as that shown in Fig. 8-15a. As before, it is reasonable to assume that the utility-supplied line-frequency voltage $v_s(t)$ is sinusoidal, with an rms value of V_s and a frequency $f_1 (= \frac{\omega_1}{2\pi})$. Based on Eq. 8-7, which states that the product of the cross-frequency terms has a zero average, the average power P drawn by the load in Fig. 8-15a is due only to the fundamental-frequency component of the current:

$$P = \frac{1}{T_1} \int_{T_1} v_s(t) \cdot i_s(t) \cdot dt = \frac{1}{T_1} \int_{T_1} v_s(t) \cdot i_{s1}(t) \cdot dt \qquad (8\text{-}24)$$

Therefore, in contrast to Eq. 8-1 for a linear load, in a load that draws distorted current, similar to Eq. 8-1

$$P = V_s I_{s1} \cos\phi_1 \qquad (8\text{-}25)$$

where ϕ_1 is the angle by which the fundamental-frequency current component $i_{s1}(t)$ lags behind the voltage, as shown in Fig. 8-15a.

At this point, another term called the Displacement Power Factor (*DPF*) needs to be introduced, where

$$DPF = \cos\phi_1 \qquad (8\text{-}26)$$

Therefore, using the *DPF* in Eq. 8-25,

$$P = V_s I_{s1}(DPF) \qquad (8\text{-}27)$$

In the presence of distortion in the current, the meaning and therefore the definition of the power factor, at which the real average power P is drawn, remains the same as in Eq. 8-2, that is, the ratio of the real power to the product of the rms voltage and the rms current:

$$PF = \frac{P}{V_s I_s} \qquad (8\text{-}28)$$

Substituting Eq. 8-27 for P into Eq. 8-28,

$$PF = \left(\frac{I_{s1}}{I_s}\right)(DPF) \qquad (8\text{-}29)$$

In linear loads that draw sinusoidal currents, the current-ratio (I_{s1}/I_s) in Eq. 8-29 is unity, hence $PF = DPF$. Eq. 8-29 shows the following: a high distortion in the current waveform leads to a low power factor, even if the *DPF* is high. Using Eq. 8-13, the ratio (I_{s1}/I_s) in Eq. 8-29 can be expressed in terms of the Total Harmonic Distortion as

$$\frac{I_{s1}}{I_s} = \frac{1}{\sqrt{1+\left(\frac{\%THD}{100}\right)^2}} \tag{8-30}$$

Therefore, in Eq. 8-29,

$$PF = \frac{1}{\sqrt{1+\left(\frac{\%THD}{100}\right)^2}} \cdot DPF \tag{8-31}$$

The effect of *THD* on the power factor is shown in Fig. 8-17 by plotting (PF/DPF) versus *THD*. It shows that even if the displacement power factor is unity, a total harmonic distortion of 100 percent (which is possible in power electronic systems unless corrective measures are taken) can reduce the power factor to approximately 0.7 (or $\frac{1}{\sqrt{2}} = 0.707$ to be exact), which is unacceptably low.

Fig. 8-17 Relation between PF/DPF and THD.

8-4-3-5 Deleterious Effects of Harmonic Distortion and a Poor Power Factor

There are several deleterious effects of high distortion in the current waveform and the poor power factor that results due to it. These are as follows:

- Power loss in utility equipment such as distribution and transmission lines, transformers, and generators increases, possibly to the point of overloading them.
- Harmonic currents can overload the shunt capacitors used by utilities for voltage support and may cause resonance conditions between the capacitive reactance of these capacitors and the inductive reactance of the distribution and transmission lines.

- The utility voltage waveform will also become distorted, adversely affecting other linear loads, if a significant portion of the load supplied by the utility draws power by means of distorted currents.

In order to prevent degradation in power quality, recommended guidelines (in the form of the IEEE-519) have been suggested by the IEEE (Institute of Electrical and Electronics Engineers). These guidelines place the responsibilities of maintaining power quality on the consumers and the utilities as follows: 1) on the power consumers, such as the users of power electronic systems, to limit the distortion in the current drawn, and 2) on the utilities to ensure that the voltage supply is sinusoidal with less than a specified amount of distortion.

The limits on current distortion placed by the IEEE-519 are shown in Table 8-1, where the limits on harmonic currents, as a ratio of the fundamental component, are specified for various harmonic frequencies. Also, the limits on the *THD* are specified. These limits are selected to prevent distortion in the voltage waveform of the utility supply.

Table 8-1 Harmonic current distortion (I_h / I_1)

I_{sc}/I_1	Odd Harmonic Order h (in %)					Total Harmonic Distortion(%)
	$h < 11$	$11 \leq h < 17$	$17 \leq h < 23$	$23 \leq h < 35$	$35 \leq h$	
< 20	4.0	2.0	1.5	0.6	0.3	5.0
$20 - 50$	7.0	3.5	2.5	1.0	0.5	8.0
$50 - 100$	10.0	4.5	4.0	1.5	0.7	12.0
$100 - 1000$	12.0	5.5	5.0	2.0	1.0	15.0
> 1000	15.0	7.0	6.0	2.5	1.4	20.0

Therefore, the limits on distortion in Table 8-1 depend on the "stiffness" of the utility supply, which is shown in Fig. 8-18a by a voltage source $\overline{V}_s$ in series with internal impedance Z_s. An ideal voltage supply has zero internal impedance. In contrast, the voltage supply at the end of a long distribution line, for example, will have large internal impedance. To define the "stiffness" of the supply, the short-circuit current I_{sc} is calculated by hypothetically placing short-circuit at the supply terminals, as shown in Fig. 8-18b. The stiffness of the supply must be calculated in relation to the load current. Therefore, the stiffness is defined by a ratio called the Short-Circuit-Ratio *(SCR)*:

$$\text{Short-Circuit-Ratio } SCR = \frac{I_{sc}}{I_{s1}} \tag{8-32}$$

where I_{s1} is the fundamental-frequency component of the load current. Table 8-1 shows that a smaller short-circuit ratio corresponds to lower limits on the allowed distortion in the current drawn. For the short-circuit-ratio of less than 20, the total harmonic distortion in the current must be less than 5 percent. Power electronic systems that meet this limit would also meet the limits of more stiff supplies.

Figure 8-18 (a) Utility Supply, (b) Short-Circuit Current.

It should be noted that the IEEE-519 does not propose harmonic guidelines for individual pieces of equipment but rather for the aggregate of loads (such as in an industrial plant) seen from the service entrance, which is also the point-of-common-coupling (PCC) with other customers. However, the IEEE-519 is frequently interpreted as the harmonic guidelines for specifying individual pieces of equipment such as motor drives. There are other harmonic standards, such as the IEC-1000, which apply to individual pieces of equipment.

8-4-3-6 Active Filters

To prevent harmonic currents produced by power electronics loads can be prevented from entering the utility system by means of filters. These filters are often passive filters tuned to certain harmonic frequencies, for example, in use in HVDC terminals. Lately, active filters have also been employed where a current is produced by power electronics means and is injected into the utility system such as to nullify the harmonic currents produced by the nonlinear load. Therefore, only a sinusoidal current is drawn from the utility source by the combination of the nonlinear load and the active filter.

8-5   LOAD MANAGEMENT [6, 7]

This is a topic that is likely to become extremely important in coming years as the utilities are stretched to meet the load demand. The load management can take many forms. Utilities can implement time-of-day rates, thus giving customers incentives to shift their loads to off-peak hours. They can implement Demand-Side Management (DMS) where certain loads, such as air conditioners, can be interrupted remotely during peak-load hours and in return, customers who sign up for it, get rebates on their electricity bills. Large customers can often negotiate to pay a reduced rate for the energy (kWh) used, in addition to a Demand Charge based on the peak power (kW) they draw in a given month. Load shedding based on voltage and frequency can be an important strategy for maintaining proper system operation and preventing voltage collapse and blackouts.

8-6   PRICE OF ELECTRICITY [3]

It is informative to know the average retail price of electricity to ultimate customers by the end-use sector and it has changed recently, as shown in Fig. 8-19.

	Residential	Commercial	Industrial	Total
■ 2006	9.55	8.82	5.71	8.28
□ 2005	8.49	7.98	5.07	7.42

Cents/kWh

Fig. 8-19 Average retail price of electricity to ultimate customers [3].

REFERENCES

1. IEEE Std 141-1986.
2. N. Mohan and J.W. Ramsey, Comparative Study of Adjustable-Speed Drives for Heat Pumps, EPRI Report, 1986.
3. U.S. Department of Energy (www.eia.doe.gov).
4. N. Mohan, First Course on Power Electronics, published by MNPERE, 2005 (www.MNPERE.com).
5. United States Department of Agriculture, Rural Utilities Service, Design Guide for Rural Substations, RUS BULLETIN 1724E-300.
6. J. Casazza and F. Delea, Understanding Electric Power Systems: An Overview of the Technology and the Marketplace, IEEE Press and Wiley-Interscience, 2003
7. Electric Utility Systems and Practices, 4th Edition by Homer M. Rustebakke (Editor), John Wiley & Sons, August 1983.

PROBLEMS

8-1   Describe voltage distribution inside homes and residential buildings.

8-2   What is the role of Ground Fault Interrupters (GFI) and how do they work?

8-3   What is meant by the Load Factor in describing the daily load curve on utility systems?

8-4   What is a typical make up of utility loads and what are their real and reactive power sensitivities to voltages?

8-5 What is the characteristic of power electronics based load; explain.

8-6 A load in steady state is characterized by $P = 1\,pu$ and $Q = 0.5\,pu$ at a voltage $V = 1\,pu$. Represent it as a constant-impedance load.

8-7 What are the main power quality considerations?

8-8 Describe in words the nature of the CBEMA curve.

8-9 What are interruptible power supplies?

8-10 What is meant by the dual feeder arrangement?

8-11 What are Dynamic Voltage Restorers (DVRs) and how do they work?

8-12 What means are used in sub-stations to regulate voltages?

8-13 What are STATCOMs and how do they work?

8-14 How is the Total Harmonic Distortion defined in current waveforms?

8-15 What is meant by Power-Factor-Correction (PFC) circuits?

8-16 How do active filters work?

8-17 In a single-phase power electronics load, $I_s = 10\,A(rms)$, $I_{s1} = 8\,A(rms)$, and $DPF = 0.9$. Calculate $I_{distortion}$, %THD, and PF.

8-18 In a single-phase power electronics load, the following operating condition are given: $V_s = 120V(rms)$, $P = 1kW$, $I_{s1} = 10\,A$, and $THD = 80\%$. Calculate the following: DPF, $I_{distortion}$, I_s, and PF.

8-19 What are active filters and how do they work?

8-20 Define the following terms and their significance: load management, demand-side management, load shedding, demand charges, time-of-day rates, load forecasting, and annual load-duration curve.

Problems using PSCAD/EMTDC:

8-21 Calculate the displacement power factor, power factor and the total harmonic distortion associated with the power-electronics interface, as described on the accompanying CD.

CHAPTER 9

SYNCHRONOUS GENERATORS

9-1 INTRODUCTION

In most power plants, hydro, steam or gas turbines provide mechanical input to synchronous generators that convert mechanical input to three-phase electrical power output. Synchronous generators, by means of their voltage excitation system called the voltage regulator, are also the primary means of supporting and regulating the system voltage to its nominal value. Thousands of such generators operate in synchronism in the interconnected system in North America. In this chapter, we will briefly look at the basic structure of synchronous generators and the fundamental principles of the electromagnetic interactions that govern their operation. These synchronous generators can be classified into two broad categories:

- Turbo Alternators which are used with steam turbines, as shown in Fig. 9-1a, or with gas turbines that rotate at high speeds such as at 1800 rev per minute for 60 Hz or 1500 rev per minute for 50 Hz, and

- Hydro Generators used in hydro power plants, as shown in Fig. 9-1b, where the turbines rotate at very slow speed (few hundred rpm) and hence these generators are very large with a large number of poles to produce the output at the line frequency of 60 or 50 Hz.

We will focus on the high speed turbo-alternators of Fig. 9-1a, although the basic principles involved also apply to the hydro generators. Such generators can be several hundred MVA in ratings at voltages around 20 kV.

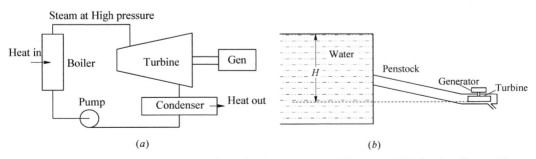

Fig. 9-1 Synchronous generators driven by (a) steam turbines, and (b) hydraulic turbines.

9-2 STRUCTURE

Electrical generators are designed to be long and cylindrical as shown in Fig. 9-2a. To discuss their characteristics, we will describe them by their cross-section by hypothetically slicing them by a plane perpendicular to the shaft axis in Fig. 9-2b by a plane. Looking from one side, Fig. 9-2b shows the stationary part, called the stator, made up of magnetic material such as silicon steel and firmly affixed to the foundation. The rotor on a set of bearings is free to rotate, and the stator and the rotor are separated by a very small air gap.

Fig. 9-2 Machine cross-section.

Winding placed on the stator and the rotor produce magnetic flux; Fig. 9-3 shows the representation of flux lines in various types of generators. Figs. 9-3a and b show a round rotor (non-salient) generator, where the generator is a 2-pole generator in Fig. 9-3a and a 4-pole generator in Fig. 9-3b. The cross-section in Fig. 9-3c illustrates a 4-pole salient pole generator where there are distinct poles, called salient poles, on the rotor. Hydro generators may consist of dozens of such pole-pairs in a salient construction where the magnetic reluctance to flux lines is much smaller in the radial path through the rotor-pole axis as compared to a path that is in between the two adjacent poles.

Fig. 9-3 Machine structure.

In multi-pole generators with more than 1 pole-pair, as shown in Figs. 9-3b and c, it is sufficient to consider only one pole-pair consisting of adjacent north and south poles due to complete symmetry around the periphery in the air gap. Other pole-pairs have identical conditions of magnetic fields and currents.

In order to minimize the ampere-turns required to create flux lines shown crossing the air gap in Fig. 9-3, both the rotor and the stator are made up of high permeability ferromagnetic materials and the length of the air gap is kept as small as possible, which is shown highly exaggerated for the ease of drawing. As in transformers, to reduce eddy-current losses, the stator consists of silicon-steel laminations, which are insulated from each other by a layer of thin varnish. These laminations are stacked together, perpendicular to the shaft axis. Conductors, which run parallel to the shaft axis, are placed in the slots cut into these laminations. Hydrogen, oil or water are often used as coolants.

In the following description, we will assume a 2-pole generator (with $p=2$). This analysis can be generalized to multi-pole generators.

9-2-1 Stator with Three-Phase Windings

In synchronous generators, the stator has three-phase windings, with their respective magnetic axes, as shown in Fig. 9-4a. The windings for each phase ideally should produce a sinusoidally-distributed flux density in the air gap in the radial direction. Theoretically, this requires a sinusoidally-distributed winding in each phase. In practice, this is approximated in a variety of ways. To visualize this sinusoidal distribution, consider the winding for phase a, shown in Fig. 9-4b, where, in the slots, the number of turns-per-coil for phase-a progressively increases away from the magnetic axis, reaching a maximum at $\theta = 90^0$. Each coil, such as the coil with sides 1 and 1', spans 180 degrees where the current into coil-side 1 returns in 1' through the end-turn at the back of the generator. This coil (1,1') is connected in series to coil-side 2 of the next coil (2,2'), and so on. Graphically, these windings are simply drawn as shown in Fig. 9-4a with the understanding that each is sinusoidally distributed, with its magnetic axis as shown.

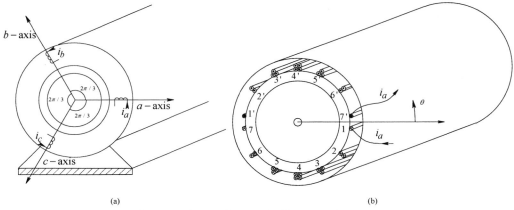

(a)   (b)

Fig. 9-4 Three phase windings on the stator.

In Fig. 9-4b, we focused only on phase-a, which has its magnetic axis along $\theta = 0^0$. There are two more identical sinusoidally-distributed windings for phases b and c, with magnetic axes along $\theta = 120^0$ and $\theta = 240^0$, respectively, as represented in Fig. 9-5a. These three windings are generally connected in a wye-arrangement by connecting terminals a', b', and c' together, as shown in Fig. 9-5b. Flux-density distributions in the air gap due to currents i_b and i_c, identical in shape to that due to i_a, peak along their respective phase-b and phase-c magnetic axes.

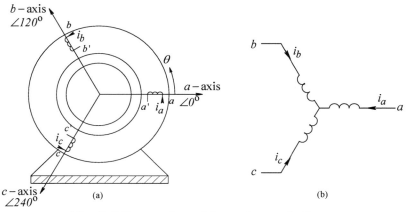

Fig. 9-5 Connection of three phase windings.

9-2-2 Rotor with dc field winding

Rotor of a synchronous generator contains a field winding in its slots. This winding is supplied by a dc voltage, resulting in a dc current I_f. The field-current I_f in Fig. 9-6 produces the rotor field in the air gap. It is desired that this field flux-density be sinusoidally distributed in the air gap in the radial direction, effectively producing north and south poles, as shown in Fig. 9-6. By controlling I_f and hence the rotor-produced field, it is possible to control the induced emf of this generator, and control the reactive power delivered by it. This voltage excitation system is discussed later in this chapter.

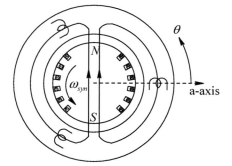

Fig. 9-6 Field winding on the rotor that is supplied by a dc current I_f.

9-3   INDUCED-EMF IN THE STATOR WINDINGS

To discuss induced emfs, we will concentrate on phase-a, realizing that similar emfs are induced in the other two phase windings. The phase-a winding is shown in Fig. 9-7 by a single coil where it is understood that it is sinusoidally distributed as discussed earlier. Current i_a in the direction shown in Fig. 9-7 is so chosen that it results in flux-lines that peak along the phase-a magnetic axis. The induced emf polarity in Fig. 9-7 is chosen to be positive where the current exits, since we are interested in the generator-mode of operation (as opposed to the motoring mode, where following the passive sign-convention would require that the current enter the positive terminal of the induced voltage).

Fig. 9-7 Current direction and voltage polarities; the rotor position shown induces maximum e_a.

In the stator windings, there are two causes of induced emfs, which will be discussed one-at-a-time, and assuming that there is no magnetic saturation, these two induced emfs will be superimposed to yield the resultant induced emf.

9-3-1   Induced EMF due to Rotation of the Field-Flux with the Rotor

Produced by the field winding, the density of the flux-lines in ϕ_f that links the stator is distributed co-sinusoidally in the radial direction, peaking along the field-winding axis, as shown in Fig. 9-8a.

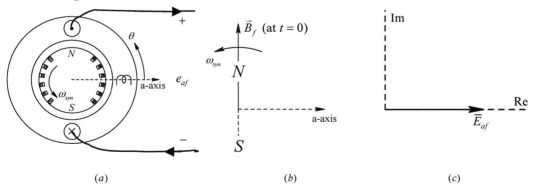

(a)   (b)   (c)

Fig. 9-8 Induced emf e_{af} due to rotating rotor field with the rotor.

Corresponding to the field-winding axis, which is shown to be vertical in Fig. 9-8a, this field-flux density distribution at any instant can be represented by a space vector $\vec{B}_f$ as shown in Fig. 9-8b. The length of the space vector represents the value of the flux-density peak and its angle, measured with respect to phase-a axis, represents its orientation. This space vector is distinguished from phasors by an "arrow" on top. As the rotor rotates, so does the $\vec{B}_f$ space vector.

Due to the rotor field-flux lines rotating with the rotor and cutting the stationary windings in the stator, voltages are induced in the stator phase-windings in accordance with the Faraday's law. At an instant when the rotor and the $\vec{B}_f$ orientation are as shown in Figs. 9-8a and b respectively, and rotating, the voltage induced at this instant will be maximum in phase-a since highest density of field-flux lines are cutting the highest density of phase-a conductors. If the rotor is rotating counterclockwise, then by Lenz's law, we can determine the polarity of the induced voltage in phase-a at $t = 0$ to be positive, as indicated in Fig. 9-8a. As the rotor rotates with time, the induced emf in phase-a will vary co-sinusoidally with time which is represented by a phasor, as shown in Fig. 9-8c.

Arbitrarily, considering the orientation in Figs. 9-8a and b to be at $t = 0$, the phasor $\overline{E}_{af}$ representing the induced voltage in phase-a due to field-flux, will be along the real axis as shown in Fig. 9-8c. That is, it is maximum at time $t = 0$. Both, the space vector $\vec{B}_f$ in the space vector diagram of Fig. 9-8b, and $\overline{E}_{af}$ in the phasor diagram of Fig. 9-8c are complex variables, that is, they both have amplitudes and orientations. Therefore, from Figs. 9-8b and c, these two can be related as follows:

$$\overline{E}_{af} = (-j)k_f \omega \vec{B}_f(0) \tag{9-1}$$

where $\vec{B}_f(0)$ is the space vector at time $t = 0$, k_f is a constant of proportionality depending on the machine construction details, and ω is the synchronous speed (equal to $\omega_{syn} = 2\pi f$ in a 2-pole machine) in rad/s in a counterclockwise direction. The reason for $(-j)$ in Eq. 9-1 is that the induced voltage in the phasor diagram lags behind $\vec{B}_f$ (at $t = 0$) in the space-vector diagram.

9-3-2   Induced EMF due to the Rotating Magnetic Field called the Armature Reaction, Created by the Stator Currents

When the generator phases are connected to the electrical grid, sinusoidal phase currents would flow. These currents are necessary to produce power that is supplied to the grid. Flow of these phase currents produces a rotating magnetic field that, in addition to the rotating field flux, also "cuts" the stator phase windings that are stationary.

In Fig. 9-9a, each phase current results in a flux-density distribution that is stationary in space and peaks along its phase axis, and is proportional to instantaneous value of the phase current; at any instant, it drops off co-sinusoidally away from its axis. Therefore, the flux-density distribution produced by each phase winding can be represented by a space vector, oriented along the respective phase axis. Each of these space vectors is stationary in position but its amplitude pulsates with time as the phase-current value changes with time, and can be expressed as

$$\vec{B}_{i_a} = \left(k_1 i_a\right) e^{j0} \quad \vec{B}_{i_b} = \left(k_1 i_b\right) e^{j2\pi/3} \quad \vec{B}_{i_c} = \left(k_1 i_c\right) e^{j4\pi/3} \tag{9-2}$$

where k_1 is a machine constant that relates the phase-current and the peak flux-density values. The resultant flux-density distribution can be obtained by vectorially summing the three space vectors, using the principle of superposition and assuming a linear magnetic circuit:

$$\vec{B}_{AR} = k_1 \left(i_a e^{j0} + i_b e^{j2\pi/3} + i_c e^{j4\pi/3}\right) \tag{9-3}$$

where the subscript AR refers to the Armature Reaction as it is commonly called.

Fig. 9-9 Armature reaction due to phase currents.

Let the three phase currents be as below, where $t = 0$ corresponds to the rotor position as shown in Fig. 9-8a

$$i_a = I_a \cos(\omega t - \theta) \quad i_b = I_a \cos(\omega t - \theta - 2\pi/3) \quad i_c = I_a \cos(\omega t - \theta - 4\pi/3) \tag{9-4}$$

where I_a is the rms value of each phase current. The sinusoidal current i_a is represented by a phasor $\bar{I}_a$ in Fig. 9-9b; similarly other phase currents can be represented as phasors. By Substituting currents in Eq. 9-4 into Eq. 9-3, it simplifies as below

$$\vec{B}_{AR} = \left(\frac{3}{\sqrt{2}} k_1 I_a\right) e^{j(\omega t - \theta)} \tag{9-5}$$

where $\vec{B}_{AR}$ is the space vector that represents the flux-density distribution due to all three phase currents at any instant t. In steady state, the peak of this space vector remains constant for a given current rms magnitude I_a, and it rotates counterclockwise at the synchronous speed ω (equal to $2\pi f$ in a 2-pole machine) with time, where ω in Eq. 9-5 is the same as in Eq. 9-1. Considering Eqs 9-4 and 9-5, we note that the orientation of $\vec{B}_{AR}$ at time $t = 0$ in the space-vector diagram of Fig. 9-9c is the same as the orientation of $\overline{I}_a$ in the phasor diagram of Fig. 9-9b.

Just like the rotating field-flux density distribution $\vec{B}_f$ induces field voltages $\overline{E}_{af}$ etc in the stationary stator phase windings, similarly $\vec{B}_{AR}$ induces armature-reaction voltages $\overline{E}_{a,AR}$ etc. Using the analogy with Eq. 9-1, $\overline{E}_{a,AR}$ in Fig. 9-9b lags behind $\vec{B}_{AR}$ (at $t = 0$) in Fig. 9-9c by 90^0, and it can be expressed as follows:

$$\overline{E}_{a,AR} = (-j)k_2\omega\vec{B}_{AR}\,(\text{at}\,t = 0) \tag{9-6}$$

where k_2 is another constant of proportionality. Figs. 9-9b and c show that the orientation of $\vec{B}_{AR}$ at $t = 0$ in the space-vector diagram is the same as that of $\overline{I}_a$ in the phasor diagram, and the magnitude of both these variables are related. Making use of this information in Eq. 9-6, from Eqs. 9-5 and 9-6

$$\overline{E}_{a,AR} = -jk_{AR}\omega\overline{I}_a \tag{9-7}$$

where k_{AR} is a constant of proportionality. Eq. 9-7 shows that for a given speed ω, $\overline{E}_{a,AR}$ lags behind $\overline{I}_a$ by 90^0, and the magnitude of these two are proportional to each other, related by ω. This is the property of the voltage drop across an inductive reactance. Therefore, Eq. 9-7 can be written as

$$\overline{E}_{a,AR} = -jX_m\overline{I}_a \tag{9-8}$$

where X_m is the magnetizing reactance of the synchronous generator.

9-3-3   Combined Induced EMFs due to the Field Flux and the Armature Reaction
We saw in the above two sub-sections that the induced emf in phase-a (and similarly in the other phases b and c) is due to two mechanisms. In a magnetic circuit, assuming no saturation, these two emfs can be combined to determine the resultant emf:

$$\overline{E}_a = \overline{E}_{af} + \overline{E}_{a,AR} = \overline{E}_{af} - jX_m\overline{I}_a \tag{9-9}$$

as shown in Fig. 9-10a. The relationship of Eq. 9-9 can be represented by a per-phase equivalent shown in Fig. 9-10b. Including the effect of the leakage flux by a voltage drop across the leakage reactance $X_{\ell s}$, and including the voltage drop across the phase-winding resistance R_s, we can write the terminal voltage expression as

$$\overline{V}_a = \overline{E}_{af} - jX_s\overline{I}_a - R_s\overline{I}_a \tag{9-10}$$

where $X_s\left(= X_{\ell s} + X_m\right)$ is called the synchronous reactance, which is the sum of the leakage reactance $X_{\ell s}$ of each stator winding and X_m is the magnetizing reactance.

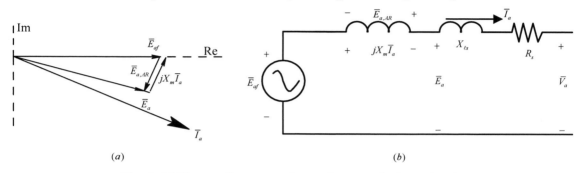

(a)   (b)

Fig. 9-10 Phasor diagram and per-phase equivalent circuit.

9-4   POWER OUTPUT, STABILITY AND THE LOSS OF SYNCHRONISM

Induced emfs in stator windings cause phase currents to flow, which produce an electromechanical torque that opposes the torque supplied by the turbine. In the circuit of Fig. 9-11a, consider a generator connected to an infinite bus (an ideal voltage source) $\overline{V}_\infty$ through a radial line.

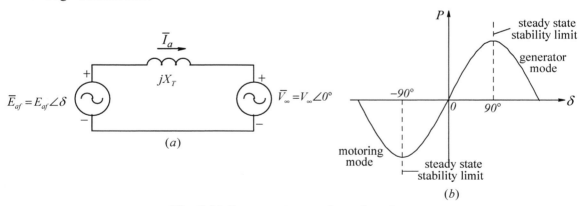

Fig. 9-11 Power output and synchronism.

The reactance X_T is the sum of the generator synchronous reactance and the internal reactance of the utility grid (plus the leakage reactance of transformer(s) if any). Choosing $\overline{V}_\infty$ as the reference phasor (i.e., $\overline{V}_\infty = V_\infty \angle 0$) and neglecting the circuit resistance in comparison to the reactance, the power from the fundamental concepts in Chapter 3 can be written for all three phases as

$$P = 3\frac{E_{af}V_{\infty}}{X_T}\sin\delta \qquad (9\text{-}11)$$

where the rotor angle δ associated with $\overline{E}_{af}(= E_{af}\angle\delta)$ is positive in the generator mode. If the field current is kept constant, then the magnitude E_{af} is also constant in steady state, and thus the power output of the generator is proportional to the sine of the torque angle δ between $\overline{E}_{af}$ and $\overline{V}_{\infty}$. This power-angle relationship is plotted in Fig. 9-11b for both positive and negative values of δ, where for negative values of δ, this machine goes into its motoring mode.

9-4-1 Steady State Stability Limit

Fig. 9-11b shows that the power supplied by the synchronous generator reaches its peak at $\delta = 90^{0}$. This is the steady-state limit, beyond which the synchronism is lost. This can be explained as follows: Initially, assuming no losses, at a value δ_1 below 90 degrees, the turbine is supplying power P_{m1} that equals the electrical output P_{e1}, as shown in Fig. 9-12a. To supply more power, the power input from the turbine is increased (for example, by letting more steam into the turbine). This momentarily speeds up the rotor, causing the torque angle δ associated with the rotor-induced voltage $\overline{E}_{af}$ to increase. Finally, a new steady state is reached at $P_{e2}(= P_{m2})$ a higher value of the torque angle δ_2 as shown in Fig. 9-12a.

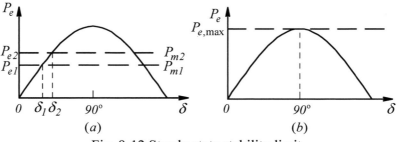

Fig. 9-12 Steady state stability limit.

However, at and beyond $\delta = 90^{0}$, if the power input from the turbine is increased as shown in Fig. 9-12b, then increasing δ causes the electrical output power to decline, which results in a further increase in δ (because more mechanical power is coming in, while less electrical power is going out). This increasing δ causes an intolerable increase in generator currents and the protection relays cause the circuit breakers to trip to isolate the generator from the grid, thus saving the generator from being damaged.

The above sequence of events is called the "loss of synchronism," and the stability is lost. In practice, the transient stability, in which there may be a sudden change in the electrical power output, forces the maximum value of the steady-state torque angle δ to be much less than 90 degrees, typically in a range of 40 to 45 degrees.

9-5   FIELD EXCITATION CONTROL TO ADJUST REACTIVE POWER

Reactive power associated with synchronous generators can be controlled in magnitude as well as in sign (leading or lagging). To discuss this, let us assume, as a base case, that a synchronous generator is supplying a constant power, and the field current I_f is adjusted such that this power is supplied at a unity power factor, as shown in the phasor diagram of Fig. 9-13a.

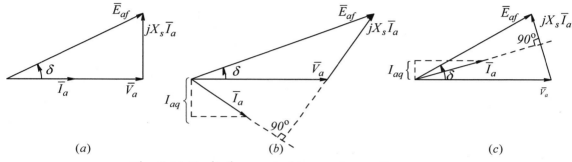

Fig. 9-13 Excitation control to supply reactive power.

9-5-1   Over-Excitation

Now, an increase in the field current, called over-excitation, will result in a larger magnitude of $\overline{E}_{af}$, since assuming no magnetic saturation, E_f depends linearly on the field-current I_f. However, $E_{af}\sin\delta$ must remain constant from Eq. 9-11, since the power output is constant. Similarly, the projection of the current phasor $\overline{I}_a$ on the voltage phasor $\overline{V}_a$ must remain as in Fig. 9-13a. This results in the phasor diagram of Fig. 9-13b, where the current $\overline{I}_a$ is lagging behind $\overline{V}_a$. Considering the utility grid to be a load, the grid absorbs reactive power as an inductor does. Therefore, a synchronous generator operating in an over-excited mode supplies reactive power, like a capacitor does. The three-phase reactive power Q can be computed from the reactive component of the current I_{aq} as

$$Q = 3V_a I_{aq} \tag{9-12}$$

9-5-2   Under-Excitation

In contrast to the over-excitation, decreasing I_f results in a smaller magnitude E_{af}, and the corresponding phasor diagram, assuming that the power output remains constant as before, can be represented as in Fig. 9-13c. Now the current $\overline{I}_a$ leads the voltage $\overline{V}_a$, and the load (the utility grid) supplies reactive power, as a capacitor does. Thus, a synchronous generator in the under-excited mode absorbs reactive power like an inductor does. The three-phase reactive power Q can be computed from the reactive component of the current I_{aq}, similar to Eq. 9-12.

9-5-3 Synchronous Condensers

Sometimes in power systems, grid-connected synchronous machines are operated in a motoring mode to supply reactive power, as shown in Fig. 9-14. A similar control over the reactive power in these synchronous condensers, as they are often called, can be exercised by controlling the field excitation as explained above. There is no need for a turbine and the small amount of power loss accrued in operating the synchronous machine as a motor are supplied by the grid.

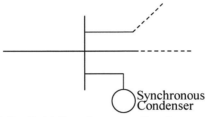

Fig. 9-14 Synchronous Condenser.

9-6 FIELD EXCITERS FOR AUTOMATIC VOLTAGE REGULATION (AVR)

Field excitation of synchronous generators can be controlled to regulate the voltage at their terminals or at some other bus in the system for that matter, usually to its nominal value. This is possible since the voltage regulation and the supply of reactive power are related, and it is the desire to regulate the voltage at a designated bus dictates what reactive power the generator should supply. Most generators are equipped with an automatic voltage regulator that senses the bus voltage to be regulated and compares it with its desired value. The error between the two, as shown in Fig. 9-15 controls the voltage applied to field-excitation winding to adjust the field current I_f appropriately.

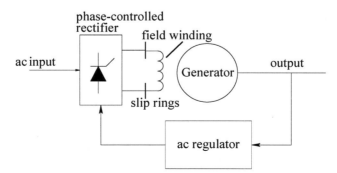

Fig. 9-15 Field exciter for automatic voltage regulation (AVR).

These field-excitation systems can take several forms based on where the input power is derived from, and the desire to avoid slip-ring and brushes because the field winding to be supplied is rotating with the rotor.

9-7 SYNCHRONOUS, TRANSIENT AND SUB-TRANSIENT REACTANCES

The analysis above assumes a steady state operation. However, for example, during and after a short-circuit fault, the rotor oscillations ensue, prior to the rotor coming to another steady state. During these rotor oscillations, the synchronous generator is under a transient condition.

To study transient phenomena, the steady state per-phase equivalent circuit shown in Fig. 9-10b needs to be modified. Modeling of synchronous machines can be carried out with increasing levels of complexities, resulting in increasing accuracy. However, in most fault analysis, a "ballpark" value of fault current is needed. Similarly in stability studies, most often all that is desired is to determine if the system would remain stable subsequent to a fault and its clearing. Therefore in these studies, most often a model termed Constant-Flux Model usually suffices, at least for educational purposes. A discussion of this model and the resulting equivalent circuit for use in such studies is described below.

9-7-1 Constant-Flux Model

The field winding of a synchronous generator is supplied by a dc voltage source V_f such that in steady state, it results in the desired field current $I_f (= V_f / R_f)$ whose dc value is determined by the field resistance R_f. Assuming this dc-excitation voltage to be constant during transients because it cannot change very rapidly, the field winding is essentially a short-circuited coil with a very small resistance, relative to its self-inductance L_{ff}, and thus has a large time-constant. According to the Theorem of Constant Flux-Linkage, the flux linkage of a short-circuited coil remains constant that cannot change very quickly. Therefore, under brief transient conditions as the stator currents suddenly change causing the armature-reaction flux to change, the field current also suddenly changes to an appropriate value to keep the flux-linkage of the field winding constant.

In steady state, the armature-reaction flux can penetrate the rotor as shown in Fig. 9-16. Therefore, the steady state phasor diagram of Fig. 9-10a and the per-phase equivalent circuit of Fig. 9-10b were obtained using the principle of superposition. Also, since the armature-reaction flux in steady state can penetrate the rotor, the resulting synchronous reactance X_s is large, generally nearly 1 per unit on the generator base. The field flux-linkage in steady state is the sum of the field flux produced by I_f and the armature-reaction flux going through it. At the armature terminal, the conditions are $\overline{E}_a$ and $\overline{I}_a$, as shown in Fig. 9-10a.

Fig. 9-16 Armature reaction flux in steady state.

However, immediately following an electrical disturbance such as a short-circuit fault on the electrical network causing the stator currents to suddenly change, the machine is considered in a sub-transient condition. In this sub-transient condition, the armature reaction flux cannot enter the field winding due to the Constant Flux-Linkage theorem mentioned earlier and much of the armature reaction flux is forced to flow through the air gap, thus resulting in a path of higher magnetic reluctance and hence a smaller reactance. Therefore, the sub-transient reactance $X_s^{''} < X_s$, where the ratio between the two can be as large as 4 to 7, where X_s is around 1 per-unit on the machine base. The armature current and the field current, subsequent to a sudden three-phase short circuit at the terminals, are shown in Fig. 9-17a and Fig. 9-17b respectively. The sub-transient interval corresponds to a few cycles subsequent to the fault, where the armature current is very large and the field current suddenly jumps to maintain the field-flux linkage constant.

Fig. 9-17 Armature (a) and field current (b), after a sudden short circuit [source: 4].

A few cycles after the electrical disturbance causing the stator currents to change but prior to steady state, the machine is considered in a transient state. In this condition, some flux lines manage to penetrate the field winding and the transient reactance $X_s^{'}$ has a value such that $X_s^{''} < X_s^{'} < X_s$, where $X_s^{'}$ is generally twice of $X_s^{''}$.

To make use of the sub-transient and the transient conditions in fault-current calculations and transient stability studies, we will modify the steady state per-phase equivalent circuit in Fig. 9-10b for later chapters. We should note that prior to the fault, the machine is in steady state and the terminal conditions $\overline{E}_a$ and $\overline{I}_a$ are as shown in Fig. 9-10a, resulting in the per-phase equivalent circuit of Fig. 9-10b. Therefore, our model should be such that it results in the appropriate voltage and current at the machine terminal in the steady state, and yet it is valid in the sub-transient and the transient conditions. This can be accomplished in Fig. 9-10 by modifying the phasor diagram and the per-phase equivalent circuit as shown in Fig. 9-18, where

$$\overline{E}_{af} = \overline{E}_a + jX_s\overline{I}_a \qquad \overline{E}'_{af} = \overline{E}_a + jX'_s\overline{I}_a \qquad \overline{E}''_{af} = \overline{E}_a + jX''_s\overline{I}_a \qquad (9\text{-}13)$$

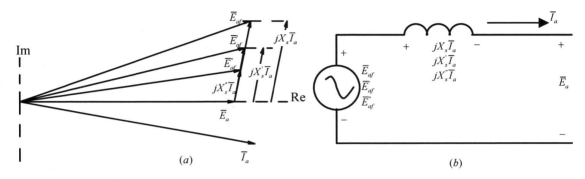

Fig. 9-18 Synchronous generator modeling for transient and sub-transient conditions.

Therefore, for a given terminal voltage $\overline{E}_a$ and the current $\overline{I}_a$, ignoring the machine resistance, the field-induced voltage can be calculated from Eq. 9-13 based on the type of condition being studied.

REFERENCES

1. N. Mohan, Electric Drives: An Integrative Approach, 2003, MNPERE (www.mnpere.com).
2. P. Anderson, Analysis of Faulted Power Systems, June 1995, Wiley-IEEE Press.
3. Prabha Kundur, *Power System Stability and Control*, McGraw-Hill, 1994.
4. PSCAD/EMTDC.

PROBLEMS

9-1   Assume that the rotor position in Fig. 9-8a corresponds to time $t = 0$. Plot e_{af}, e_{bf}, and e_{cf} as functions of $\omega_{syn}t$.

9-2   Assume that the rotor position in Fig. 9-8a corresponds to time $t = 0$. Draw the rotor flux-density space vector $\vec{B}_f$ at $\omega_{syn}t$ equal to 0, $\pi/6$, $\pi/3$, and $\pi/2$ radians.

9-3   If the stator phase current angle θ in Eq. 9-4 is zero, then plot the armature-reaction flux-density space vector $\vec{B}_{AR}$ at $\omega_{syn}t$ equal to 0, $\pi/6$, $\pi/3$, and $\pi/2$ radians.

9-4   In the problem of 9-3, plot i_a and $e_{a,AR}$ as functions of $\omega_{syn}t$.

9-5   In the per-phase equivalent circuit of Fig. 9-10b, assume $R_s = 0$ and $X_s = 1.2\,pu$. The terminal voltage $\overline{V}_a = 1\angle 0\,pu$ and $\overline{I}_a = 1\angle -\pi/6\,pu$. Calculate $\overline{E}_{af}$ and draw a phasor diagram similar to Fig. 9-10a.

9-6   In Problem 9-5, with E_{af} kept constant at the magnitude calculated and $V_a = 1\,pu$, calculate the maximum power in per unit that this machine can supply.

9-7   In a synchronous generator, assume $R_s = 0$ and $X_s = 1.2\,pu$. The terminal voltage $\overline{V}_a = 1\angle 0\,pu$. It is supplying 1 pu power. Calculate all the relevant quantities to draw the phasor diagrams in Fig. 9-13 if the synchronous generator field-excitation is controlled such that the reactive power Q is as follows: (a) $Q = 0$, (b) supplying $Q = 0.5\,pu$, and (c) absorbing $Q = 0.5\,pu$.

9-8   Repeat Problem 9-7, assuming that the synchronous machine is a synchronous condenser where the real power $P = 0$.

9-9   In the per-phase equivalent circuit of Fig. 9-18b, assume $R_s = 0$, $X_s = 1.2\,pu$, $X_s' = 0.33\,pu$ and $X_s'' = 0.23\,pu$. The terminal voltage $\overline{V}_a = 1\angle 0\,pu$ and the current $\overline{I}_a = 1\angle -\pi/6\,pu$. Draw the phasor diagram similar to Fig. 9-18a for the steady state, transient and the sub-transient operation.

PSCAD/EMTDC-based Problem:

9-10   Simulate a sudden short circuit at the terminals of a synchronous generator, as described on the accompanying CD.

CHAPTER 10

VOLTAGE REGULATION AND STABILITY IN POWER SYSTEMS

10-1 INTRODUCTION

As transmission lines are loaded more towards their capacities, the voltage stability has become a serious consideration. There have been several blackouts caused by voltage collapse. In this chapter, we will examine the causes of voltage stability, the role of reactive power in maintaining voltage stability and means to supply reactive power.

10-2 RADIAL SYSTEM AS AN EXAMPLE

To understand voltage dependence phenomenon, consider a simple radial system as shown in Fig. 10-1a, where an ideal source is supplying a load through a transmission line of series reactance X_L and shunt susceptances as shown. For simplification, the transmission line resistance is ignored. To analyze such a system, the susceptances on both sides are combined as parts of the sending-end and the receiving-end systems and represented by the equivalent circuit in Fig. 10-1b. To analyze real and reactive powers in the equivalent system of Fig. 10-1b, assuming the receiving-end voltage to be the reference, that is, $\overline{V}_R = V_R\angle 0$:

$$\overline{I} = \frac{\overline{V}_s - \overline{V}_R}{jX_L} \tag{10-1}$$

(a)   (b)

Fig. 10-1 A radial system.

At the receiving end, the complex power can be written as

$$S_R = P_R + jQ_R = V_R \overline{I}^* \tag{10-2}$$

Using the complex conjugate from Eq. 10-1 into 10-2 and expressing $\overline{V}_S$ in its polar form as $\overline{V}_S = V_S \angle \delta$,

$$P_R + jQ_R = V_R \left(\frac{V_S \angle (-\delta) - V_R}{-jX_L} \right) = \frac{V_S V_R \sin \delta}{X_L} + j \left(\frac{V_S V_R \cos \delta - V_R^2}{X_L} \right) \tag{10-3}$$

Equating the real parts on both sides of the equation,

$$P_R = \frac{V_S V_R}{X_L} \sin \delta \tag{10-4}$$

where, assuming no transmission-line losses, P_R is the same as the sending-end power P_S. And

$$Q_R = \frac{V_S V_R \cos \delta}{X_L} - \frac{V_R^2}{X_L} \tag{10-5}$$

Dividing both sides of Eq. 10-5 by $\dfrac{V_R^2}{X_L}$ and rearranging terms,

$$\frac{V_R}{V_S} = \cos \delta \left(\frac{1}{1 + \dfrac{Q_R}{V_R^2 / X_L}} \right) \tag{10-6}$$

In power systems, utilities try to keep bus voltage magnitudes close to their nominal values of 1 per unit. Therefore from Eq. 10-4, a higher value of P_R drawn through the transmission line would require a higher value of $\sin \delta$, and therefore a lower $\cos \delta$. Hence, to maintain both voltages close to one per-unit, the reactive power Q_R must be negative, that is, at higher power loading of the transmission line, the receiving-end must supply reactive power to prop up its bus voltage.

The above requirement for the receiving-end to supply reactive power to maintain its voltage can be further explained by the phasor diagram of Fig. 10-2a. By Kirchhoff's voltage law in Fig. 10-2b,

$$\overline{V}_S = \overline{V}_R + jX_L \overline{I} \tag{10-7}$$

Assuming both bus voltage magnitudes at 1 per unit and $\overline{V}_R$ as the reference voltage, the phasor diagram is shown in Fig. 10-2a where $\overline{V}_S$ leads by an angle δ.

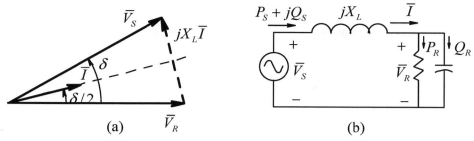

Fig. 10-2 Phasor diagram and the equivalent circuit with $V_S = V_R = 1\text{pu}$.

The angle between the two voltages depends on the power transfer over the line, given by Eq. 10-4. If both bus voltages are of equal magnitude, $\overline{I}$ from Eq. 10-1 is as shown in Fig. 10-2a, exactly at an angle $\delta/2$. This phasor diagram clearly shows $\overline{I}$ in Fig. 10-2a leading $\overline{V}_R$, implying that Q_R is negative. This means that to achieve V_R equal to 1 per unit voltage, similar to that at the sending-end, the receiving-end should "equivalently" appear as shown in Fig. 10-2b, where the equivalent resistance absorbs P_R and the equivalent capacitor supplies the reactive power equal to $\left|Q_R\right|$. Higher the load, greater would be δ and I , resulting in a higher demand for the reactive power.

It is useful to know as well what is happening at the sending-end of the transmission line. From the phasor diagram of Fig. 10-2a, it can be observed that the sending-end reactive power is the same in magnitude as Q_R but opposite in polarity

$$Q_s = -Q_R \tag{10-8}$$

Therefore, the sending-end supplies reactive power, for example the generator at the sending-end operates over-excited and the sending-end side susceptance contributes to it as well to a certain extent.

In the transmission line, the reactive power consumed can be calculated as

$$Q_{Line} = I^2 X_L \tag{10-9}$$

Just like real powers, the reactive power supplied to a system must equal the sum of the reactive powers consumed, and therefore,

$$Q_S = Q_R + \underbrace{I^2 X_L}_{Q_{Line}} \tag{10-10}$$

Using Eq. 10-8 into Eq. 10-10, the reactive power consumed by the line is twice $\left|Q_R\right|$:

$$I^2 X_L = Q_{Line} = 2\left|Q_R\right| \tag{10-11}$$

In Fig. 10-1, the transmission line is represented by lumped elements and the following discussion above shows what happens at the terminals, with which we are mainly concerned. However, the transmission line has distributed parameters as shown in Fig. 10-3a. Assume that the voltages at the two ends are maintained at 1 per unit. If this transmission line, assumed to be lossless, is surge-impedance loaded to $P_R = SIL$, then the voltage profile along the transmission-line length would be flat, as shown by the solid line in Fig. 10-3b where the reactive power consumed per unit line length is supplied by its distributed shunt capacitance. Under a heavy load condition with $P_R > SIL$, the voltage profile would sag as shown in Fig. 10-3b, and reactive power must be supplied by both ends. The opposite is true under light loadings with $P_R < SIL$, as shown in Fig. 10-3b, where the reactive power supplied by the transmission-line shunt capacitances must be absorbed at both ends to hold voltages at 1 per unit.

Fig. 10-3 Voltage profile along the transmission line.

10-3   VOLTAGE COLLAPSE

Once again, let us consider a radial system similar to Fig. 10-1b, shown in Fig. 10-4a, supplying a load at the receiving end. To begin with, consider a unity power factor load with $Q_R = 0$.

Fig. 10-4 Voltage collapse in a radial system (example of 345-kV line, 200 km long).

From Eq. 10-5,

$$V_R = V_S \cos \delta \tag{10-12}$$

and substituting it into Eq. 10-4,

$$P_R = \frac{V_S^2}{X_L}\cos\delta\sin\delta \tag{10-13}$$

To determine the maximum power transfer, taking the partial derivative in Eq. 10-13 with respect to angle δ and substituting it to zero results in

$$\frac{\partial P_R}{\partial \delta} = \frac{V_S^2}{X_L}\left(\cos^2\delta - \sin^2\delta\right) = 0 \tag{10-14}$$

from which,

$$\delta = \pi/4 \tag{10-15}$$

Therefore the maximum power transfer occurs at $\delta = \pi/4$, and using this condition into Eq. 10-13

$$P_{R,\max} = \frac{V_s^2}{2X_L} \tag{10-16}$$

and

$$V_R \simeq 0.7V_s \tag{10-17}$$

For normalizing P_R, it is divided by the Surge Impedance Loading, SIL. With $Q_R = 0$, corresponding to a unity power factor load, the voltage-ratio (V_R/V_S) is plotted in Fig. 10-4b as a function of the normalized real power transfer P_R. Similar curves are plotted for loads at lagging and leading power factor of 0.9 for illustration. These "nose" curves show that as the line loading is increased, the receiving end voltage drops and reaches a "critical" point, that depends on the power factor, beyond which further loading (by reducing the load resistance) at the receiving end results in actually lower power, until the voltage at the receiving end collapses. Lagging power factor loading is worse for the voltage stability compared to the unity power factor load.

As shown in Fig. 10-4b, leading power factor loads result in a higher voltage compared to lagging power factor loads. However, even at leading power factor where one would think that the receiving-end voltage is higher than normal and the voltage stability should be of no concern, slight increase in power can lead to the critical point and a possible voltage collapse.

10-4 PREVENTION OF VOLTAGE INSTABILITY

As the analysis above shows, the voltage instability is the result of highly loaded systems. Although this has been illustrated using a simple radial system, the same manner of analysis can be applied to a highly integrated system. Voltage instability is associated with the lack of reactive power, and therefore it is necessary to have a reactive power reserve. Several such means are discussed below.

10-4-1 Synchronous generators

Synchronous generators can supply inductive and capacitive vars by their excitation control, and are the primary source of reactive power. As discussed earlier, heavier loading requires more reactive power support at the receiving end as well as the sending end. However, synchronous generators are limited on how much vars they can supply, as shown in Fig. 10-5 by a family of curves corresponding to various pressures of hydrogen used for cooling, at the rated voltage. A positive value of Q signifies reactive power supplied by the generator in the over-excited mode. There are three distinct regions of reactive power capabilities as shown, as a function of the real power P that depends on the mechanical input.

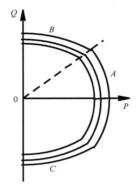

Fig. 10-5 Reactive power supply capability of synchronous generators.

In region A, the reactive power capability is limited by the heating due to the armature (stator) current and therefore, the magnitude of the apparent power $|S| (= \sqrt{P^2 + Q^2})$ must not exceed its rated value in steady state. In region B, the generator is operating over-excited and is limited by the field-current heating. In region C, the generator is operating under-excited and the end rings are not saturated and their heating can be problem that limits the armature current. Generally, the intersection of regions A and B indicates the rating of the synchronous generator in MVA and power factor at the rated voltage. Curves similar to that in Fig. 10-5 can be plotted for voltages other than 1 per unit.

Synchronous generators have to be located in the area where ever the voltage support is needed. From Fig. 10-4b it can be seen that obtaining a near 1 per unit receiving end voltage at a lagging power factor load would require the sending-end voltage to be unacceptably high.

In synchronous generators, the conventional excitation control may be too slow to react therefore it is preferable to use a thyristor-based fast acting excitation control in conjunction with the Power System Stabilizer (PSS) for damping rotor oscillations. Another possible solution for fast response is to operate the generator over-excited so normally it is producing more vars than needed, where extra vars are consumed by shunt reactors. Under voltage contingencies, shunt reactors can be quickly disconnected, making those extra vars available to the system.

10-4-2 Static Reactive Power Compensators

Need for reactive power in an area can be met by a shunt device as shown in Fig. 10-6a, where the system looking into, including the load at that bus where the device is to be connected, can be represented by its Thevenin equivalent, for explanation purposes. The Thevenin impedance is mostly reactive and it is assumed to be purely so to simplify explanation. From Fig. 10-6a,

$$\overline{V}_{bus} = \overline{V}_{Th} - jX_{Th}\overline{I} \qquad\qquad (10\text{-}18)$$

As the phasor diagrams in Fig. 10-6b show, if $\overline{I}$ is leading $\overline{V}_{bus}$, then V_{bus} becomes higher than V_{Th} due to the voltage drop across the Thevenin reactance; the opposite effect occurs if $\overline{I}$ is lagging $\overline{V}_{bus}$. It is important to recognize from Eq. 10-18 that the shunt device affects the bus voltage magnitude by means of the drop across X_{Th}: smaller the Thevenin reactance, smaller would be the affect on the bus voltage. For example, if X_{Th} is nearly zero, no amount of current would affect the bus voltage.

Fig. 10-6 Effect of leading and lagging currents due to the shunt compensating device.

The shunt compensating device may consist of capacitor banks which are switched in or out by mechanical means or by back-to-back connected thyristors shown in Fig. 10-7a. A small inductance shown in series is mainly to minimize transient current at turn-on. Absence of gate pulses to the thyristors keeps them from conducting, whereas applying continuous gate pulses to both thyristors ensures that the current through the pair can flow in either direction, as if it were a mechanical switch that is switched-in. Often, thyristor-switched capacitor banks are referred as Static Var Compensators (SVC). The $V-I$ characteristic of an SVC is a straight line as shown in Fig. 10-7b, where the current magnitude I_C varies linearly with bus voltage as $(\omega C)V_{bus}$.

Fig. 10-7 V-I characteristic of SVC.

The shunt compensating device may consist of a shunt reactor as shown in Fig. 10-8a. Here, the thyristor pair may be designed to act as a switch, as discussed earlier with shunt capacitor banks, switching the reactor in or disconnecting it. However, it is possible to control each thyristor firing angle, as shown by Fig. 10-8b, and hence control the current through the reactor, thus controlling its effective reactance and the vars provided by it. In this mode, this compensating device is called thyristor controlled reactor (TCR). The $V - I$ characteristic of a TCR is as shown in Fig. 10-8c, where at high voltages the reactor is fully "in" with a delay angle of 90^0 or less. Below a certain threshold voltage, the controller begins to increase the delay angle, also purposely giving a slope to this characteristic as shown. When the delay angle reaches 180^0, the reactor is completely switched out.

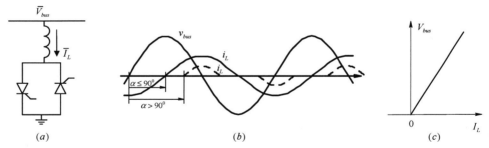

Fig. 10-8 Thyristor-Controlled Reactor (TCR).

10-4-2-1   Parallel Combination of SVC and TCR

It is possible to have both SVC and TCR in parallel as shown in Fig. 10-9a. Now, the characteristic is the parallel combination of the characteristics in Fig. 10-7b and 10-8c, as shown in Fig. 10-9b. Intentionally, a finite gain is introduced in the control of the thyristor conduction angles associated with the TCR to give the slope of V-I characteristic as shown in Fig. 10-9b. In Fig. 10-9c, this combined characteristic is superimposed on the system characteristic looking into the system from that bus. At nominal loading represented by characteristic A, the bus voltage is nominal at 1 per unit, without having to drawn any current $\overline{I}$. At heavier system loading, the system characteristic represented by B will result in the bus voltage to sag to V_1', but by drawing a capacitive current, it can be held at V_1. At light system loading represented by characteristic C, the bus voltage will swell to V_2' but can be maintained at V_2 by drawing an inductive current from the parallel combination of SVC and TCR.

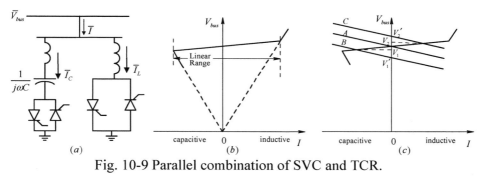

Fig. 10-9 Parallel combination of SVC and TCR.

10-4-2-2   STATCOMs

In addition to SVCs and TCRs, it is possible to employ STATCOMs, which are based on voltage-link converters, as shown in Fig. 10-10a. As discussed in the chapter dealing with HVDC transmission lines, it is possible to synthesize three-phase sinusoidal voltages from a dc source, for example from the dc voltage across the capacitor. A small inductor is at the ac output of the STATCOM, which is not shown in Fig. 10-10a, is mainly for filtering purposes and has a very little drop across it a fundamental frequency.

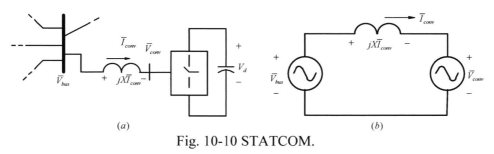

Fig. 10-10 STATCOM.

On a per-phase basis, the circuit diagram is as shown in Fig. 10-10b, where $\overline{V}_{conv}$ is the line-frequency voltage synthesized by the converter from the dc bus voltage V_d, which itself is created and maintained by transferring a small amount of real power from the ac system to the converter to overcome losses in it. Otherwise, there is no real transfer of power through the converter, only controlled reactive power as in an inductor or as in a capacitor. Assuming the direction of current through the filter inductor to be as shown in Fig. 10-10b, assuming $\overline{V}_{conv}$ to be the reference phasor,

$$\overline{V}_{conv} = \overline{V}_{bus} - jX\overline{I}_{conv} \qquad (10\text{-}19)$$

10-9

If $\overline{I}_{conv}$ is leading $\overline{V}_{conv}$ as it does through a capacitor, then by Eq. 10-19, both voltages are in phase but V_{conv} is greater than V_{bus} by XI_{conv}, similar to the phasor diagram of Fig. 10-6b. On the other hand, if $\overline{I}_{conv}$ is lagging $\overline{V}_{conv}$ as it does through an inductor, then by Eq. 10-19, both voltages are again in phase but V_{conv} is less than V_{bus} by XI_{conv}. Thus synthesizing $\overline{V}_{conv}$ in phase with $\overline{V}_{bus}$ but controlling its magnitude, we can control reactive power supplied by the converter.

A STATCOM can draw controllable capacitive or inductive currents independent of the bus voltage. Therefore, it can be considered a controllable reactive current source on the bus to which it is connected and its *V-I* characteristic is shown in Fig. 10-11, where the vertical lines represent the current rating of the device. Also, if the power transfer between two systems or areas takes place using a voltage-link HVDC line, then rather that consuming reactive vars as an ac line does under heavy loading, the converters on both sides of a voltage-link HVDC line can supply, or absorb if needed, reactive power.

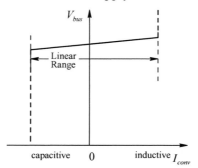

Fig. 10-11 STATCOM VI characteristic.

10-4-3 Thyristor-Controlled Series Capacitor (TCSC)

Other means for voltage support are series capacitors which reduce the effective value of X_L in the power equation of Eq. 10-4. In addition to series capacitors, it is possible to insert a Thyristor-Controlled Series Capacitor (TCSC) as shown in Fig. 10-12a.

(*a*)   (*b*)   (*c*)

Fig. 10-12 Thyristor-Controlled Series Capacitors (TCSC) [source: Siemens Corp.].

In TCSCs, the effective inductance of the inductor, in parallel with the capacitor, can be controlled by the conduction angles of the thyristors, and thus controlling the effective reactance of the TCSC to appear more capacitive or inductive, as shown in Fig. 10-12b. One such unit used in the western part of the U.S. is shown in Fig. 10-12c.

REFERENCES

1. P. Kundur, *Power System Stability and Control*, McGraw-Hill, 1994.
2. C.W. Taylor, Power System Voltage Stability, McGraw-Hill, 1994 (for reprints, Email: cwtaylor@ieee.org).
3. *PowerWorld* Computer Program, (http://www.powerworld.com).
4. N. Hingorani, L. Gyugyi, *Understanding FACTS : Concepts and Technology of Flexible AC Transmission Systems*, Wiley-IEEE Press, 1999.

PROBLEMS

10-1   In the power flow example of Chapter 5 in the 3-Bus power system, what reactive power compensation needs to be provided at Bus-3 to bring its voltage to 1 pu.

10-2   In the power flow example of Chapter 5 in the 3-Bus power system, what will be the voltage at Bus-3 if the power demand at Bus-3 is reduced by 50%.

10-3   Based on the voltage sensitivity to reactive power change at Bus-3, as calculated in Chapter 5 for the example power system, what is reactive power needed at Bus-3 to bring its voltage to 1 pu. Compare this result with that of Problem 10-1.

10-4   Calculate the reactive power consumed by the three transmission lines in the example power system of Chapter 5.

10-5   If the reactive power compensation in Problem 10-1 is provided by shunt capacitors, calculate their value.

10-6   If the reactive power compensation in Problem 10-1 is provided by a STATCOM, calculate equivalent $\bar{V}_{conv}$ in pu; assume X as shown in Fig. 10-10 to be 0.01 pu.

10-7   In the power flow example of Chapter 5, what will be the effect on the Bus-3 voltage if lines 1-3 and 2-3 are 50% compensated by series capacitors.

10-8   In the power flow example of Chapter 5, what must be the voltage at Bus-1 to bring the Bus-3 voltage to 1 pu.

10-9   Why is the performance of STATCOMs superior to that of shunt capacitors?

PSCAD/EMTDC-based Problems:

10-10   Model a TCR, as described on the accompanying CD.

10-11   Model a TCSC, as described on the accompanying CD.

PowerWorld-based Problems:

10-12   Confirm results of Problem 10-1.

10-13   Confirm results of Problem 10-2.

10-14   Confirm results of Problem 10-4.

10-15 Confirm results of Problem 10-5.

10-16 Confirm results of Problem 10-6.

10-17 Confirm results of Problem 10-7.

10-18 Confirm results of Problem 10-8.

CHAPTER 11

TRANSIENT AND DYNAMIC STABILITY OF POWER SYSTEMS

11-1 INTRODUCTION

In an interconnected power system such as that in North America, thousands of generators operate normally in synchronism with each other. They share load based on economic dispatch and optimum power flow as discussed in the next chapter. But major disturbances, even momentarily, such a fault on the system, loss of generation or sudden loss of load can threaten this synchronous operation. Therefore, the ability of the power system to maintain synchronism when subjected to any of the major disturbances previous mentioned is called the transient stability. Such an interconnected system should also have enough damping to retain dynamic stability, as explained later in this chapter.

11-2   PRINCIPLE OF TRANSIENT STABILITY

The principle of transient stability can be illustrated by a simple system with one generator connected through a transformer to an infinite bus, considered to be an ideal voltage source with a voltage of $\overline{V}_B(= V_B\angle 0)$, as shown in Fig 11-1a by two parallel lines.

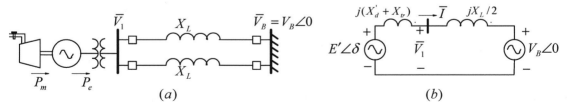

Fig. 11-1 Simple one-generator system connected to an infinite bus.

Power being delivered by the mechanical source is P_m, which equals the generator electrical output P_e in steady state, assuming all the generator losses to be zero. As discussed in Chapter 9, under transient conditions, using the Constant Flux model, a synchronous generator can be represented by a voltage source of constant amplitude at

11-1

the back of the transient reactance X_d' of the generator, as shown in Fig. 11-1b, where $\overline{E}'(= E'\angle\delta)$ is such that in steady state, prior to the fault, the equivalent circuit of Fig. 11-1b results in $P_e = P_m$. In Fig. 11-1b, X_{tr} is the leakage reactance of the transformer. Ignoring all the losses in the system of Fig. 11-1b, as derived in Chapter 2, the electrical power in MW delivered by the generator to the infinite bus is:

$$P_e = \frac{E'V_B}{X_{T1}}\sin\delta \qquad (11\text{-}1)$$

where E' and V_B are the magnitudes of the two voltages in kV that are an angle δ (in electrical radians) apart and are connected through the total reactance X_{T1} (in Ω), which is the sum of the generator transient reactance X_d', the transformer leakage reactance X_{tr}, and the reactance of the two transmission lines in parallel, $X_L/2$. If this study lasts may be a second or less, it is reasonable to assume as a first-order approximation that the exciter system of the generator cannot respond in such a short time. Therefore the magnitude of the voltage behind the transient reactance can be assumed constant. Similarly, the turbine governor control, be it a steam or a hydro turbine, cannot react within this short time. Hence, the mechanical input P_m from the turbine to the generator can be assumed constant.

In steady state, the generator is rotating at a mechanical speed ω_m (in mechanical radians/s) which equals the synchronous speed. The electrical power output of the generator, P_e, based on Eq. 11-1 is plotted in Fig. 11-2a as a function of the rotor angle δ (in electrical radians) associated with the generator voltage. In steady state prior to the disturbance, $P_e = P_m$ and the initial rotor angle is δ_0, as shown in Fig. 11-2a.

Fig. 11-2 Power-angle characteristics.

If a fault were to occur, for example on one of the transmission lines, as shown in Fig. 11-2b, then during the fault, the capability to transfer electrical power transfer P_e, shown by the dashed-dotted curve in Fig. 11-2a, goes down because the bus-1 voltage goes down. It takes a finite clearing time to isolate the faulted line by the circuit breakers at both ends, and subsequent to the fault-clearing time, the generator and the infinite bus are connected by the remaining transmission line. Using an equation similar to Eq. 11-1, the power-angle curve for the post-fault curve is shown dotted in Fig. 11-2a. It is clear from Fig. 11-2a that if the system is stable following the faulted line taken out of service, the new steady state rotor-angle value will be δ_1. In this section, we will look at the dynamics of how the rotor-angle reaches this new steady state, assuming that the transient stability is maintained.

11-2-1 Rotor-Angle Swing

During and following a disturbance, until a new steady state is reached, $P_e \neq P_m$. As explained in Appendix 11A, this will result in the electrical torque T_e that does not equal the mechanical torque T_m, and therefore the difference of these torques will cause the rotor speed ω_m to deviate slightly from the synchronous speed. Therefore, the rotor angle δ_m in mechanical radians per second can be described as

$$J_m \frac{d^2 \delta_m}{dt^2} = T_m - T_e \qquad (11\text{-}2)$$

where J_m is the moment-of-inertia of the rotational system, which is acted upon the acceleration torque, which is the difference of the mechanical torque input T_m and the electrical torque T_e opposing it. Multiplying both sides of Eq. 11-2 by the rotor mechanical speed ω_m, and recognizing that the product of the torque and speed equals power, Eq. 11-2 can be written as

$$\omega_m J_m \frac{d^2 \delta_m}{dt^2} = P_m - P_e \qquad (11\text{-}3)$$

To express the above equation in per unit, a new inertia-related parameter H_{gen} is defined whose value lies is in a narrow range of 3-11 s for turbo-alternators and in a 1-2 s range for hydro generators. It is defined as the ratio of the kinetic energy of the rotating mass at the rated synchronous speed $\omega_{syn,m}$ in mechanical radians/s to the three-phase volt-ampere rating $S_{rated,gen}$ of the generator:

$$H_{gen} = \frac{\frac{1}{2} J_m \omega_{syn,m}^2}{S_{rated,gen}} \qquad (11\text{-}4)$$

Substituting for J_m in terms of H_{gen} defined in Eq. 11-4, Eq. 11-3 can be written as

$$\left(\frac{\omega_m}{\omega_{syn,m}^2}\right)2H_{gen}\frac{d^2\delta_m}{dt^2} = P_{m,gen,pu} - P_{e,gen,pu} \tag{11-5}$$

where P_m and P_e are in per unit of the generator MVA base $S_{rated,gen}$. Often, the system MVA base S_{system} is chosen to be 100 MVA. Regardless of the chosen value of S_{system}, in per unit of the system MVA base, Eq. 11-5 can be written as

$$\left(\frac{\omega_m}{\omega_{syn,m}^2}\right)2H\frac{d^2\delta_m}{dt^2} = P_{m,pu} - P_{e,pu} \tag{11-6}$$

where $P_{m,pu}$ and $P_{e,pu}$ are in per unit of the system MVA base S_{system} and

$$H = H_{gen}\left(\frac{S_{rated,gen}}{S_{system}}\right) \tag{11-7}$$

We should note that even under the transient condition, it is reasonable to assume in Eq. 11-6 that the rotor mechanical speed ω_m is approximately equal to the synchronous speed corresponding to the frequency of the infinite bus, that is $\omega_m \approx \omega_{syn,m}$. Therefore, Eq. 11-6 can be written as

$$\frac{2H}{\omega_{syn,m}}\frac{d^2\delta_m}{dt^2} = P_{m,pu} - P_{e,pu} \tag{11-8}$$

In Eq. 11-8, both the angle deviation and the synchronous speed can be expressed in terms of electrical radians

$$\frac{2H}{\omega_{syn}}\frac{d^2\delta}{dt^2} = P_{m,pu} - P_{e,pu} \tag{11-9}$$

The above equation is called the swing equation that describes how the angle δ swings or oscillates due to unbalance between the mechanical power input and the electrical power output of the generator. To calculate the dynamics of speed and angle as functions of time, several sophisticated numerical methods can be used. However to illustrate the basic principle, here we will assume that the integration with time is carried out with a sufficiently small time increment Δt during which $(P_m - P_e)$ can be assumed to be constant. With this assumption, integrating both sides of Eq. 11-7 with time,

$$\left.\frac{d\delta}{dt}\right|_t = \omega(t) = \omega(t - \Delta t) + \frac{\omega_{syn}}{2H}(P_{m,pu} - P_{e,pu})\Delta t \tag{11-10}$$

11-4

Similarly assuming the speed in Eq. 11-10 to be constant at $\omega(t - \Delta t)$ during Δt,

$$\delta(t) = \delta(t - \Delta t) + \omega(t - \Delta t)\Delta t \qquad (11\text{-}11)$$

Eqs. 11-10 and 11-11 show the rotor dynamics in terms of its speed ω and the angle δ as functions of time. In a simple system with one generator connected to an infinite bus, Example 11-1 below shows the rotor dynamics.

▲ **Example 11-1** Consider a simple system discussed earlier in Fig. 11-2b. The infinite-bus voltage is $\overline{V}_B = 1\angle 0\,\mathrm{pu}$. The bus 1 voltage magnitude is $V_1 = 1.05\,\mathrm{pu}$. The generator has a transient reactance $X'_d = 0.28\,\mathrm{pu}$ at a base of 22 kV (L-L) and 1,500 MVA. On the generator base, $H_{gen} = 3.5\,s$. The transformer has a leakage reactance of $X_{tr} = 0.2\,\mathrm{pu}$ at a base of 345 kV (L-L) and 1,500 MVA. The two 345-kV transmission lines are 100 km in length, and each has a series reactance of $0.367\,\Omega/km$, where the series resistance and the shunt capacitances are neglected. Initially, the three-phase power flow from the generator to the infinite-bus is 1500 MW.

A 3-phase to ground fault occurs on one of the lines, 20 percent of the distance away from bus-1. Calculate the maximum rotor-angle swing δ_m if the fault clearing is 40 ms after which the faulted transmission line is isolated from the system by the circuit breakers at both ends of the line.

Solution The solution to this example is detailed by a MATLAB program included on the accompanying CD. The rotor-angle swing is shown in Fig. 11-3.

Fig. 11-3 Rotor-angle swing in Example 11-1.

▲

11-2-2 Determining Transient Stability Using Equal-Area Criterion

Consider the simple system discussed earlier, repeated in Fig. 11-4a where a fault occurs on one of the transmission lines, which is cleared after a time $t_{c\ell}$ by isolating the faulted line from the system. In steady state prior to fault, $d\delta/dt = 0$ at δ_0, which is the initial steady state value of δ in Fig. 11-4b, given by the intersection of the horizontal line representing P_m and the pre-fault curve.

Fig. 11-4 Fault on one of the transmission lines.

The behavior of the rotor angle can be determined by multiplying both sides of Eq. 11-9 by $d\delta/dt$:

$$2\frac{d\delta}{dt}\frac{d^2\delta}{dt^2} = \frac{\omega_{syn}}{H}\left(P_{m,pu} - P_{e,pu}\right)\frac{d\delta}{dt} \tag{11-12}$$

Replacing δ in the above equation by θ, and integrating both sides with respect to time

$$\int\left(2\frac{d\theta}{dt}\frac{d^2\theta}{dt^2}\right)dt = \frac{\omega_{syn}}{H}\int\left(P_{m,pu} - P_{e,pu}\right)\frac{d\theta}{dt}dt \tag{11-13}$$

where the integral on the left side equals $(d\delta/dt)^2$. Therefore in Eq. 11-13, from the initial angle δ_0 at which $d\delta/dt = 0$, to an arbitrary angle δ

$$\left(\frac{d\delta}{dt}\right)^2 = \frac{\omega_{syn}}{H}\int_{\delta_0}^{\delta}\left(P_{m,pu} - P_{e,pu}\right)d\delta \tag{11-14}$$

In a stable system, the maximum value of the rotor angle will reach some value δ_m as shown in Fig. 11-4b at which $d\delta/dt$ once again becomes zero, and then the value of δ begins to decrease. Substituting this condition in Eq. 11-14,

$$\frac{\omega_{syn}}{H_{system}}\int_{\delta_0}^{\delta_m}\left(P_{m,pu} - P_{e,pu}\right)d\delta = 0 \tag{11-15}$$

In Eq. 11-15, $P_e = P_{e,fault}$ during the fault duration with $\delta_0 < \delta < \delta_{cl}$ and $P_e = P_{e,post-fault}$ after the fault the fault is cleared with $\delta_{cl} \le \delta \le \delta_m$. Therefore, Eq. 11-15 can be written as

$$\underbrace{\int_{\delta_0}^{\delta_{c\ell}} \left(P_{m,pu} - P_{e,fault,pu} \right) d\delta}_{Area\ A} - \underbrace{\int_{\delta_{c\ell}}^{\delta_m} \left(P_{e,post-fault,pu} - P_{m,pu} \right) d\delta}_{Area\ B} = 0 \qquad (11\text{-}16)$$

which shows that in a stable system, area A equals area B.

During the faulted line still connected to the system, $d\delta/dt$ given by Eq. 11-14 is positive in Fig. 11-4b, since the mechanical power input exceeds the electrical power output and the rotor angle increases from δ_0 to a new value $\delta_{c\ell}$ at the clearing-time $t_{c\ell}$. Area A given by Eq. 11-16 and illustrated graphically in Fig. 11-4b represents the excess energy delivered to the inertia of the rotor, causing the rotor angle to increase:

After the clearing-time $t_{c\ell}$ at which time the rotor-angle has reached $\delta_{c\ell}$, circuit breakers at both ends of the faulted transmission line open up to isolate the line from the rest of the system and the electrical output shifts to the post-fault power-angle curve, shown dotted in Fig. 11-4b. Now, the electrical power output exceeds the mechanical power input in the integral of Eq. 11-16. Therefore beyond $\delta_{c\ell}$ in Fig. 11-4b, therefore the speed begins to decrease although still above the synchronous speed, causing the angle to still keep on increasing, as shown in Fig. 11-4b. When area A equals area B, the excess energy supplied to the rotor equals that given up by it, and the rotor speed return to its synchronous speed value. At this time, the rotor angle reaches its maximum value δ_m at which $d\delta/dt = 0$ in Eq. 11-14, and the area B equals area A.

Thus the equal-area criterion given by Eq. 11-16 is able to determine the maximum swing of the rotor angle. To maintain stability, δ_m, determined by the equal-area criterion in Eq. 11-16, must be less than δ_{max}, as labeled in Fig. 11-4b, in order for the generator to remain in synchronism, as further explained in section 11-2-2-1. Beyond the time the rotor angle reaches δ_m, the electrical output in this illustration of Fig. 11-4a is still greater than the mechanical input, hence the speed begins to decline and the rotor-angle δ begins to decrease, as shown in Fig. 11-5.

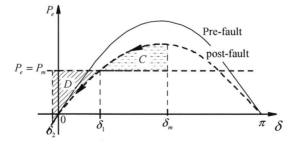

Fig. 11-5 Rotor oscillations after the fault is cleared.

11-7

With the lack of damping assumed here, the angle would oscillate forever around δ_1 in Fig. 11-5, with areas C and D equal in magnitude. However, the damping in a real system would eventually cause the rotor angle to settle down at δ_1.

11-2-2-1 Critical Clearing-Angle

The illustration above shows that the transient stability is maintained since $\delta_m < \delta_{max}$. Consider a case as shown in Fig. 11-6, where the clearing time is larger than before such that areas A and B are equal.

Fig. 11-6 Critical clearing angle.

Fig. 11-6 represents the critical case of the maximum clearing time and hence δ_{crit}, beyond which the stability would be lost. By the time the rotor angle reaches δ_{max}, if the generator inertia is not able to give up the excess energy acquired during the fault, then it will not be able to slow down. The reason is that beyond δ_{max}, the mechanical power input is greater than the electrical power output under the post-fault condition. Therefore, the rotor angle will keep on increasing, resulting in a so-called out-of-step operation. This will cause the relays to trip the circuit breakers to isolate the generator to prevent damage due to excessive currents in the system, and the stability will be lost. Therefore, for a given type and location of fault or a sudden change in electrical load, there is a critical angle δ_{crit} corresponding a maximum critical clearing time t_{crit} that results in area A to area B in magnitude as shown in Fig. 11-6, such that $\delta_{max} = \pi - \delta_1$.

Of course, the discussion above is theoretical. In practice, there should be a sufficient safety margin to prevent the transient stability to be lost.

▲ **Example 11-2** Consider a simple system discussed earlier in Fig. 11-4a. The infinite-bus voltage is $\overline{V}_B = 1\angle 0\,\text{pu}$. The voltage magnitude at Bus 1 is $V_1 = 1.05\,\text{pu}$. The generator has a transient reactance $X'_d = 0.28\,\text{pu}$ at a base of 22 kV (L-L) and 1,500 MVA. On the generator base, $H_{gen} = 3.5\,s$. The transformer has a leakage reactance of $X_{tr} = 0.2\,\text{pu}$ at a base of 345 kV (L-L) and 1,500 MVA. The two 345-kV transmission lines are 100 km in length, and each has a series reactance of $0.367\,\Omega/km$, where the series resistance and the shunt capacitances are neglected. Initially, the three-phase power flow from the generator to the infinite-bus is 1500 MW.

A 3-phase to ground fault occurs on one of the lines, 20 percent of the distance away from bus-1. Calculate the maximum rotor-angle swing δ_m if the rotor angle at the time of fault clearing is 75^0.

Solution The solution to this example is detailed by a MATLAB program included on the accompanying CD. The power angle curves for the pre-fault, during-fault and the post-fault conditions are as shown in Fig. 11-7, where initially $\delta_0 = 22.47^0$. The peak values of the power angle curves are calculated as follows on a system MVA base 0f 100 MVA: $\hat{P}_{e,pre-fault,pu} = 39.24$, $\hat{P}_{e,fault,pu} = 10.16$, and $\hat{P}_{e,post-fault,pu} = 25.57$. Using these values, the power-angle curves are as shown in Fig. 11-7.

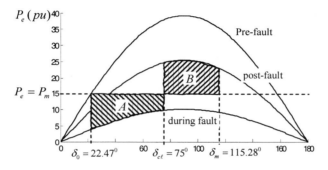

Fig. 11-7 Power angle curves and equal-area criterion in Example 11-2.

In Fig. 11-4b during the fault, the Area A in Eq. 11-14 can be calculated as follows:

$$Area\,A = \int_{\delta_0}^{\delta_{cl}} \left(P_{m,pu} - \hat{P}_{e,fault,pu} \sin\delta \right) d\delta \qquad (11\text{-}17)$$
$$= P_{m,pu}(\delta_{cl} - \delta_0) + \hat{P}_{e,fault,pu}(\cos\delta_{cl} - \cos\delta_0)$$

Similarly, the Area B in Eq. 11-16 can be calculated as

$$Area\,B = \int_{\delta_{cl}}^{\delta_m} \left(\hat{P}_{e,post-fault,pu} \sin\delta - P_{m,pu} \right) d\delta \qquad (11\text{-}18)$$
$$= \hat{P}_{e,post-fault,pu}(\cos\delta_{cl} - \cos\delta_m) - P_{m,pu}(\delta_m - \delta_{cl})$$

By applying equal-area criterion, the maximum rotor-angle swing $\delta_m = 115.28^0$, as shown in Fig. 11-6.

▲

11-3   TRANSIENT STABILITY EVALUATION IN LARGE SYSTEMS

The equal-area method describes the principle behind the transient stability. However in practice, transient stability must be evaluated in the presence of a large number of generators. In such a system, as shown in Fig. 11-8 by means of a block-diagram, the rotor electromechanical dynamics is represented in the time domain and the electrical network is represented in the phasor domain.

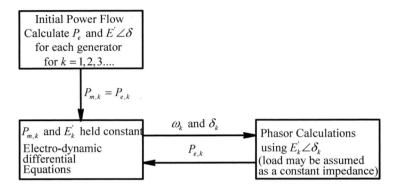

Fig. 11-8 Block diagram of transient stability program for an n-generator case.

The role of the electromechanical dynamics is to provide the rotor angles (angle of synchronous generator voltages) where as the role of the phasor calculations of the network is to calculate the electrical power that various generators are providing at that time. Phasor calculations are made assuming that the network is in quasi steady state. This way, the line frequency in the system is eliminated. This procedure, as illustrated in the block diagram of Fig. 11-7 allows large time steps to be taken based on the electromechanical time constants of the system.

It is important that the entire network not be calculated in time-domain, which otherwise would require a small simulation time-step and the execution time will be prohibitively large. A time-domain procedure needs to be adopted using a program such as EMTDC only if certain phenomenon such as the performance of Thyristor-Controlled Series-Capacitor (TCSC) is being evaluated. The procedure for stability analysis of large networks is illustrated using a three-bus system in Example 11-3.

▲ **Example 11-3**   Consider a three-bus system discussed earlier in chapter 5 and repeated in Fig. 11-9. These three buses are connected through three 345-kV transmission lines 200 km, 150 km and 150 km long, as shown in Fig. 5-1. These transmission lines, considered to consist of bundled conductors, have the line reactance of $0.376\ \Omega/km$ at 60 Hz. The line resistance is $0.037\ \Omega/km$. The per-unit susceptance is $4.5\ \mu\mho/km$, however ignore all the shunt susceptances. Bus-1 is a slack bus with $V_1 = 1.0\ pu$ and $\theta_1 = 0$. Bus-2 is a PV bus with $V_2 = 1.03\ pu$ and $P_2^{sp} = 5.0\ pu$. Bus-3 is a PQ bus with injection of $P_3^{sp} = -9.0\,pu$ and $Q_3^{sp} = -4.0\,pu$. To convert the actual quantities to per-unit, the voltage base is 345 kV (L-L).

Both the transformers and the generators have the three-phase MVA ratings of 500 MVA each. Both the generators have a transient reactance $X_d' = 0.23\,pu$ at a base of 22 kV (L-L) and its own MVA base. Also, each generator has $H_{gen} = 3.5\,s$ on the generator base. Each transformer has a leakage reactance of $X_{tr} = 0.2\,pu$ at a base of 345 kV (L-L) and its own MVA base.

A 3-phase to ground fault occurs on the line 1-2, $1/3^{rd}$ of the distance away from bus-1. Calculate the rotor-angle swings if the fault-clearing time is 0.5 s after which the faulted transmission line is isolated from the system by the circuit breakers at both ends of the line 1-2.

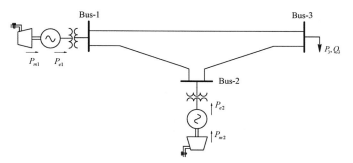

Fig. 11-9 A 345-kV test example system.

Solution   The solution to this example is detailed by a MATLAB program included on the accompanying CD. The rotor-angle swings are shown in Fig. 11-10 which show the system to be stable.

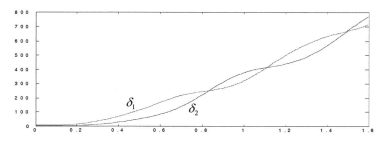

Fig. 11-10 Rotor-angle swings of δ_1 and δ_2 in Example 11-3.

11-4 DYNAMIC STABILITY [3]

Without adequate damping, an interconnected power system can develop growing power oscillations, causing it to split and possibly resulting in a blackout. One such incident took place in the western USA/Canada system on August 10, 1996, as shown by the plot of power oscillations in Fig. 11-11 [4] that left millions of customers without power.

Fig. 11-11 Growing Power Oscillations: Western USA/Canada system, Aug 10, 1996 [4].

This incident, among many, illustrates that there should be adequate damping in the system so that the oscillations caused by changes in loads, however the size of these changes, decay to a new steady state operating point. This is considered dynamic stability, which has become particularly important in modern power systems with fast-acting feedback controllers used in excitation systems, HVDC transmission systems and in FACTS devices. By proper design, for example, using power system stabilizers in conjunction with exciters for synchronous generators and HVDC control [5, 6], it is possible to provide the required damping for maintaining dynamic stability. Series-capacitor compensation of transmission lines can lead to sub-synchronous resonances take can fatigue turbine-generator shaft, and therefore must be damped out. For the dynamic stability investigation and the design of controllers accordingly, a modal analysis is required that uses the concept of eigenvectors. Therefore, as important as this topic is, it is beyond the scope of the first course on power systems.

REFERENCES

1. Prabha Kundur, *Power System Stability and Control*, McGraw-Hill, 1994.
2. Paul Anderson, Analysis of Faulted Power Systems, IEEE Press, 1995.
3. Graham Rogers, Power System Oscillations, Kluwer, 2000.
4. Dynamic Performance Validation in the Western Power System John F. Hauer et al, Presented at the APEx 2000, Kananaskis, Alberta, Canada, October 2000 (http://certs.lbl.gov/pdf/apex2000.pdf).
5. R.L. Cresap et al, "Operating Experience with Modulation of the Pacific HVDC Intertie," IEEE Transactions on PA&S. Vol. PAS-97, pp. 1053-1059.
6. D.J. Christofersen, K.N. Mortensen, G.A. Skarbakka, "CU HVDC Project Damping Control Requirements and Interaction with AC System".

PROBLEMS

11-1   Redo Example 11-1 for a fault clearing time twice as long.

11-2   In Example 11-2, what is the value of the voltage E', as defined in Fig. 11-1b.

11-3   In Example 11-2, what is the time taken by the rotor angle to reach $\delta_{cl} = 75^0$ at which time the fault is cleared?

11-4   In Example 11-2, what is the value of δ_{crit} and what is the time taken by the rotor angle to reach that value?

11-5   Redo Example 11-3 if the initial real and reactive powers at Bus-3 are 75% of their original values.

11-6   Redo Example 11-3 if the generator H_{gen} are 50% of their original value.

11-7   Redo Example 11-3 if a fault occurs on line 1-3, $1/3^{rd}$ of the distance away from Bus-1.

APPENDIX 11A   INERTIA, TORQUE AND ACCELERATION IN ROTATING SYSTEMS

Synchronous generators are of rotating type. Consider a lever, pivoted and free to move as shown in Fig. 11A-1. When an external force f is applied in a *perpendicular* direction at a radius r from the pivot, then the torque acting on the lever is

$$\underset{[Nm]}{T} = \underset{[N]}{f} \ \underset{[m]}{r} \tag{11A-1}$$

which acts in a counter-clockwise direction, considered here to be positive.

Figure 11A-1 Pivoted lever.

In the turbine-generator system, forces shown by arrows in Fig. 11A-2 are produced by the turbine. The definition of torque in Eq. 11A-1 correctly describes the torque T_m that causes the rotation of the turbine and the synchronous generator connected to it by a shaft.

Figure 11A-2 Forces and torques in a turbine-generator system.

In a rotational system, the angular acceleration due to a net torque acting on it is determined by its moment-of-inertia J_m of the entire system. The net torque T_a acting on the rotating body of inertia J causes it to accelerate. Similar to systems with linear motion where $f_a = Ma$, Newton's Law in rotational systems becomes

$$T_a = J_m \alpha_m \tag{11A-2}$$

where the angular acceleration $\alpha_m (= d\omega_m / dt)$ in rad / s^2 is

$$\alpha_m = \frac{d\omega_m}{dt} = \frac{T_m}{J_m} \tag{11A-3}$$

where the damping is neglected. In MKS units, a torque of $1\,Nm$, acting on an inertia of $1\,kg \cdot m^2$ results in an angular acceleration of $1\,rad / s^2$.

In systems such as the one shown in Fig. 11A-3a, the turbine produces an electromagnetic torque T_m. The bearing friction and wind resistance (drag) can be combined with the synchronous generator torque T_e opposing the rotation. The net torque, the difference between the mechanical torque developed by the turbine and the generator torque opposing it, causes the combined inertias of the turbine and the generator to accelerate in accordance with Eq. 11A-3:

$$\frac{d}{dt}\omega_m = \frac{T_a}{J_m} \tag{11A-4}$$

where the net torque $T_a = T_m - T_e$ as shown in Fig. 11A-3b, and J_m is the equivalent combined inertia.

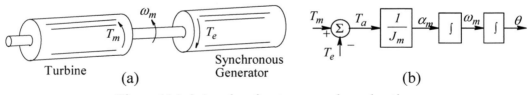

Turbine   (a)   Synchronous Generator   (b)

Figure 11A-3 Accelerating torque and acceleration.

Eq. 11A-4 shows that the net torque is the quantity that causes acceleration, which in turn leads to changes in speed and position. Integrating the acceleration $\alpha(t)$ with respect to time,

$$\text{Speed } \omega_m(t) = \omega_m(0) + \int_0^t \alpha(\tau)d\tau \tag{11A-5}$$

where $\omega_m(0)$ is the speed at t=0 and τ is a variable of integration. Further integrating $\omega_m(t)$ in Eq. 11A-5 with respect to time yields

$$\theta(t) = \theta(0) + \int_0^t \omega_m(\tau)d\tau \qquad (11A\text{-}6)$$

where $\theta(0)$ is the position at $t = 0$, and τ is again a variable of integration. Eqs. 11A-4 through 11A-6 indicate that torque is the fundamental variable for controlling speed and position. Eqs. 11A-4 through 11A-6 can be represented in a block-diagram form, as shown in Fig. 11A-3b.

In a rotational system shown in Fig. 11A-4, if a net torque T_a causes the cylinder to rotate by a differential angle $d\theta$, the differential work done is

$$dW = T d\theta \qquad (11A\text{-}7)$$

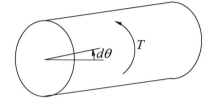

Fig. 11A-4 Torque, work and power.

If this differential rotation takes place in a differential time dt, the power can be expressed as

$$p = \frac{dW}{dt} = T\frac{d\theta}{dt} = T\omega_m \qquad (11A\text{-}8)$$

where $\omega_m = d\theta/dt$ is the angular speed of rotation.

CHAPTER 12

CONTROL OF INTERCONNECTED POWER SYSTEM AND ECONOMIC DISPATCH

12-1 CONTROL OBJECTIVES

In an interconnected power system such as that in North America, thousands of generators, connected through hundreds of thousands of miles long transmission and sub-transmission lines, operate synchronously to supply load that is constantly changing. The main Advantage of a highly interconnected system is the continuity of service to consumers making sure that the reliability is ensured in case of contingencies such as unscheduled outages. An interconnected system also affords the economy of operation using the optimum generation, making use of the lowest cost generation. As we will see shortly, frequency deviations are also smaller in a highly interconnected system.

In meeting constantly changing load demand and possibly the network structure due to outages, the network voltage and frequency are maintained by the following means:

1. voltage control by excitation control of generators and the control of reactive power
2. frequency control and the interchange of power at their scheduled values
3. optimal power flow such that the power to the load is provided in the most economic manner, considering the constraints such as the transmission-line capacities and the power system stability.

In addition to the controls mentioned above, there are supplementary controls that lead to reducing the integral of frequency error periodically to zero so that the clocks and other appliances that depend on the grid frequency get back to their normal values, and the integral of the power exchange error is also reduced to zero.

Although the voltage and the frequency controls are implemented simultaneously in time, they act fairly independent of each other as described below.

12-2 VOLTAGE CONTROL BY CONTROLLING EXCITATION AND THE REACTIVE POWER

In a power system, the quality of power is defined by keeping the voltage level at its nominal value within a fairly narrow range of ± 5 percent, for example. This is so because the change in the voltage level can disturb the load, at lower voltages dimming lights and slowing down induction motors and at higher voltages causing magnetic saturation of transformers and motors. As discussed in the voltage stability chapter, lack of reactive power can cause voltage instability and possibly voltage collapse, and to avoid this, certain reactive power reserve must be maintained.

Although there are other means, the primary means of voltage control is by excitation control of synchronous generators within power plants. As discussed earlier, overexciting these generators allows them to supply reactive power to the system, where as underexciting them allows them to absorb reactive power. Other means of reactive power control to maintain voltages are the following, which are discussed in the voltage stability chapter: shunt capacitors, shunt reactors, static var controllers (SVCs), STATCOM, series capacitors including thyristor-controlled series capacitors, and HVDC Terminals. Voltage can also be controlled by transformer tap-changing. The last-resort scheme includes automatic load shedding. However, as mentioned earlier, the primary means to obtain voltage control objective is by Automatic Voltage Regulation (AVR) of synchronous generators, as discussed below.

12-2-1 Automatic Voltage Regulation (AVR) through Excitation Control

As discussed in the synchronous generator chapter, the field winding on the rotor is supplied by a dc current to establish the field flux. This requires an excitation system. There are many types of excitation systems in use but one of the fast acting excitation systems is shown in Fig. 12-1.

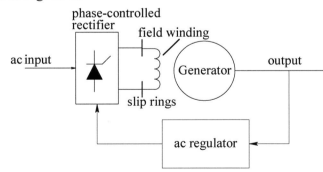

Fig. 12-1 Field exciter for automatic voltage regulation (AVR).

It consists of a thyristor rectifier supplied by a three-phase ac derived from the generator output or from an auxiliary supply. The dc output is supplied to the field winding, which rotates with the rotor, through brushes and slip rings. A voltage exciter such as shown in

Fig. 12-1 can be designed to regulate the voltage at other than the generator output; for example at the high-voltage bus after the step-up transformer. This can be accomplished by a load compensation network which takes account of the voltage drop across the impedance between the generator and the point of regulation, mainly the transformer leakage inductance. In this exciter, several safety features are built in, for example limiting under-excitation to exceed the steady state stability limit and over-excitation to prevent thermal over-loading.

As discussed in the chapter on transient and dynamic stability, the fast excitation response can play a beneficial role in improving transient stability. But, in addition, a power system stabilizer (PSS) should be used to introduce damping to prevent rotor oscillations, by using the rotor speed oscillations as a signal in controlling the field excitation of the generator to maintain dynamic stability.

12-3 AUTOMATIC GENERATION CONTROL (AGC)

As mentioned earlier, as the load demand continuously and randomly fluctuates, and the real power being generated must be adjusted to meet instantaneous change in load demand. For this purpose, the interconnected power system, for example the North American power grid, is divided into four Interconnections as shown in Fig. 12-2a.

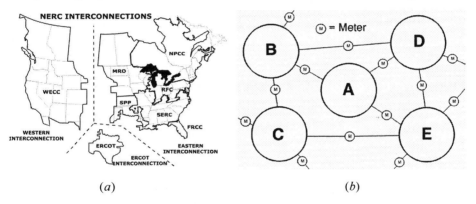

(a)   (b)

Fig. 12-2 (a) The Interconnections in North America, (b) Control Areas [Source: 2]

To operate safely and reliably, each Interconnection comprises of several control areas, as shown in Fig. 12-2b for example, which continuously monitor and control the power flow. The Eastern Interconnection has 109 control areas, the Western has 33, and ERCOT has 10, for a total of 152. The Quebec Interconnection operates as a single area. Each area consists of a part, entire, or a group of companies, consisting of many generators. These control areas are interconnected to each other through transmission lines, which are called tie lines, in a small example shown in Fig. 12-2b. There is scheduled interchange of power between these control areas to realize the benefits of having them interconnected. On a dynamic basis, most of the generators from all the areas participate in meeting a change in load demand in any one of the areas. However in steady state, each control area, if it can, consistent with the definition of a control area, meets the entire change in load demand within its own area. This requires Automatic Generation Control (AGC) and most of the generators are equipped with this. AGC also requires a certain amount of spinning reserve that can quickly meet the instantaneous change in load demand that fluctuates randomly.

12-3-1 Load-Frequency Control

Turbines of most generators above a certain rating are governed to provide automatic generation control (AGC). To understand turbine-governor control, consider a single turbine as shown in Fig. 12-3a. In such a system, if the electrical load were to increase, then the rotor will slow down, resulting in reduced speed and hence reduced frequency. The frequency is sent as a feedback signal to the regulator that acts (with a negative sign) on the turbine governor to change the valve position to let more steam in. In steady state, neglecting losses, the mechanical input, the electrical output and the load power are all the same: $P_m = P_e = P_{Load}$.

The load-frequency plot is shown in Fig. 12-3b by a drooping straight line GG. Initially, at a load equal to P_m, the operating frequency is f_0. If the load were to increase in steady state by an amount ΔP_m, then the frequency decreases by a value equal to Δf which allows, as shown in Fig. 12-3a, to let more steam in. (Note that when frequency decreases, Δf is a negative value and the regulator output is multiplied by a negative sign, thus resulting in a change in power ΔP_m which is positive).

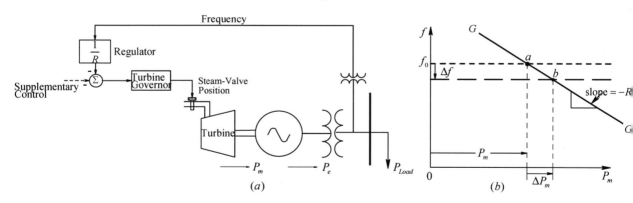

Fig. 12-3 Load-frequency control (ignore the supplementary control at present).

As shown in Fig. 12-3b, the slope of the load-frequency control characteristic is $(-R)$, where R is called the Speed Regulation, which has a positive value

$$R(\text{in \%}) = -\frac{\Delta f(\text{in \%})}{\Delta P_m(\text{in pu})} \tag{12-1}$$

12-4

For example, Regulation R equal to 5% implies that a 0.1 per unit change in the electrical load corresponds to 0.5% change in the base frequency. If the base frequency is 60 Hz, it corresponds to a decrease of 0.3 Hz, that is, the new frequency will be 59.7 Hz.

Now consider the case of two generators interconnected, supplying the load as shown in Fig. 12-4a, where in steady state, neglecting losses,

$$P_{e1} = P_{m1} \qquad P_{e2} = P_{m2} \quad \text{and} \quad P_{m1} + P_{m2} = P_{Load} \tag{12-2}$$

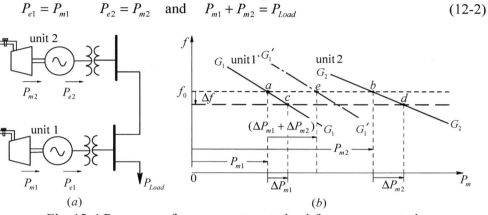

Fig. 12-4 Response of two generators to load-frequency control.

Both turbines have the governor feedback mechanisms that give their units drooping characteristics as shown by the solid lines $G_1 G_1$ and $G_2 G_2$ in Fig. 12-4b, with regulation values R_1 and R_2. Initially at the rated frequency f_0 of 60 Hz (or 50 Hz), the operating points are "a" and "b", and $P_{m1} + P_{m2} = P_{Load}$. For the given characteristics $G_1 G_1$ and $G_2 G_2$, if the electrical load were to increase by an amount ΔP_{Load}, the new steady state frequency (common to both the units) will drop, and from Eq. 12-1

$$\Delta f = -R_1 \Delta P_{m1} \quad \text{and} \qquad \Delta f = -R_2 \Delta P_{m2} \tag{12-3}$$

and the operating points will shift to "c" and "d", such that

$$\Delta P_{m1} + \Delta P_{m2} = \Delta P_{Load} \tag{12-4}$$

From Eqs. 12-3 and 12-4

$$\Delta f = -\frac{\Delta P_{Load}}{(1/R_1 + 1/R_2)} \tag{12-5}$$

In general, if many such generators are interconnected, then from Eq. 12-5

$$\Delta f = -\frac{1}{\sum_i 1/R_i} \Delta P_{Load} \tag{12-6}$$

12-5

Therefore, the equivalent speed regulation is

$$R_{eq} = \frac{1}{\sum_i 1/R_i} \tag{12-7}$$

and the change in frequency for a given change in load is much smaller compared to the case if a single generator were to accommodate this change in load. As a consequence, interconnected generators result in a much "stiffer" system where all the generators initially participate in accommodating the change in load and thus the change in frequency is very small.

▲ **Example 12-1**   Consider two generators in parallel operating at 60 Hz and having widely different regulation, with $R_1 = 5\%$ and $R_2 = 16.7\%$. A load change of 0.1 pu occurs. Calculate the equivalent value of the regulation, the initial decrease in frequency and how the change in load is shared by the two generators initially.

Solution   From Eq. 12-7, $R_{eq} = 3.85 (\text{in }\%)$. Therefore, from Eq. 12-6,

$$\Delta f = -0.385 (\text{in }\%) = -0.231 Hz \ .$$

New frequency initially after the load change will be 59.769 Hz. Using Eq. 12-1,

$$\Delta P_{m1} = \frac{0.385}{5.0} = 0.077 \, \text{pu} \ , \text{ and } \Delta P_{m2} = \frac{0.385}{16.7} = 0.023 \, \text{pu} \ ,$$

which shows that unit 1 with small value of regulation picks up initially a greater share of the load.   ▲

12-3-2 Automatic Generation Control (AGC)

In order to restore the frequency and the tie-line flow to their original and scheduled values in the system of Fig. 12-4a where the load change occurs on unit 1, a supplementary control called the Automatic Generation Control (AGC) raises the generation characteristic of unit 1 in steady state to $G_1'G_1'$ as shown in Fig. 12-4b, such that the entire load change is provided by unit 1 and the operating point for unit 1 shifts to a new point "e", whereas the operating point for unit 2 returns to its original value "b".

If units 1 and 2 were to represent two control areas as shown in Fig. 12-5, then for each area, an Area Control Error (ACE) is defined as a sum of the tie-line flow deviation, and the frequency deviation multiplied by a frequency-bias factor B. Therefore, defining the increase in power flow out of one area to the other area, for example the increase ΔP_{12} from area 1 to area 2 to be positive,

$$ACE_1 = \Delta P_{12} + B_1 \Delta f \qquad\qquad (12\text{-}8)$$

Similarly,

$$ACE_2 = \Delta P_{21} + B_2 \Delta f \qquad (\text{where, } \Delta P_{21} = -\Delta P_{12}) \qquad (12\text{-}9)$$

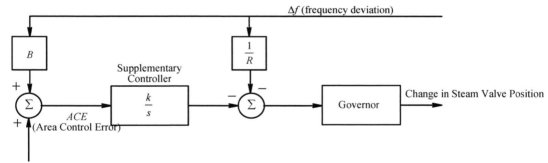

Fig. 12-5 Two control areas.

A negative value of ACE for an area indicates that there is not enough generation in that area. In the block diagram of Fig. 12-5, following a load change in either one of the two areas, the final steady state is reached only if each ACE, as defined by Eqs. 12-8 and 12-9 comes to zero when the tie-line flow and the frequency are restored to their original values. This implies that in steady state, an area with a load change completely absorbs its own load change. This was earlier illustrated in Fig. 12-4, where the change in load on unit 1 results in the load-reference setting by the bias motor of unit 1 in steady state shifting the generation curve to $G_1'G_1'$ such that it supplies the entire change in that area, and the unit 2 generation remains unchanged at $G_2 G_2$.

Each generator participating in the Area Generation Control (AGC) has a supplementary controller that has the Area Control Error (ACE) as the input, as shown in Fig. 12-6. The supplementary controller output and the regulation feedback act on the governor to change the steam-valve position, as shown in Fig. 12-6.

Fig. 12-6 Area Control Error (ACE) for Automatic Generation Control (AGC).

In steady state, the results are the same regardless of the values of the frequency-bias settings, B_1 and B_2 in Eqs. 12-8 and 12-9, provided the control is stable. During dynamic operation, field experience has shown that the selection of the frequency-bias factor of approximately $B = 1/R$ in each area gives good dynamic results. When a control area has more than one tie line as is almost always the case, the AGC action described above brings the net control-area exchange to its original scheduled value. This is illustrated in the example power system of Fig. 12-7, where there are two control areas connected through two tie-lines. There are two Revenue Meters (M) to measure power flows at the boundaries of the two control areas. Therefore, in defining ACE in Eqs. 12-8 and 12-9, the tie-line deviation between the two control areas is $\Delta P_{12} = \Delta P_{1-2} + \Delta P_{1-3}$, where ΔP_{1-2} and ΔP_{1-3} are the line flows at the boundaries of the two control areas.

Fig. 12-7 Two control areas in the example power system with 3 buses.

▲ **Example 12-2** Consider the example 3-bus power system described in the Power Flow chapter. Ignoring the line losses, calculate the power flow on the three lines. Repeat this when the load has increased to 600 MW but due to AGC applied to both units, the net power flow between the two areas is to remain the same.

Solution Using the MATLAB program developed in the Power Flow chapter and reducing all line resistances to zero, the line flows are as shown in Fig. 12-8a for the load of 500 MW. In case of a 600 MW and both units under AGC, the net flow from Area 1 to Area 2 remains the same, and the entire load change in area 2 is absorbed by unit 2. The line flows are shown in Fig. 12-8b.

Fig. 12-8 Line flows in Example 12-2.

▲

In practice, the AGC is run every 2 to 4 seconds and the area control error (ACE) has to be brought to zero within every 10-minute interval.

12-3-3 Dynamic Performance of Interconnected Areas
So far, we have examined the interconnections of various areas on a steady state basis. However, the load can change as a step and the interconnected system reacts to it on a

dynamic basis. In doing so, it is important that there is enough damping, otherwise, the system can go unstable. The dynamic response of the system depends on many parameters: inertias of the interconnected systems, damping, regulators, gain values of the supplementary controller in Fig. 12-6 to correct the area control error (ACE), etc.

Another important parameter is the magnitude of the synchronizing torque coefficient between the areas, which can be explained by means of a simple two-area example shown in Fig. 12-9 where all the generating units in a control area are represented by an equivalent generator since the objective is to study the inter-area oscillations, not the intra-area oscillations.

Fig. 12-9 Electrical equivalent of two area interconnection.

In Fig. 12-9, X_1 and X_2 are the reactances of each of the equivalent generators with E_1 and E_2 as the internal emfs, and X_{12} is the tie-line reactance. Thus,

$$X_T = X_1 + X_{12} + X_2 \tag{12-10}$$

The power flow from area 1 to area 2 is

$$P_{12} = \frac{E_1 E_2}{X_T} \sin \delta_{12} \tag{12-11}$$

where $\delta_{12} = \delta_1 - \delta_2$. Therefore, linearizing Eq. 12-11 around a steady state operating point with initial power as P_0 and the initial angle difference as δ_0, we can write Eq. 12-11 as

$$P_0 + \Delta P_{12} = \frac{E_1 E_2}{X_T} \sin(\delta_0 + \Delta \delta_{12}) \tag{12-12a}$$

Noting that $\sin(a+b) = \sin a \cdot \cos b + \cos a \cdot \sin b$, expanding the sine term in Eq. 12-12a results in the following for small values of the perturbation $\Delta \delta_{12}$:

$$P_0 + \Delta P_{12} = \frac{E_1 E_2}{X_T} \left(\sin \delta_0 \cdot \underbrace{\cos \Delta \delta_{12}}_{(\approx 1)} + \cos \delta_0 \cdot \underbrace{\sin \Delta \delta_{12}}_{(\approx \Delta \delta_{12})} \right) \tag{12-12b}$$

Therefore, from Eq. 12-12b, recognizing that $\Delta \delta_{12} = \Delta \delta_1 - \Delta \delta_2$,

$$\Delta P_{12} = \left(\underbrace{\frac{E_1 E_2}{X_T} \cos \delta_0}_{T_{12}} \right) (\Delta \delta_1 - \Delta \delta_2) \tag{12-13}$$

where the quantity within the brackets is the synchronizing torque coefficient T_{12} between areas 1 and 2:

$$T_{12} = \frac{E_1 E_2}{X_T} \cos \delta_0 \tag{12-14}$$

Eq. 12-14 shows that smaller the initial operating angle δ_0, larger will be the magnitude of the synchronizing torque coefficient that determines the period and the magnitude of the tie-line oscillations following a load change. These inter-area oscillations in a two-area system are illustrated by an example below.

▲ **Example 12-3** Consider a two-area system shown in Fig. 12-10 where both areas are identical and both are under AGC. The system parameters are specified in a MATLAB file associated with this example, on the accompanying CD. There is a step-change of load in area 1. Plot the following: ΔP_{m1}, ΔP_{m2} and ΔP_{12}.

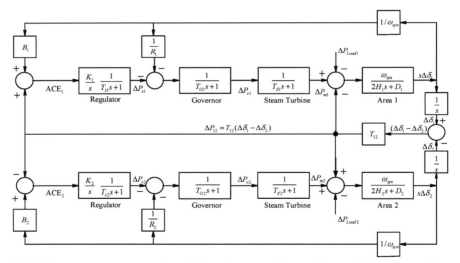

Fig. 12-10 Two-area system with AGC. **Source**: Adapted from Reference 6, Leon K. Kirchmayer, *Economic Control of Interconnected Systems*, John Wiley & Sons, 1959.

Solution This system is modeled in *Simulink* and included in the accompanying CD. The results, which are plotted in Fig. 12-11, show that for a load change in area 1, initially both areas participate but in steady state, the load change is entirely satisfied by area 1 and hence, $\Delta P_{m1} = \Delta P_{Load1}$, and $\Delta P_{m2} = 0$. The tie-line power deviation ΔP_{12}

oscillates and eventually will settle down to zero. The frequency of these oscillations depends on the system parameters.

Fig. 12-11 Simulink results of the two-area system with AGC in Example 12-3.

▲

12-4   ECONOMIC DISPATCH AND OPTIMUM POWER FLOW

One of the advantages of an interconnected system is the optimum allocation of generation for the least overall production cost, making sure that the transmission line loadings are within their capacities and the system transient stability margins are maintained.

12-4-1 Economic Dispatch

In power plants, the cost of generating electricity depends on the fixed operating costs (that depend on the capital investment etc and are independent of the power being produced), and on the variable operating costs, including fuel costs, which depend on the power being produced. However, once the power plants have been built, the operating strategy from the economic point of view is to minimize the total fuel cost to generate the required amount of power.

In the normal operating range, the efficiency of a thermal power plant increases somewhat with increasing power level. In other words, the Heat Rate, which is the primary energy in MBTU being consumed per hour divided by the electrical power P, decreases slightly with the power level, as shown in Fig. 12-12.

Fig. 12-12 Heat Rate at various generated power levels.

12-11

Contrary to what the heat-rate curve of Fig. 12-12 would suggest, in practice due to various considerations, the fuel cost is taken to increase with power as shown in Fig. 12-13a.

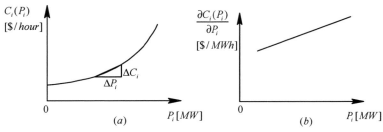

Fig. 12-13 (a) Fuel cost and (b) Marginal cost, as functions of the power output.

In general, the fuel-cost curve for a unit i can be expressed as a quadratic function of the power P_i that is generated:

$$C_i(P_i) = a_i + b_i P_i + c_i P_i^2 \qquad (12\text{-}15)$$

The slope of the fuel-cost curve in Fig. 12-13a at any power level is the marginal cost, which is the cost of generating 1 MWh at a particular power level. This marginal cost, in dollars/MWh, can also be calculated by taking the partial derivative of the cost in Eq. 12-15 with respect to P_i:

$$\frac{\partial C_i(P_i)}{\partial P_i} = b_i + 2c_i P_i \qquad (12\text{-}16)$$

which is a straight line with an upward (positive) slope as shown in Fig. 12-13b.

Consider an example where an area has three generators. Then there will be three marginal cost equations similar to Eq. 12-16 and there will be three marginal-cost curves, as plotted in Fig. 12-14.

Fig. 12-14 Marginal costs for the three generators.

Another equation is based on power balance that is the sum of the generation must equal the sum of the load and the losses

$$\sum_i P_i = P_{Load} + P_{Losses} \qquad (12\text{-}17)$$

We are searching for the values of P_1, P_2, and P_3 that result in the total minimum fuel cost while the power balance equation is satisfied. An intuitively solution is to operate such that all three generators have the same marginal cost and the power balance is satisfied. The reason is as follows: if one of the generators is operating at a higher marginal cost, shifting generation from it to the lower marginal-cost generators would result in lower overall cost. This will continue until all generators have equal marginal costs, as plotted in Fig. 12-14.

A more formal solution to this well-known optimization problem can be obtained using what is called the Lagrangian Multiplier Method, where a Lagrangian cost function is defined as follows for this three-generator system:

$$L = C_1(P_1) + C_2(P_2) + C_3(P_3) - \lambda[P_1 + P_2 + P_3 - (P_{Load} + P_{Losses})] \tag{12-18}$$

where λ is the Lagrangian multiplier. This Lagrangian function has four variables: P_1, P_2, P_3, and λ, assuming P_{Losses} to be a constant. To minimize this Lagrangian, we will take its partial derivative with respect to each of these four variables and set them to zero. Therefore, from Eq. 12-18,

$$\frac{\partial L}{\partial P_1} = \frac{\partial C_1(P_1)}{\partial P_1} - \lambda = 0 \tag{12-19}$$

$$\frac{\partial L}{\partial P_2} = \frac{\partial C_2(P_2)}{\partial P_2} - \lambda = 0 \tag{12-20}$$

$$\frac{\partial L}{\partial P_3} = \frac{\partial C_3(P_3)}{\partial P_3} - \lambda = 0 \tag{12-21}$$

$$P_1 + P_2 + P_3 - (P_{Load} + P_{Losses}) = 0 \qquad (\because \frac{\partial L}{\partial \lambda} = 0) \tag{12-22}$$

The last equation is the power-balance equation. From 12-19 through 12-22, the cost function in Eq. 12-18 is minimized if

$$\frac{\partial C_1(P_1)}{\partial P_1} = \frac{\partial C_2(P_2)}{\partial P_2} = \frac{\partial C_3(P_3)}{\partial P_3} = \lambda \quad \text{(assuming } P_{Losses} \text{ to be constant)} \tag{12-23}$$

The solution given by Eq. 12-23 is the same as the intuitively solution, that the overall cost is minimized if all three generators are operating at equal marginal costs while satisfying the power balance. Therefore, from equations similar to Eq. 12-16,

$$b_1 + 2c_1 P_1 = \lambda \tag{12-24}$$

$$b_2 + 2c_2 P_2 = \lambda \tag{12-25}$$

$$b_3 + 2c_3 P_3 = \lambda \tag{12-26}$$

and,

$$P_1 + P_2 + P_3 = P_{Load} + P_{Losses} \tag{12-27}$$

From these four equations, the four variables P_1, P_2, P_3, and λ can be solved, where λ is the system optimum marginal cost in \$/MWh (that is, the cost in \$/hour of supplying an increase of 1 MW in system load and losses). In practice, there is a maximum limit on the power that can be produced by a generator, and also a lower limit that a unit must produce unless taken offline. These limits can be indicated by vertical lines in the marginal cost curves as shown in Fig. 12-14.

▲ **Example 12-4**　In a control area, there are two generators, 100 MW each. The marginal costs for these two generators can be as expressed as follows:

$$\frac{\partial C_1}{\partial P_1} = 1.8 + 0.01 P_1 \qquad \text{(in \$/MWh)}$$

$$\frac{\partial C_2}{\partial P_2} = 1.5 + 0.02 P_2 \qquad \text{(in \$/MWh)}$$

If this area has to supply a total of 150 MW, calculate the area optimum marginal cost λ and the power supplied by each generator.

Solution　Equating the two marginal costs and equating the sum of two powers to 150 MW,

$$1.8 + 0.01 P_1 = 1.5 + 0.02 P_2 \qquad \text{and} \qquad P_1 + P_2 = 150$$

Solving the above two equations, $P_1 = 90\,MW$ and $P_2 = 60\,MW$. From any of these, the area marginal cost is $\lambda = 2.7[\$/MWh]$.　　　　　　　　　　　　　　　▲

12-4-2 Unit Commitment and Spinning Reserve [4]

The economic dispatch discussed above is based on the generation capacity that has been put into service. However, there are other factors that dictate the capacity that must be in service for a given load, in order for the angle and voltage stability, and for the ability to meet the load change in a control area (now referred to as a Balancing Authority) quickly. This requires that each control area maintains a certain level, 15 to 20 percent for example, of spinning reserve which represents the aggregate power plant capacity in a control area that is not utilized at a given time, and can respond immediately being on-line, because a cold star, especially of thermal plants, may take a long time – tens of minutes if not hours. If this spinning reserve is not enough, a new generator may be committed, and this is called unit commitment.

12-4-3 Optimal Power Dispatch and Flow

In the analysis above of economic dispatch to minimize overall fuel cost, the transmission line losses are represented as constant, independent of the values of P_1, P_2, and P_3. This is not so since a generator far away will incur higher transmission line losses and the cost of these losses must be included in the cost minimization problem. Also, no consideration was given to transmission line capacities and the system transient stability. When constraints such as these are factored in, the cost minimization is called optimal power dispatch and under those conditions, power flow on various lines is the optimal power flow.

REFERENCES

1. Prabha Kundur, *Power System Stability and Control*, McGraw Hill, 1994.
2. Control Area Concepts and Obligations, NERC Document.
3. United States Department of Agriculture, Rural Utilities Service, Design Guide for Rural Substations, RUS BULLETIN 1724E-300.
4. Leon K. Kirchmayer, *Economic Operation of Power Systems*, John Wiley & Sons, 1958.
5. Nathan Cohn, *Control of Generation and Power Flow on Interconnected Systems*, John Wiley & Sons, 1967.
6. Leon K. Kirchmayer, *Economic Control of Interconnected Systems*, John Wiley & Sons, 1959.
7. A. Wood, B. Wollenberg, *Power Generation, Operation, and Control*, 2nd edition, Wiley-Interscience, 1996.

PROBLEMS

12-1   Three generators operating at 60 Hz are connected in parallel and have the following regulation values: $R_1 = 5\%$, $R_2 = 10\%$ and $R_3 = 15\%$. A load change of 0.1 pu occurs. Calculate the equivalent value of the regulation, the initial decrease in frequency and how the change in load is shared by the three generators initially.

12-2   Repeat Example 12-2 using MATLAB or PowerWorld to compute line flows if the load on bus-3 decreases from 500 MW to 400 MW.

12-3   Repeat Example 12-3 using Simulink, where eliminate the low-pass filtering in the regulators by setting $T_{s1} = T_{s2} = 0$. Compare the results with those in Example 12-3.

12-4   The marginal costs in \$/MWh of three generators can be expressed as follows: (1.0+0.02P) for generator 1, (2.0+0.015P) for generator 2, and (1.5+0.01P) for generator 3, where P is in MW. The total power supplied by these generators is 500 MW. Calculate the system marginal cost λ and the load shared by each of the three generators.

12-5   Repeat Problem 12-4, if the power output of generator 3 is limited in a range of 25 MW to 75 MW.

12-6   The daily load-duration curve over a 24-hour period is as shown in Fig. P12-6, where it varies from 200 MW to 600 MW. It is being supplied by three generators whose marginal cost curves are described in Problem 12-4. If an economic dispatch is implemented, calculate the daily fuel cost in dollars for each of the generators and the total, to meet this power demand.

Fig. P12-6 Load-duration curve.

CHAPTER 13

TRANSMISSION LINE FAULTS, RELAYING AND CIRCUIT BREAKERS

Transmission lines stretch over large distances and are subject to faults involving one or more phases and ground. Such faults in a form of a short circuit not only cause momentary power outages, but more importantly, if protective action is not taken, can cause permanent damage to transmission equipment such as the line itself and the transformers. In this chapter, we will analyze the causes and the types of faults, the relays to detect them and the circuit breakers to isolate these faults and then restore the power system back to normal.

13-1   CAUSES OF TRANSMISSION LINE FAULTS

A common cause of such faults is tree branches near the right-of-way falling on transmission lines and shorting them to ground. Sagging transmission lines touching the trees underneath were a part of the major blackout on August 14, 2003 in the northeast United States. Another common fault occurrence is due to backflash when the transmission-line tower or one of the ground wires is struck by lightning that represents a current source of several thousand kilo-amperes. This current flowing through the tower footing impedance can raise the tower potential above the local ground to such a level that without surge arresters (discussed in the next chapter), the insulator string flashes over.

The lightning current is momentary and lasts just a few tens of micro seconds, but the arc established due to such an insulator-string flashover results in a short-to-ground of the power-frequency voltages through the arc impedance to the line-frequency voltage of 60 or 50 Hz. If short circuit currents are not detected by a relay that sends a signal to open circuit breakers to interrupt this current, the current at the power frequency would keep flowing until a serious damage such as a fire would damage the equipment. Therefore, it is essential that these faults be detected and circuit breakers interrupt them quickly. A few cycles after the fault has been cleared, the circuit breakers can be closed and the normal operation resumes.

The reason to analyze short circuit faults are 1) to set the relays so they can detect it, and 2) to make sure that the circuit breakers ratings are such that they are capable of interrupting the fault currents.

13-2   SYMMETRICAL COMPONENTS FOR FAULT ANALYSIS

More than 80 percent of the faults involve just one of the three phases and ground, for example a tree branch touches or falls on one of the phases. Such faults are called unsymmetrical faults, however easiest to analyze are symmetrical faults involving a short between all three phases and possibly to ground.

We will begin with the discussion of the analytical approach to analyze unsymmetrical faults of which symmetrical faults are just a subset. To keep this discussion simple yet practical, we will assume that the system is balanced, although the fault at a location is unsymmetrical. Such a fault results in fault currents i_a, i_b and i_c as shown in Fig. 13-1a. In analyzing fault currents, we will assume that they have reached their steady state at the line frequency of 60/50 Hz. Therefore, in steady state at the line frequency, even though i_a, i_b and i_c in Fig. 13-1a are unbalanced, they can be represented by phasors $\overline{I}_a$, $\overline{I}_b$, and $\overline{I}_c$ as shown in Fig. 13-1b.

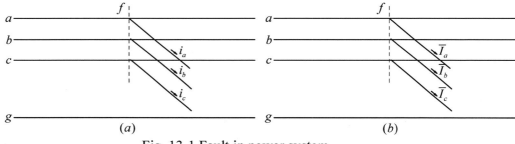

Fig. 13-1 Fault in power system.

13-2-1 Calculating the Symmetrical Components

To analyze power system with unsymmetrical fault, Fortesque [1] showed long ago that the unbalanced currents can be expressed as sums of components that are symmetrical and balanced. Assuming the power system to be a linear network where the Principle of Superposition can be applied, the voltages and currents in the faulted system can be obtained by summing the components in each of the balanced sequence network.

To apply the above principle to unbalanced currents in Fig. 13-2a, they can be shown to be composed of three components as follows:

$$\overline{I}_a = \overline{I}_{a1} + \overline{I}_{a2} + \overline{I}_{a0}$$
$$\overline{I}_b = \overline{I}_{b1} + \overline{I}_{b2} + \overline{I}_{b0} \qquad\qquad (13\text{-}1)$$
$$\overline{I}_c = \overline{I}_{c1} + \overline{I}_{c2} + \overline{I}_{c0}$$

where as shown in Fig. 13-2b, the subscript 1 refers to the positive-sequence, 2 to the negative-sequence and 0 to zero-sequence components.

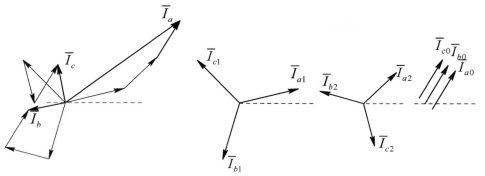

Fig. 13-2 Sequence components.

Within each sequence, the three phases are balanced and sinusoidal at the line frequency. Positive-sequence components $\overline{I}_{a1}$, etc are balanced in amplitude and are of the same a-b-c sequence as the power system voltages and currents, that is phase $\overline{I}_{b1}$ lags $\overline{I}_{a1}$ by 120^0 and so on. The negative-sequence components are also balanced in amplitude but are of the sequence a-c-b, that is, $\overline{I}_{c2}$ lags $\overline{I}_{a2}$ by 120^0 and so on. The zero-sequence components are also balanced in amplitude but, in contrast to both the positive and the negative-sequence components, $\overline{I}_{a0} = \overline{I}_{b0} = \overline{I}_{c0}$ have the same phase, and thus, are equal to each other and hence the name zero-sequence. Given these properties of the sequence components in Eq. 13-1, for ease of writing we will define the following operators:

$$a = 1\angle 120^0 = -0.5 + j0.866$$
$$a^2 = 1\angle 240^0 = -0.5 - j0.866$$

(13-2)

Therefore, the sequence components in phases b and c in Eq. 13-1 can be written in terms of the phase-a components as follows:

$$\overline{I}_{b1} = a^2 \overline{I}_{a1}; \ \overline{I}_{c1} = a\overline{I}_{a1}$$
$$\overline{I}_{b2} = a\overline{I}_{a2}; \ \overline{I}_{c2} = a^2 \overline{I}_{a2}$$

(13-3)

Therefore, substituting the above, the fault currents in terms of phase-a components can be written as

$$\overline{I}_a = \overline{I}_{a1} + \overline{I}_{a2} + \overline{I}_{a0}$$
$$\overline{I}_b = a^2 \overline{I}_{a1} + a\overline{I}_{a2} + \overline{I}_{a0}$$
$$\overline{I}_c = a\overline{I}_{a1} + a^2 \overline{I}_{a2} + \overline{I}_{a0}$$

(13-4)

which in a matrix form can be written as

$$
\begin{bmatrix} \overline{I}_a \\ \overline{I}_b \\ \overline{I}_c \end{bmatrix} = \begin{bmatrix} 1 & 1 & 1 \\ a^2 & a & 1 \\ a & a^2 & 1 \end{bmatrix} \begin{bmatrix} \overline{I}_{a1} \\ \overline{I}_{a2} \\ \overline{I}_{a0} \end{bmatrix}
\tag{13-5}
$$

Inverting the matrix in Eq. 13-5, we can solve for the three sequence components of the phase-a current in terms of the fault currents:

$$
\begin{bmatrix} \overline{I}_{a1} \\ \overline{I}_{a2} \\ \overline{I}_{a0} \end{bmatrix} = \frac{1}{3} \begin{bmatrix} 1 & a & a^2 \\ 1 & a^2 & a \\ 1 & 1 & 1 \end{bmatrix} \begin{bmatrix} \overline{I}_a \\ \overline{I}_b \\ \overline{I}_c \end{bmatrix}
\tag{13-6}
$$

▲ **Example 13-1** In Fig. 13-2, the three phase currents are unbalanced and have the following values: $\overline{I}_a = 2.2027\angle 26.6319^0\, A$, $\overline{I}_b = 0.6034\angle -156.857^0\, A$, $\overline{I}_c = 0.4706\angle 138.6949^0\, A$. Calculate the symmetrical components $\overline{I}_{a1}$, $\overline{I}_{a2}$, and $\overline{I}_{a0}$.

Solution   Applying Eq. 13-6 with the above values of phase current, these phase currents are made of symmetrical components with the positive-sequence $\overline{I}_{a1} = 1.0\angle 15^0\, A$, the negative-sequence $\overline{I}_{a2} = 0.75\angle 30^0\, A$, and the zero-sequence $\overline{I}_{a0} = 0.5\angle 45^0\, A$.

▲

13-2-2 Applying the Sequence-Components to the Network and the Superposition

Looking into the system from the fault point for each sequence, the system is balanced and therefore the three-phase system can be represented on a per-phase basis as discussed in Chapter 3, in terms of phase-a for example. For each sequence, the power system network can be drawn in terms of that sequence for phase-a, for example, as shown in Fig. 13-3. How these networks are connected depends on the type of fault. Once the currents and voltages are calculated in these sequence networks for phase-a, they can be used to calculate voltages and currents in the faulted system using equations similar to Eq. 13-5.

Fig. 13-3 Sequence networks.

13-3   TYPES OF FAULTS

There can be many different types of faults and the procedure for solving for all of them is similar. In this chapter, the following faults are considered:
-   Symmetrical Three-Phase and Three-Phase to Ground Fault

- Single-Line to Ground Fault
- Double-line to Ground Fault
- Double Line Fault (ground is not involved)
- Fault with Fault Impedances

In addition to these short-circuit faults, there can be there can be instances of open-circuit conductor(s) that can serious safety issues. Analysis of these is left as a homework exercise.

13-3-1 Symmetrical Three-Phase and Three-Phase to Ground Fault

In a balanced system, three-phase or three-phase-to-ground fault are identical where the voltage at the faulted point is zero with respect to ground, and the current flowing into ground is zero since $\overline{I}_a + \overline{I}_b + \overline{I}_c = 0$ in Fig. 13-4a.

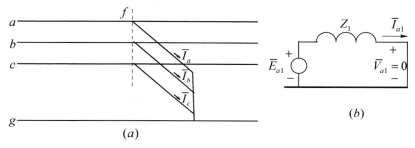

(a)

(b)

Fig. 13-4 Three-phase symmetrical fault.

Since, these three fault currents form a balanced three-phase set, the negative and the zero sequence components are zero and only the positive sequence network, on a per-phase basis needs to be considered as shown in Fig. 13-4b, where, $\overline{I}_a = \overline{I}_{a1}$ since the other components are zero.

13-3-2 Single-Line to Ground Fault

This is shown in Fig. 13-5a, where phase-a is faulted to ground through a fault impedance Z_f.

The fault conditions result in the following conditions:

$$\overline{I}_b = \overline{I}_c = 0 \tag{13-7}$$

$$\overline{V}_a = 0 \tag{13-8}$$

Substituting $\overline{I}_b$ and $\overline{I}_c$ as zero in Eq. 13-6,

$$\overline{I}_{a1} = \overline{I}_{a2} = \overline{I}_{a0} \tag{13-9}$$

and

Fig. 13-5 Single line to ground fault.

$$\overline{I}_{a1} = \frac{\overline{I}_a}{3} \qquad (13\text{-}10)$$

From the voltage fault condition,

$$\overline{V}_a = \overline{V}_{a1} + \overline{V}_{a2} + \overline{V}_{a0} = Z_f \overline{I}_a \qquad (13\text{-}11)$$

Substituting for $\overline{I}_a$ from Eq. 13-10 into Eq. 13-11,

$$\overline{V}_a = \overline{V}_{a1} + \overline{V}_{a2} + \overline{V}_{a0} = 3Z_f \overline{I}_{a1} \qquad (13\text{-}12)$$

Eqs. 13-9 and 13-12 are satisfied by connecting the three sequence networks in series as shown in Fig. 13-5b from which

$$\overline{I}_{a1} = \overline{I}_{a2} = \overline{I}_{a0} = \frac{\overline{E}_{a1}}{Z_1 + Z_2 + Z_0 + 3Z_f} \qquad (13\text{-}13)$$

Knowing the sequence currents, all the three sequence networks can be solved and any of the currents and voltages can be computed in the faulted network.

13-3-3 Double-line to Ground Fault

This is shown in Fig. 13-6a, where phases b and c are faulted to ground. The fault conditions result in the following conditions:

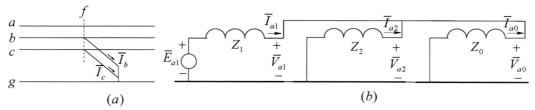

Fig. 13-6 Double line to ground fault.

$$\overline{I}_a = 0 \qquad (13\text{-}14)$$

13-6

$$\overline{V}_b = \overline{V}_c = 0 \tag{13-15}$$

Using the condition in Eq. 13-15 for voltages into an equation similar to Eq. 13-6,

$$\overline{V}_{a1} = \overline{V}_{a2} = \overline{V}_{ao} \tag{13-16}$$

From Eq. 13-16, it is clear all three sequence networks are in parallel as shown in Fig. 13-6b, and applying the Kirchhoff's current law in this circuit, Eq. 13-14 is satisfied in light of Eq. 13-4.

13-3-4 Double-Line Fault (ground is not involved)

This is shown in Fig. 13-7a, where phases b and c are shorted to each other through Z_f. The fault result in the following conditions:

$$\overline{I}_a = 0 \tag{13-17}$$

$$\overline{I}_b = -\overline{I}_c \tag{13-18}$$

$$\overline{V}_b = \overline{V}_c + Z_f \overline{I}_b \tag{13-19}$$

Fig. 13-7 Double line fault (ground not involved).

By observation of the faulted system, there is no connection to ground and hence there cannot be any zero-sequence current

$$\overline{I}_{a0} = 0 \tag{13-20}$$

and hence, in the zero-sequence network, all the zero-sequence voltage would be zero;

$$\overline{V}_{a0} = 0 \tag{13-21}$$

Since $\overline{I}_a$ is zero and so is $\overline{I}_{a0}$,

$$\overline{I}_{a1} = -\overline{I}_{a2} \tag{13-22}$$

Therefore, from Eq. 13-5

$$\overline{I}_b = (a^2 - a)\overline{I}_{a1} \tag{13-23}$$

From the voltage fault condition of Eq. 13-19, with $\overline{V}_{a0} = 0$, from the voltage equation similar to Eq. 13-5 and using Eq. 13-23

$$a^2\overline{V}_{a1} + a\overline{V}_{a2} = a\overline{V}_{a1} + a^2\overline{V}_{a2} + Z_f(a^2 - a)\overline{I}_{a1}$$ (13-24)

From the above equation

$$\overline{V}_{a1} = \overline{V}_{a2} + Z_f\overline{I}_{a1}$$ (13-25)

Using the voltage and the current equations of the fault, the sequence networks are connected as shown in Fig. 13-7b.

13-4   SYSTEM IMPEDANCES FOR FAULT CALCULATIONS

Since unsymmetrical faults involve positive, negative and the zero-sequence components, various power system components must be represented by their appropriate impedances.

13-4-1 Transmission Lines

Transmission lines are assumed to be perfectly transposed and their positive and negative sequence impedances are the same. Their zero-sequence impedance that involves ground return is greater in value and it can be calculated using a line-constants program such as EMTDC, as described in the chapter dealing with transient over-voltages on transmission lines.

13-4-2 Simplified Synchronous Generator Representation

For calculating fault currents within a few cycles of the fault inception, sub-transient reactance of the generators are used. Assuming that it is a round-rotor machine, the positive sequence impedance equals $X_d^{"}$ for the d-axis, whereas that of the q-axis sub-transient reactance may be slightly smaller. Typically, it can be approximated that $X_d^{"} = 0.12\,pu$.

In the negative sequence, the voltage and currents are of the negative sequence a-c-b, while the rotor is turning at the synchronous speed in the forward direction dictated by the positive sequence a-b-c excitation. In this situation, the armature reaction mmf produced by the negative sequence currents would rotate in the direction opposite to the rotor. This would be at twice the synchronous speed with respect to the rotor. Therefore, the d- and q-axis damper winding would shield the flux due to the negative-sequence armature reaction from going past the damper windings. Therefore, the negative sequence reactance of the synchronous generator can be written as

$$X_2 = \frac{X_d^{"} + X_q^{"}}{2}$$ (13-26)

Typically, it can be approximated as $X_2 = 0.12\,pu$.

The zero-sequence impedance depends on the leakage reactance per-phase plus three times the impedance that is usually connected from the neutral to ground through a transformer. If the neutral for some reason is floating with respect to ground and this neutral impedance is infinite, then, the zero sequence impedance would also be infinite, indicating that the zero-sequence current cannot flow through the generator. Typically, the internal zero-sequence reactance of a turbo-generator can be approximated as $X_0 = 0.5X_2$.

For fault calculations, usually the positive-sequence network for the generator is represented by the sub-transient reactance and a voltage source behind it, such that, together they yield the pre-fault voltages and currents in the network.

13-4-3 Transformer Representation in Fault Studies

Generally, only the leakage impedance of the transformers need be included in fault studies. On per unit basis, normally the transformer turns-ratio does not appear in calculations. Transformer leakage reactances are the same for the positive and the negative sequences. The zero sequence impedance depends on how the three phase windings are connected. For example, a delta-connected winding does not provide a path of zero sequence current in the currents flowing to the delta connection as shown in Fig. 13-8a.

(a)   (b)   (c)

Fig. 13-8 Path for zero-sequence currents in transformers.

Similarly, the wye-connected windings with an isolated neutral will appear as an open-circuit to zero sequence, as shown in Fig. 13-8b. As shown in Fig. 13-8c, a grounded-wye with delta-connected secondary windings provides a short-circuit path that allows zero-sequence currents to flow. This will also be the case if the secondary was connected in a grounded-wye. However, the grounded-wye in Fig. 13-8c will appear as an open-circuit if the secondary was wye-connected with an isolated neutral. If zero-sequence currents can flow, a neural-to-ground impedance Z_n, as shown in Fig. 13-9a, will appear as $3Z_n$ in the zero sequence network of Fig. 13-9b.

(a)   (b)

Fig. 13-9 Neutral grounded through an impedance.

In case of three single-phase transformers, the zero-sequence impedance Z_0 in Fig. 13-9b equals the positive-sequence leakage impedance. This will also be the case in three-phase transformers with shell-type construction.

▲ **Example 13-2** Consider a simple system with a 1 pu load being supplied by a single generator, as shown in Fig. 13-10, where all the quantities are in per unit. Calculate the fault current in per unit at Bus-2 for (a) three-phase fault, and (b) single-line to ground (SLG) fault with the fault impedance as zero.

Fig. 13-10 (a) One-line diagram of a simple power system and bus voltages.

Solution   Bus-1 is assumed to be the slack bus with $\overline{V}_1 = 1.0\angle 0\,pu$. Using the MATLAB program developed in Chapter 5 on Power Flow or the *PowerWorld*, both of which are included on the accompanying CD, the pre-fault voltage at bus-3 is calculated as $\overline{V}_3 = 0.98\angle -11.79^0\,pu$ and shown in Fig. 13-10.

(a)   In case of a three-phase fault on bus-2, the positive-sequence per-phase circuit is shown in Fig. 13-11, where $\overline{I}_{Load}$ and hence $\overline{E}''$ at the back of the sub-transient reactance can be calculated as $\overline{V}_3 \overline{I}_{Load}^* = 1.0\,pu$, therefore, $\overline{I}_{Load} = 1.0204\angle -11.79^0\,pu$ before the fault. Therefore in Fig. 13-11, $\overline{E}'' = 1.0\angle 0 + j0.12\overline{I}_{Load} = 1.032\angle 6.67^0\,pu$. With a short on bus-2 to ground, with the switch closed in Fig. 13-11, $\overline{I}_{fault} = 4.69\angle -83.32^0\,pu$.

Fig. 13-11 Positive-sequence circuit for calculating a 3-phase fault on bus-2.

(b)   In case of a single-line to ground (SLG) fault on bus-2, the sequence per-phase networks are connected in series as the analysis in Fig. 13-5 shows. With the fault impedance $Z_f = 0$, the circuit diagram is shown in Fig. 13-12. In the zero-sequence network, the generator zero-sequence impedance is shorted out because of the grounded-wye-delta connection. Also, the 30^0 phase shift introduced by the transformer connection is ignored because it has no effect on the magnitude of the fault current. From Fig. 13-12, $\overline{I}_{fault} = 5.71\angle-85.7^0 \, pu$. The MATLAB and the PowerWorld files are included on the accompanying CD.

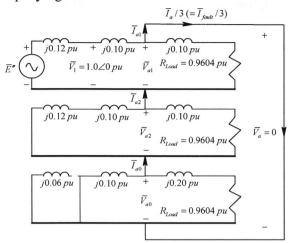

Fig. 13-12 Sequence networks for calculating fault current due to SLG fault on bus-2.

▲

13-5 CALCULATION OF FAULT CURRENTS IN LARGE NETWORKS

The above procedure shows the underlying principles for fault calculation which can be used for analyzing a power system with a few buses. In most practical networks with thousands of buses, computer programs have been developed to carry these out. One of the procedures used in computing fault currents in such network is described below.

Earlier, we have discussed the nodal equation formulation of the network for the positive sequence

$$\overline{I}_{pos} = Y_{pos}\overline{V}_{pos} \qquad (13\text{-}27)$$

where the subscript "pos" is used to indicate positive sequence, in place of "1", which may be a bus number. Eq. 13-37 can be written in terms of the impedance matrix as

$$\overline{V}_{pos} = Z_{pos}\overline{I}_{pos} \qquad (13\text{-}28)$$

where $Z_{pos}(=Y_{pos}^{-1})$ is the inverse of the Y-matrix. The impedance matrix in large networks is created without taking the inverse of the Y-matrix. Similar equations can be written to relate negative-sequence and the zero-sequence voltages and currents. From these networks, the fault currents for any type of fault can be computed using a computer program such as PowerWorld.

13-11

▲ **Example 13-3** Consider the example three-bus power system discussed in earlier chapters and repeated in Fig. 13-13. This system under the pre-fault operating conditions is modeled in PowerWorld and described on the accompanying CD. A single-line to ground (SLG) fault occurs on the line 1-2, $1/3^{rd}$ of the distance away from bus-1. Calculate the fault current and the current on various lines.

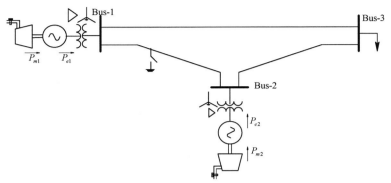

Fig. 13-13 A SLG fault in the example 3-bus power system.

Solution The solution to this example is detailed by a PowerWorld program included on the accompanying CD.

▲

13-6 PROTECTION AGAINST SHORT-CIRCUIT FAULTS

Although, open-circuit can sometimes result in hazardous safety situation to personnel and must be guarded against, it is the over-current phenomena due a short-circuit fault that is of focus here. To minimize the interval of power disturbance and more importantly preventing power equipment from permanent damage, it is important that currents larger than the load currents, that the apparatus is designed for, not be allowed to flow for intervals that can be destructive. For this purpose, all power system apparatus for normal operation are equipped with over-current protection equipment. This protection equipment can be categorized as follows, as shown in the block diagram of Fig. 13-14 for one of the circuit breakers (CB):

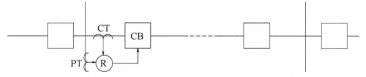

Fig. 13-14 Protection equipment.

- – Current and voltage transformers for sensing these line values
- – Relays which determine if a fault has occurred and issue a command to this effect
- – Circuit Breakers which open contacts to interrupt the fault and subsequently reclose them to resume normal operation

All these are described briefly in the sub-sections below.

13-6-1 Current and Voltage Transformers

The currents and voltages in a power system must be sensed to determine in a relay if a fault has occurred. However, these are at extremely high values and must be stepped down to voltage signals with reference to a logic ground.

The current transformer (CT), as shown in Fig. 13-15a is a transformer in which the power system current flows through its primary which is usually has a single turn as shown in Fig. 13-15b. The secondary generally has a large number of turns and produces a much smaller current, primary current divided by the turn-ratio, which flows through a small load referred to as "burden". The current-sense signal associated with it is used in the relay logic.

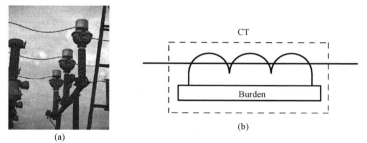

(a)

(b)

Fig. 13-15 Current Transformer (CT) [5].

The capacitor-coupled voltage transformer (CCVT) in Fig. 13-16a uses the capacitive voltage-divider principle where the output voltage of this divider is isolated through a transformer for safety purposes, as shown in Fig. 13-16b.

(a)   (b)

Fig. 13-16 Capacitor-Coupled Voltage Transformer (CCVT) [5].

13-6-2 Relays

Relays, based on the sensed voltages and currents, and other signals like time and so on, decide if a fault has occurred and if it should be interrupted by the circuit breaker. It is important that relays operate, when they should, in order to protect power system but it is equally important that they don't operate falsely in order to avoid causing unnecessary power disturbances. Therefore, in relays, three things are important: selectivity, speed and reliability.

Relays are of many types but they can be basically categorized in the following manner:

- Differential Relays: These relays may be used, for example to protect a generator, a bus or a transformer against internal faults, as shown in Fig. 13-17.

Fig. 13-17 Differential relay.

Under normal conditions, as shown in Fig. 13-17, the differential current through the relay, which is the difference between the measured currents, is zero. This is not so under an internal fault condition, causing the fault current to trip the circuit breaker.

- Over-Current Relays: In these relays, if the current being measured exceeds a minimum value that is greater than the maximum load current by a certain factor, the relay determines that a fault has occurred, giving a "trip" command to the circuit breaker to operate. Generally, such relays operate on a delay time basis where this delay time is nonlinear function of the magnitude of the fault current; larger the current magnitude, shorter the delay time.

- Directional Over-current Relays: The protection offered by this relay is for faults only in one direction. For example, in Fig. 13-18, if the fault occurs right of its CT location, the current $\bar{I}$ sensed by this relay would be lagging with respect to the voltage at this location, causing the relay to trip the circuit breaker. Whereas for the fault left of its CT location, the current would be leading and the relay would be blocked from tripping the circuit breaker.

Fig. 13-18 Directional over-current Relay.

- Ground Directional Over-current Relays: These are zero-sequence relays which as Fig. 13-19 shows, act instantaneously in issuing a trip command to the circuit breaker if the fault is within 85% of the line; otherwise the time is increased as shown.

Fig. 13-19 Ground directional over-current Relay.

- Distance (Impedance) Relays: By calculating the ratio of the measured voltage magnitude and the measured current magnitude, these bidirectional relays determine the impedance, and hence the name, which is an indication of the distance along the line that the fault has occurred. In an $R - X$ plane shown in Fig. 13-20, if the calculated impedance falls within the circle, the relay will trip; otherwise it is blocked.

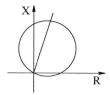

Fig. 13-20 Impedance (distance) relay.

- Pilot Relays: Pilot relays use the communication channel, like the microwave shown in Fig. 13-21, power-line carrier or the fiber-optics, to communicate between the two terminals of a transmission line being protected by such relays. If a fault occurs that is internal to the transmission line, the relays issue commands to circuit breakers at both ends of this line to interrupt the fault.

Fig. 13-21 Microwave terminal [5].

Zones of Protection: The power system is divided into zones of protection, for example as shown in Fig. 13-22.

Fig. 13-22 Zones of protection.

Each zone encompasses one or more power system equipment, and adjacent zones are overlapping so that no part of the power system is left unprotected.

- The first zone for the relay at A encompasses for example 90% of the line. The remaining 10% is protected by the relay at B. If the fault occurs in A's first zone, the relay acts instantly without any time delay

- The second zone for the relay at A encompasses for example 120% of the line, thus overreaching in the next section. If the fault occurs in the second zone assigned to it, it operates with a time delay of a few hundred msec, thus allowing it to coordinate with the relay that is its first zone.

- The adjacent zone consisting of line CD is the third zone for the relay A for which it provides backup protection with a further time delay of 1 to 3 seconds.

Protection of Generator and the Step-up Transformer: Fig. 13-23 shows the relaying scheme for protecting a generator and the step-up transformer associated with it. The generator neutral is grounded through an impedance that is connected to the secondary of a transformer, as shown in Fig. 13-23. If a fault is detected, the circuit breaker is tripped, the field-excitation is removed and steam is vented out.

Fig. 13-23 Protection of generator and the step-up transformer.

▲ **Example 13-4** In the example 3-bus power system shown in Fig. 13-24, what are the relays that act on the circuit breakers A and B.

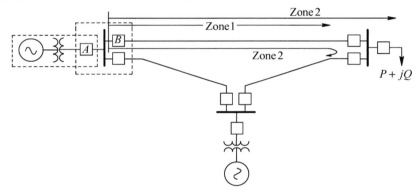

Fig. 13-24 Relaying in the example 3-bus power system.

Solution The overlapping zones of protection are as shown in Fig. 13-24. The circuit breaker A is acted upon a differential protection relay shown in Fig. 13-23 to protect the generator and the step-up transformer, and a differential relay shown in Fig. 13-17 to protect the bus. The circuit breaker B is acted upon several relays: a differential relay shown in Fig. 13-17 to protect the bus, an impedance relay shown in Fig. 13-20 to protect against phase-phase faults (not involving ground) between a-b, b-c and c-a phases, where zone 1 and zone 2 are shown in Fig. 13-24 (zone 3, beyond zone 2, is for backup protection), and a ground direction over-current relay shown in Fig. 13-19 for single-line to ground (SLG) faults. ▲

13-6-3 Circuit Breakers

Circuit breakers are large apparatus which, commanded by relays, interrupt the flow of current and break the circuit, as the name implies, in order to protect power equipment from short-circuit faults. There are circuit breakers available that can operate in two cycles and further improvements are continuously being made. Various different principles are used to elongate and cool the arc established by the parting contacts as they try to interrupt the current through them; this process is helped in case of ac circuits where current goes to zero naturally every half-cycle. Circuit breakers use a method of arc interruption based on their voltage level. At 345-kV and above, most circuit breakers use sulfur hexafluoride (SF_6) as shown in Fig. 13-25 and SF_6 gas-puffer. SF_6 is a greenhouse gas but there is no good substitute available.

Fig. 13-25 SF_6 circuit breaker [5].

13-6-3-1   Automatic Reclosure

From stability considerations, high-speed reclosing is important. Since most faults are of transitory nature, many utilities allow EHV circuit breakers a single reclosing automatically. If the fault is still persisting, the circuit breakers trip the line without further attempts to reclose automatically and only the system operator can reclose the line. Such automatic reclosing is not recommended for lines leaving a generating station, since reclosing into a persistent fault can fatigue the shaft of the turbine-generator. In distribution systems, where it is important to maintain continuity of service to customer loads, several attempts for automatic reclosing may be allowed.

13-6-3-2   Single-Phase (or Independent-Pole) Operation

In conventional relaying and circuit breaker schemes, all three phases are tripped for any type of fault. However, most faults involve only one of the phases, whereas tripping all three phases represents a more serious interruption. Therefore, certain utilities opt to open only the faulted phase. Of course, these schemes are more complex and costly than the conventional schemes.

13-6-3-3   Circuit Breaker Ratings

Circuit breakers as discussed above are rated for their interrupting times in cycles of the line frequency. In addition, they have voltage ratings based on their insulation and current ratings based on the current they can safely carry and interrupt.

Symmetrical and Asymmetrical Current Ratings:

A sudden fault in power system can result in current transients that decay based on the ratio of circuit inductance to resistance. The fault calculations discussed earlier in the chapter determined the *symmetrical* (with equal positive and negative peak values) line-frequency current following a fault. In these calculations, it was assumed that the current transients have decayed away. However, with fast circuit breakers it is important to take into account the initial current offset that results in *asymmetrical* current, called so because the positive and negative peak values are not the same. The asymmetrical current can be higher than the symmetrical current by a factor depending on the reactance over the resistance ratio, X/R, of the network.

This initial current offset that decays can be understood by a simple R-L circuit with a sinusoidal source, as shown in Fig. 13-26a, where $v_s(t) = \hat{V}\sin(\omega t + \phi)$.

Fig. 13-26 Current in an *RL* circuit.

Choosing the switch-closing time as $t = 0$, across the impedance, the voltage $v(t)$, which was initially zero, can be expressed as $v(t) = \hat{V}\sin(\omega t + \phi)$. Therefore, in the circuit of Fig. 13-26a,

$$Ri + L\frac{di}{dt} = \hat{V}\sin(\omega t + \phi) \qquad (t > 0) \qquad (13\text{-}29)$$

The natural current component, recognizing that this component decays with time, is

$$i_n(t) = Ae^{-t/\tau} \qquad \text{(where, } \tau = L/R \text{ is the time constant)} \qquad (13\text{-}30)$$

The steady state ac current component in this R-L circuit is

$$i_{ac} = \hat{I}_{ac}\sin(\omega t + \phi - \beta) \qquad (13\text{-}31)$$

13-18

where, $\hat{I}_{ac} = \dfrac{\hat{V}}{\sqrt{R^2 + (\omega L)^2}}$ and $\beta = \tan^{-1}\left(\dfrac{\omega L}{R}\right)$.

Therefore, the complete current solution, using Eqs. 13-30 and 13-31, is

$$i(t) = Ae^{-t/\tau} + \hat{I}_{ac}\sin(\omega t + \phi - \beta) \tag{13-32}$$

where the unknown A can be calculated from the initial condition, that is, at time $t = 0$, the current $i = 0$. Therefore, from Eq. 13-32, $A = \hat{I}_{ac}\sin(\beta - \phi)$, and thus

$$i(t) = \underbrace{\hat{I}_{ac}\sin(\beta - \phi)e^{-t/\tau}}_{\text{offset } I_{dc}(t)} + \hat{I}_{ac}\sin(\omega t + \phi - \beta) \qquad (t > 0) \tag{13-33}$$

This *asymmetrical* current $i(t)$, where the decaying dc offset is superimposed on the ac (symmetrical) component, is plotted in Fig. 13-26b. As can be seen from Eq. 13-33, the offset $I_{dc}(t)$ is a *dc* component that decays exponentially with time, based on the circuit time constant $\tau = L/R$, as $e^{-(R/L)t}$. In low resistance networks that are typical of power systems, the dc component decays slowly, compared to the power frequency, and can be assumed constant at the time of the circuit-breaker opening at a value I_{dc} over one or two power-frequency cycles. Therefore, the rms value I_{rms} of the asymmetrical current can be calculated, recognizing that the rms value of the ac component is $I_{ac} = \hat{I}_{ac}/\sqrt{2}$, as:

$$I_{rms} = \sqrt{I_{dc}^2 + I_{ac}^2} \tag{13-34}$$

The above discussion shows that in low resistance network that is typical of power systems, high-speed circuit breakers that interrupt current soon after the fault, have to interrupt a current that is factor S higher than the ac current, where $S = 1.2$ for a 2 cycle breaker (this includes ½-cycle minimum relay time and plus the opening time of the breaker contacts) [8]. This factor S varies inversely proportional to the breaker contact parting-time, as defined in the ANSI/IEEE Standard C37.010 Application Guide [8]. For circuit breakers at above 115-kV voltage levels, the closing and latching capabilities for momentary symmetrical rms current are defined to be 1.6 times the rated rms short-circuit current [9].

REFERENCES

1. C.L.Fortescue, "Method of Symmetrical Coordinates Applied to the Solution of Polyphase Networks," AIEE, vol. 37, pp 1027-1140, 1918.
2. Prabha Kundur, *Power System Stability and Control*, McGraw-Hill, 1994.

3. Paul Anderson, Analysis of Faulted Power Systems, IEEE Press, 1995.
4. Power World Computer Program (www.powerworld.com).
5. United States Department of Agriculture, Rural Utilities Service, Design Guide for Rural Substations, RUS BULLETIN 1724E-300.
6. Electric Utility Systems and Practices, 4th Edition by Homer M. Rustebakke (Editor), John Wiley & Sons, August 1983.
7. A. Phadke, J. Thorp, *Computer Relaying for Power Systems*, Institute of Physics Publishers, 2005.
8. H. O. Simmons, Jr., "Symmetrical versus Total Current Rating of Power Circuit Breakers," Applications of Power Circuit Breakers, IEEE Tutorial Course, 75CH0975-3-PWR.
9. ANSI/IEEE Standard C37.04.

PROBLEMS

13-1   Due to a single-line to ground fault on phase-a, $\overline{I}_{fa} = 5\angle 0\, pu$ and $\overline{I}_{fb} = \overline{I}_{fc} = 0$. Calculate the symmetrical components $\overline{I}_{fa1}$, $\overline{I}_{fa2}$ and $\overline{I}_{fa0}$.

13-2   Due to a line-to-line fault between phase-b and phase-c $\overline{I}_{fa} = 0$ and $\overline{I}_{fb} = -\overline{I}_{fc} = 5\angle 0\, pu$. Calculate the symmetrical components $\overline{I}_{fa1}$, $\overline{I}_{fa2}$ and $\overline{I}_{fa0}$.

13-3   At a point f in the system, there is an open-circuit fault on phase-a with a voltage across the open-circuit as $\overline{V}_{fa}$, whereas $\overline{V}_{fb} = \overline{V}_{fc} = 0$. Similar to the calculations of the short-circuit currents by making use of the sequence networks, calculate the sequence components $\overline{V}_{fa1}$, $\overline{V}_{fa2}$ and $\overline{V}_{fa0}$ at the fault-point.

13-4   Repeat Example 13-2 if the single-line to ground (SLG) fault is through a fault impedance $Z_f = 0.15\angle 0\, pu$.

13-5   Repeat Example 13-2 if before the fault, the load is zero, that is, $P_{Load} = 0$.

13-6   Repeat Example 13-2 if it is a Double-Line fault between phases b and c.

13-7   Repeat Example 13-2 if it is a Double-Line fault between phases b and c with a fault impedance $Z_f = 0.15\angle 0\, pu$.

13-8   Repeat Example 13-2 if it is a Double-Line to ground fault with phases b and c grounded.

13-9   Repeat Example 13-2 if it is a Double-Line to ground fault with phases b and c grounded through a fault impedance $Z_f = 0.15\angle 0\, pu$.

13-10   Repeat Example 13-2 if there is a single-line to ground fault on phase-a of Bus-1. The generator neutral is grounded through a resistance $R_n = 0.10\, pu$.

13-11 Repeat Example 13-2 if there is a line-line to ground fault involving phases b and c of Bus-1. The generator neutral is grounded through a resistance $R_n = 0.10\,pu$.

13-12 Repeat Example 13-2 for an open-circuit fault by calculating the sequence voltages at the fault-point on line 2-3 near bus-2, where the contact opens up on phase-a.

13-13 Explain how the Differential relay of Fig. 13-17 operates to protect in case of a fault within the protected zone.

13-14 For the impedance relay of Fig. 13-20 applied to protect line 2-3 in Example 13-2, calculate the point in the impedance plane for a three-phase fault that is 85% of the line-length away from Bus-2. Repeat this if the fault is 15% of the line-length away from Bus-2.

13-15 Explain how the Differential relaying scheme of Fig. 13-23 works to protect in case of a fault either at point *F1* or *F2*.

13-16 Prove Eq. 13-34.

Problem using PowerWorld:
13-17 Repeat Example 13-3 for a Double-Line and a Double-Line to ground fault.

CHAPTER 14

TRANSIENT OVER-VOLTAGES, SURGE PROTECTION AND INSULATION COORDINATION

14-1   INTRODUCTION

Transmission and distribution lines form a large network spread over thousands of miles. A variety of reasons discussed below can cause abnormally high over-voltages that, unless protected properly against, can disrupt service momentarily at best, and cause prolonged outage and expensive damage to the power systems apparatus at worst. In this chapter, we will examine the causes of over-voltages and the measures that can be taken to protect against.

14-2   CAUSES OF OVER-VOLTAGES

Over-voltages are caused primarily by lightning strikes and switching of extra-high voltage transmission lines, both are examined below.

14-2-1 Lightning Strikes

As mentioned earlier, transmission lines stretched over thousands of miles are frequently subjected to lightning strokes. Frequency of such strikes depends on the geographical location. Lightning is not a very well understood phenomenon but it would suffice here to say that a lightning strike to an apparatus results in a brief discharge of current pulse to it with respect to ground as shown in Fig. 14-1. This pulse is commonly represented as shown in Fig. 14-1, where it reaches its peak I_{peak} in time t_1 and exponentially tapers off to half its peak value at in t_2. The peak current stroke of as high as 200 kA have been recorded, though generally a peak of 10 kA to 20 kA is assumed, to protect against the resulting over-voltages.

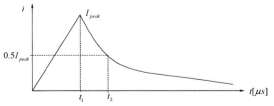

Fig. 14-1 Lightning current impulse.

14-2-1-1　Lightning Strike to Shield Wires

Many transmission lines have shield-wires as shown in the tower structure in Fig. 14-2a. These shield wires are located higher than the transmission line conductors and hence protect them from being hit directly by lightning strokes. They provide an approximately 30 degree protection zone in Fig. 14-2a. These shield wires are grounded through the tower to ground where it is desirable to keep the tower footing impedance as small as possible. It should be noted however that not all transmission systems have shield wires.

Fig. 14-2 Lightning strike to the shield wire.

When a current impulse due to a lightning stroke occurs to a shield wire, current flows in both direction and passes through the towers to ground, as shown in Fig. 14-2b. Due to the tower footing resistance and the $L(di/dt)$ effect due to the rapidly rising current-front causes the tower potential to exceed the insulation strength of the insulator string, causing it to flashover (called backflash). Generally, this will cause momentary power outage but soon the normal operation results, until the insulator string is seriously damaged, resulting in follow-on current which may require circuit breaker operation to interrupt it and allowing it to be self-repaired. Many utilities find it more economical to use surge arresters more extensively (although not at every tower) rather than employing shield wires.

14-2-1-2　Lightning Strike to the Conductor

Another scenario is where the conductor itself is struck by lightning. Resulting traveling waves proceed in both directions and insulator strings may flashover or when it reaches the termination, surge arresters would prevent voltage from rising to a level that can damage apparatus.

14-2-2　Switching Surges

At extra-high voltage levels, switching of transmission lines, as shown in Fig. 14-3a can result in over-voltages, as shown in Fig. 14-3b, that can exceed that by lightning strikes. These switching surges are of longer duration than those caused by the lightning impulse; the length of the over-voltage duration, in addition to its amplitude, also influences the requirement of the needed insulation. These switching over-voltages can be minimized by the use of pre-insertion resistors where switching-in a transmission line, a resistor in series is inserted which is later bypassed for normal operation.

Fig. 14-3 Over-voltages due to switching of transmission lines.

14-3   TRANSMISSION LINE CHARACTERISTICS AND REPRESENTATION

It should be understood from the very beginning that the term transmission lines here also includes distribution lines. In the following analysis, we will assume a transposed three-phase line and make use of the discussion in Chapter 4 dealing with transmission lines in steady state. Assuming this line to be lossless, the voltage and current magnitudes of these traveling waves are related by the characteristic impedance Z_c of this transmission line, where as calculated in Chapter 4,

$$Z_c = \sqrt{\frac{L}{C}} \tag{14-1}$$

and these waves propagate at a velocity c that is related to its parameters in the following manner:

$$c = \sqrt{\frac{1}{LC}} \tag{14-2}$$

where L and C are inductance and capacitance per-unit length of the transposed three-phase line. From Chapter 4, the per-phase inductance per-unit length is

$$L = 2 \times 10^{-7} \ln \frac{\sqrt[3]{D_{12}D_{23}D_{31}}}{r} \quad H/m \tag{14-3}$$

where the current is assumed to be at the outer surface of the conductor with radius r.

Also from Chapter 4, the per-phase capacitance per-unit length in air is

$$C = \frac{2\pi \times 8.85 \times 10^{-12}}{\ln \dfrac{\sqrt[3]{D_{12}D_{23}D_{31}}}{r}} \quad F/m \tag{14-4}$$

Using Eqs. 14-3 and 14-4, the traveling wave speed in Eq. 14-2 is $c = 3 \times 10^8 \, m/s$, which is less for practical transmission lines with losses, particularly in the zero-sequence mode.

The transient disturbances are usually not balanced, for example only one of the transmission-line phases is normally subjected to lightning impulse. Therefore, the zero-sequence path involving ground return must be carefully included in modeling to get correct over-voltages. Similarly, transmission lines are not perfectly balanced and most lines are not transposed, and hence may require to be represented as un-transposed. Moreover, associated with these transient phenomena, we are no longer dealing with a steady state line frequency of 60 or 50 Hz; rather the transient operation that involves very high frequencies. Fig. 14-4 illustrates the frequency dependence of the line parameters for positive (and negative) sequence quantities and the zero-sequence quantities as well, and this dependence should also be included.

Fig. 14-4 Frequency dependence of the transmission line parameters [Source: 2].

14-3-1 Calculation of Over-Voltages

In very simple cases, over-voltages can be calculated by means of keeping track of traveling waves by means of what is called Bewley diagram named after the Mr. L.V. Bewley of the General Electric Company who pioneered it, or by means of using Laplace transforms. However, even a simplest three-phase system with un-transposition and frequency dependence of parameters is too complex to be amenable to such methods, where traveling waves in various modes combine to result in the resultant voltage. Prof. Hermann Dommel of the University of British Columbia,who pioneered the Electro-Magnetic Transients Program (EMTP), explains this viewpoint very clearly in the quote below [2]:

> *"Readers fresh out of university, or engineers who have read one or one too many textbooks on electric circuits and networks, may have been misled to believe that Laplace transform techniques should be used for solving systems with lumped elements. Laplace transform techniques are only useful for "hand solutions" of rather small network and more or less useless for computer solutions of problems of the size typically analyzed with the EMTP."*

Calculation of surge voltages due to transmission-line switching are illustrated by means of an example below, using *EMTDC* [3].

▲ **Example 14-1** In the 3-bus example power system, the transmission line between buses 1 and 3 is opened at both ends following a fault, as shown in Fig. 14-5. It is switched in first at bus-1 end, with the end at bus-3 still open. Calculate the switching over-voltages at the bus-3 end of this transmission line using *EMTDC*.

Fig. 14-5 Calculation of switching over-voltages on a transmission line.

Solution The modeling of this system and the resulting over-voltages are calculated using EMTDC and the results are included on the accompanying CD.   ▲

14-4 INSULATION TO WITHSTAND VOLTAGES

Power systems apparatus is designed with insulation to withstand a certain amount of voltages. The insulation level to withstand voltages depends on factors such as the shape of the voltage wave and its duration, condition of the insulation in terms of its age, humidity and the contamination levels. Power systems apparatus can be categorized into having two types of insulations: self-restoring and non-self-restoring. Insulator strings on transmission lines represent self-restoring type of insulation which can be allowed to breakdown occasionally and restores itself after the resulting fault clears. However, insulation for transformers, generators etc is of non-self-restoring type, which if allowed to fail at any time will result in a severe and permanent damage that will be very expensive to repair.

For self-restoring insulation such as the insulator string of transmission lines, it is cost-prohibitive to insulate against all expected over-voltages and hence a statistical approach is used where certain probability of failure is acceptable. On the other hand, the non-self-restoring insulation of transformers, for example, is protected against failure using surge arresters, as discussed later in this chapter.

As mention earlier, the withstand voltage capability of insulation depends on the shape of the voltage wave and its duration, which differs based on lightning or switching surges. These voltage levels that a given insulation can withstand are defined below.

14-4-1 Basic Insulation Level (BIL)

For the lightning impulse, the level of insulation is specified as the Basic Insulation Level (BIL), which is the peak of the withstand voltage of a standard lightning impulse voltage wave. This lightning impulse wave, as shown in Fig. 14-6, is assumed to rise to its peak value in $1.2\,\mu s$, and tapers off exponentially to one-half the peak value in $50\,\mu s$. For the insulation-coordination purposes discussed later on, an $8 \times 10 \mu s$ lightning current discharge (where in Fig. 14-1, $t_1 = 8\mu s$, and $t_2 = 20\mu s$) through an arrester is assumed to cause this voltage impulse wave of Fig. 14-6.

Fig. 14-6 Standard Voltage Impulse Wave to define BIL.

The basic insulation level (BIL), as an example, for a 345-kV transformer is shown in Fig. 14-7 as 1175 kV, which is the peak line-to-ground voltage.

Fig. 14-7 A 345-kV transformer voltage insulation levels.

14-4-2 Switching Insulation Level (BSL)

As shown in Fig. 14-3, voltages applied at one end of a transmission line result in traveling waves of voltage and current with steep fronts. However, these switching surges do not have as steep a front as those resulting from lightning impulse; these switching surges are also of longer duration. The standard switching impulse voltage wave is assumed to rise to a peak value in $250\mu s$ and tapers off exponentially to one-half the peak value in $2500\mu s$. The withstand insulation level for the peak of such as switching surge is called the basic switching insulation level (*BSL*). As shown in Fig. 14-7, an apparatus with a particular BIL has a lower withstand capability to switching surges, that is, it has a lower BSL than BIL due to the fact that switching surges are of longer duration.

14-4-3 Chopped Wave Insulation Level

As shown in Fig. 14-7, the same apparatus insulation can withstand higher voltages than BIL if the voltage impulse beyond the peak is chopped to bring it to zero in 3-4 μs.

14-6

14-5   SURGE ARRESTERS AND INSULATION COORDINATION

In power systems apparatus, their insulation is protected against voltage impulses by means of surge arresters. The role of surge arresters is similar to that of Zener diodes in low power electronic circuits. Surge arresters appear as open-circuit at normal voltages and draw almost negligible current. However, they allow whatever current that needs to flow, of course within their rating, thus "clamping" the voltage across the device being protected to a threshold voltage plus a small *IR* current-discharge voltage, as shown in Fig. 14-7. The surge arrester should also be able to dissipate the associated energy without damage to itself, thus allowing quick return to the normal operation where it should once again appear as an open-circuit. In power systems, modern practice is to use ZnO arresters which have a highly nonlinear *i-v* characteristic, for example, as given by the following relationship:

$$ i = 2500 \left(\frac{V}{V_{ref}} \right)^{26} A \qquad (14\text{-}5) $$

The arrester discharge voltage level should be sufficiently below the apparatus insulation level this arrester is to protect, and provide a margin of at least 15-20%. Insulation coordination requires coordinating and selecting BIL and BSL of various apparatus and the ratings of the arresters to protect them.

REFERENCES

1. Electric Power Research Institute (EPRI), *Transmission Line Reference Book: 345 kV and above*, 2nd edition.
2. Hermann W. Dommel, *EMTP Theory Book*, BPA, August 1986.
3. PSCAD/EMTDC, Manitoba HVDC Research Centre: www.hvdc.ca.
4. Surge Protection in Power Systems, IEEE Tutorial Course, 79EH0144-6-PWR.
5. United States Department of Agriculture, Rural Utilities Service, Design Guide for Rural Substations, RUS BULLETIN 1724E-300.

PROBLEMS

EMTDC-based Problem:

14-1   As described on the accompanying CD, calculate the positive-sequence and the zero-sequence impedances of the transmission line in Example 14-1.

14-2   As described on the accompanying CD, calculate the switching surges with and without the use of pre-insertion resistors.

14-3   As described on the accompanying CD, calculate the switching surges with and without the use of surge arresters.

DETAILED CHAPTER CONTENTS

Chapter 14 TRANSIENT OVER-VOLTAGES, SURGE PROTECTION AND INSULATION COORDINATION   14-1